International Trends
in Mental Health

McGraw-Hill Series in International Development

ALDERFER · *Local Government in Developing Countries*

BENJAMIN · *Higher Education in the American Republics*

BRANNEN AND HODGSON · *Overseas Management*

BRYCE · *Industrial Development: A Guide for Accelerating Economic Growth*

BRYCE · *Policies and Methods for Industrial Development*

CURRIE · *Accelerating Development: The Necessity and the Means*

DAVENPORT · *Financing the Small Manufacturer in Developing Countries*

DAVID · *International Resources in Clinical Psychology*

DAVID · *International Trends in Mental Health*

DUNN · *International Handbook of Advertising*

EICHER AND WITT · *Agriculture in Economic Development*

ETTINGER · *International Handbook of Management*

HARBISON AND MYERS · *Education, Manpower, and Economic Growth: Strategies of Human Resource Development*

HARBISON AND MYERS · *Manpower and Education: Country Studies in Economic Development*

MEIER · *Developmental Planning*

MONTGOMERY AND SIFFIN · *Approaches to Development: Politics, Administration and Change*

POWELSON · *Latin America: Today's Economic and Social Revolution*

REIDY · *Strategy for the Americas*

REIMANN AND WIGGLESWORTH · *The Challenge of International Finance*

SINGER · *International Development: Growth and Change*

STALEY AND MORSE · *Modern Small Industry for Developing Countries*

WALINSKY · *The Planning and Execution of Economic Development: A Nontechnical Guide for Policy Makers and Administrators*

International Trends
in Mental Health

Edited by

Henry P. David

International Research Institute
American Institutes for Research
Washington, D.C.

Prepared with the support of
the Human Ecology Fund

McGRAW–HILL BOOK COMPANY

New York   London   Sydney   Toronto

INTERNATIONAL TRENDS IN MENTAL HEALTH

DEDICATED TO INTERNATIONAL COOPERATION YEAR 1965
TWENTIETH ANNIVERSARY OF THE UNITED NATIONS

*If humanity is to survive and to make
progress, the peoples of the United
Nations have no choice but to co-operate.*

U Thant
Secretary-General
United Nations

List of Contributors

ARTHUR J. BINDMAN, Ph.D., M.P.H.
Director of Psychological Services,
Massachusetts Department of Mental Health,
Boston, Massachusetts, U.S.A.

DONALD F. BUCKLE, M.B., D.P.M.
Regional Officer for Mental Health, Regional Office for Europe,
World Health Organization, Copenhagen, Denmark

WILLIAM CAUDILL, Ph.D.
Chief, Section on Personality and Environment,
Laboratory of Socio-environmental Studies,
National Institute of Mental Health, Bethesda, Maryland, U.S.A.

FRANÇOIS CLOUTIER, M.D.
Director-General, World Federation for Mental Health,
Geneva, Switzerland

HENRY P. DAVID, Ph.D.
Associate Director, International Research Institute,
American Institutes for Research, Washington, D.C.

L. TAKEO DOI, M.D.
Department of Psychiatry, St. Luke's International Hospital,
Tokyo, Japan

HERBERT DÖRKEN, Ph.D.
Chief, Bureau of Psychology,
California Department of Mental Hygiene,
Sacramento, California, U.S.A.

LEON EISENBERG, M.D.
Professor of Child Psychiatry, Johns Hopkins University
School of Medicine, Baltimore, Maryland, U.S.A.

ALBERT ELIAS, M.A.
Superintendent, New Jersey State Reformatory,
Bordentown, New Jersey, U.S.A.

ASGER HANSEN, Cand. Psych.
Superintendent, Viby Statsungdomshjem, Aarhus, Denmark

KATHLEEN JONES, Ph.D.
Senior Lecturer in Social Administration, University of Manchester,
Manchester, England

JACK H. KAHN, M.D., D.P.M.
Consultant-in-Charge, Community Mental Health Services,
West Ham, Essex, England

LEWIS B. KLEBANOFF, Ph.D.
Assistant to the Director, Division of Mental Hygiene,
Massachusetts Department of Mental Health,
Boston, Massachusetts, U.S.A.

E. E. KRAPF, M.D.
Late Chief, Mental Health Unit, World Health Organization,
Geneva, Switzerland

T. ADEOYE LAMBO, M.D.
Professor of Psychiatry, University of Ibadan, Ibadan, Nigeria

SAMUEL R. LAYCOCK, Ph.D.
Dean Emeritus of Education, University of Saskatchewan,
Saskatoon, Saskatchewan, Canada

B. A. LEBEDEV, M.D.
Director, V. M. Bechterev Institute for Psychoneurological Research,
Leningrad, U.S.S.R.

SERGE LEBOVICI, M.D.
Codirector, Santé Mentale et Lutte contre l'Alcoolisme
dans le xiiie Arrondissement, Paris, France

W. W. LEWIS, Ed.D.
Director of Research, Project Re-ED, George Peabody College
for Teachers, Nashville, Tennessee, U.S.A.

LOUIS MILLER, M.D.
Director, Mental Health Services, Ministry of Health,
Jerusalem, Israel

JOY M. MOSER, M.P.H.
Mental Health Unit, World Health Organization,
Geneva, Switzerland

SHMUEL NAGLER, Ph.D.
Child Guidance Clinic of the Seminar Hakibbutzim, Orinam,
Kiriath-Tivon, Haifa, Israel

JEAN P. NURSTEN, M.S.W.
Senior Lecturer in Social Casework, College of Advanced Technology,
Bradford, Yorkshire, England

PHILIPPE PAUMELLE, M.D.
Codirector, Santé Mentale et Lutte contre l'Alcoolisme
dans le xiiie Arrondissement, Paris, France

THOMAS L. PILKINGTON, M.R.C.S., D.P.M.
Medical Director, Cranage Hall and Mary Dendy Hospitals,
Holmes Chapel, Cheshire, England;
Film Consultant, World Federation for Mental Health

PRESIDENT'S PANEL ON MENTAL RETARDATION
Disbanded in October, 1962. Inquiries may be directed
to the U.S. Department of Health, Education, and Welfare,
Washington, D.C., U.S.A.

HANS J. PRIESTER, Ph.D.
Child Guidance Center of Mercer County, Princeton,
New Jersey, U.S.A.

ARIE QUERIDO, M.D.
Professor of Social Medicine, Instituut voor Sociale Geneeskunde,
University of Amsterdam, Amsterdam, the Netherlands

J. R. REES, M.D.
Honorary President, World Federation for Mental Health,
Bickenhall Mansions, Baker Street, London, England

PHON SANGSINGKEO, M.D.
Undersecretary of State for Public Health,
Ministry of Public Health, Bangkok, Thailand

BENJAMIN SCHLESINGER, Ph.D.
School of Social Work, University of Toronto,
Toronto, Ontario, Canada

J. TIZARD, Ph.D.
Social Psychiatry Research Unit, Maudsley Hospital,
London, England

WHO SCIENTIFIC GROUP ON MENTAL HEALTH RESEARCH
Convened by the World Health Organization,
Geneva, Switzerland, April, 1964

Preface

THROUGHOUT the world, 2,000 pages of books, newspapers, and reports are published every sixty seconds. An unpublished study suggests that in 1964 there were more than 200,000 publications of all kinds in mental health alone. In a time when certain books are engineered, packaged, and promoted like soap in a supermarket, it may well be asked whether another collection of readings, with its usual handicaps, is really necessary.

Practice-oriented information is frequently lost in the flood tide of multiple-language publications, each competing for the time of already burdened mental health professionals and administrators. It is the purpose of this volume to focus on international trends in mental health practice and administration, with particular emphasis on community centers, school services, public health approaches to social issues, manpower needs, and prevention. While historical accident has fragmented the world politically, scientists and practitioners have traditionally endeavored to span geographic, linguistic, and ideological barriers. It was on the premise that those coping with similar problems have something to learn from each other that the plan for this book was developed.

It is with warm thanks that I acknowledge the generous support of the Human Ecology Fund, whose officers David E. Rhodes, Preston S. Abbott, and Walter F. Pasternak encouraged the original idea, supported changing editorial concepts, and never asked for a formal accounting until the project was completed. The extensive post-1960 literature was surveyed with the spirited assistance of Carol Spencer, who screened more than three hundred selected journals from all over the world in the libraries of the New York Academy of Medicine, Princeton University, the Educational Testing Service, and the New Jersey Neuro-Psychiatric Institute. Hans J. Priester made an immense contribution by greatly helping to refine initial editorial guidelines and sharing hours of sometimes frustrating discussion.

The project came to fruition and was completed during my two-year assignment in Geneva as Associate Director of the World Federation for Mental Health, 1963–1965. My associate Solange Cloutier was most helpful in surveying French language materials. Erica Macfadyen significantly enhanced the editorial process by patiently typing most of these pages and lovingly polishing translations and adaptations. Sources of contributions are individually acknowledged in each chapter.

In a few weeks I will be returning to the International Research Institute, American Institutes for Research, in Washington, D.C. Traveling in many lands, visiting diverse facilities, and sharing experiences with strangers who became friends provided a unique perspective. For that opportunity I owe much to François Cloutier and Pierre A. Visseur of the World Federation for Mental Health, colleagues in the WHO Mental Health Unit in Geneva, and Donald F. Buckle in the WHO Regional Office for Europe in Copenhagen. As before, the greatest sustenance came from my wife and children, who gave up a home in the United States to live temporarily amidst other people's furnishings and made innumerable trips to the airport to indulge an itinerant and far too busy father.

Henry P. David

Contents

List of Contributors vii

Preface xi

Part One: Introduction

1. On Using the Knowledge We Have: An Overview of the Volume   3
   Henry P. David (World Federation for Mental Health)

Part Two: A World View

2. The World Community 13
   J. R. Rees (United Kingdom)
3. A Survey of Mental Health Resources 23
   E. E. Krapf and Joy M. Moser (World Health Organization)
4. Mental Health Programs in Public Health Planning . . . 32
   Arie Querido (the Netherlands)
5. Mental Health in Developing Countries 55
   Phon Sangsingkeo (Thailand)
6. Preventive Psychiatry: If Not Now, When? 63
   Leon Eisenberg (United States)
7. International Activities: An Integrative Overview . . . 78
   François Cloutier (World Federation for Mental Health)

Part Three: Community Centers

8. British Experience in Community Care 87
   Kathleen Jones (United Kingdom)
9. An Experience with Sectorization in Paris 97
   Philippe Paumelle and Serge Lebovici (France)
10. Administration of Community Mental Health Services in the United States 109
    Herbert Dörken (United States)

11. Mental Hygiene in the U.S.S.R. 121
      B. A. Lebedev (U.S.S.R.)
12. Psychiatry and Culture in Japan 129
      William Caudill (United States) and L. Takeo Doi (Japan)
13. Patterns of Psychiatric Care in Developing African Countries:
      The Nigerian Village Program 147
      T. Adeoye Lambo (Nigeria)
14. Community Services in Israel: An Integrative Overview . . 154
      Louis Miller (Israel)

Part Four: Children and Schools

15. Promoting Mental Health in the School 171
      Samuel R. Laycock (Canada)
16. School Refusal: A Comprehensive View of School Phobia . . 181
      Jack H. Kahn and Jean P. Nursten (United Kingdom)
17. A Community Mental Health Program for Children: A Case Study 194
      Lewis B. Klebanoff and Arthur J. Bindman (United States)
18. Clinical Observations on Kibbutz Children 210
      Shmuel Nagler (Israel)
19. Children and Schools: A Reaction 223
      Donald F. Buckle (World Health Organization)

Part Five: Approaches to Social Problems

20. Project Re-ED: Reeducation of Emotionally Disturbed Children 231
      W. W. Lewis (United States)
21. The Inpatient Psychiatric Treatment of Children in Europe . 245
      Donald F. Buckle (World Health Organization), Serge
      Lebovici (France), and J. Tizard (United Kingdom)
22. A Community Program for the Retarded: The Hague . . 269
      President's Panel on Mental Retardation, Mission to the
      Netherlands
23. The Highfields Program for Delinquent Boys 280
      Albert Elias (United States)
24. Institutional Social Education of Severely Maladjusted Girls . 280
      Asger Hansen (Denmark)
25. Innovation and Experience in Mental Health: A Commentary . 303
      Henry P. David (World Federation for Mental Health)

Part Six: Resources

26. Mental Health Research: A Summary Report of Suggested
      Priorities 313
      WHO Scientific Group on Mental Health Research

27. Mental Health Grants: International Progress and Problems   .   319
        Henry P. David (World Federation for Mental Health)
28. Mental Health Films   332
        Thomas L. Pilkington (United Kingdom)
29. Mental Health Pocketbooks   337
        Benjamin Schlesinger (Canada)
30. Mental Health in Other Lands: Selected References .   .   .   347
        *Henry P. David (World Federation for Mental Health) and
        Hans J. Priester (United States)*

Index   357

part one

Introduction

1. On Using the Knowledge We Have: An Overview of the Volume

Henry P. David

Introduction

In the nearly two decades since its founding in 1948, the World Federation for Mental Health has been a moving force in the transfer of concepts and ideas, frequently in partnership with the Mental Health Unit of the World Health Organization, which was established in 1949. It was the consensus of a WFMH-convened international and interprofessional study group in 1961 that in this period of accelerated population growth, rapid social change, and ever-faster means of transportation and communication "the difficulties of the individual are coming increasingly to be viewed in a wider social, cross-cultural, and international perspective." [5] The group recommended reevaluation of existing knowledge, further research, and the development of appropriate professional practices.

The contents of this volume are closely attuned to these goals. In facilitating international endeavors, it has frequently been assumed that science and professional practice know no national borders. This is, of course, true in only a limited sense. As Otto Klineberg [4] observed, there are national barriers and boundaries set by lack of knowledge, by inadequacy of communication, and by the widespread tendency to read only what has been written in one's own language. And, as B. F. Riess [6] noted, similarities and dissimilarities of method tend to be of more than casual import in mental health practice and research. There are important differences in available economic resources and trained professional manpower. For example, what has been learned by trial and error in Europe and North America is not always directly applicable in newly emerging countries, where high priorities can seldom be given to mental health needs. Man as a biological organism is universal, but his experiences within a social milieu produce variations of behavior, attitude, and emotional expressivity. These very

3

differences frequently generate fresh approaches, which may be adaptable elsewhere in coping with similar problems.

The present international scene in mental health practice and administration is one of considerable ferment. The therapeutic community, the open hospital, the increased interest in children, the growth of social psychology and psychiatry, the broadened base of professional responsibility for mental health programs, the search for new sources of manpower, the reawakened concern for the mentally retarded, the development of comprehensive community mental health centers, the empirical methods of psychopharmacology, and the emphasis on epidemiologic research all reflect a recognition that the concepts of public health have penetrated the field of mental health.

Noting the significant shift from a clinical to a public health model, Nicholas Hobbs [3] described it as "mental health's third revolution." He identified the first revolution with Philippe Pinel in France, William Tuke in England, and Benjamin Rush and Dorothea Dix in the United States. This revolution was based on the then heretical notion that the mentally disordered are people and should be treated with kindness and dignity, a goal still not fully achieved. The second revolution was that of Sigmund Freud. His concepts and those of his students and followers on the nature and meaning of intrapsychic life have significantly permeated modern arts and sciences, indeed our very culture. It was the post-World War II recognition of the inapplicability of individual psychological treatment to major social problems which generated the innovations of the past two decades and prepared the stage for the third revolution in mental health. Today there appears to be a growing consensus that mental illness is not the private misery of single individuals but a social problem for which the whole community shares responsibility.

A cogent aspect of the third revolution is the recognition that full implementation of public health approaches requires significant changes in professional training programs. Throughout the volume there is repeated confirmation of George W. Albee's already classic monograph.[1] It is evident that the prospective supply of people for training in the mental health professions is limited, that demands for services will continue to grow more rapidly than the population, and that in the foreseeable future trained personnel will not be numerous enough to meet service demands. The situation is similar in most nations, although perhaps somewhat differently in the Socialist countries, where training in the mental health professions is usually a matter of state planning and private practice is largely nonexistent.

The impact of priorities and personal interest in developing lands is strikingly apparent in Henri Collomb's report on French-speaking Africa.[2] During his five years at the University of Dakar in Senegal, only two physicians selected postgraduate training in psychiatry, and one of these eventually chose a political career. It would be a mistake, however, to assume that mental health is the exclusive province of the clinical professions or of any one discipline. Attainment of enlightened public sentiment and more generous financial support will require that mental health also become a significant concern of educators, professional politicians, and broadly representative citizen groups.

To break the manpower bottleneck, bold innovations are needed. There is growing evidence of multifaceted efforts to deploy available resources to the end of obtaining greater logistic effectiveness in strengthening preventive and rehabilitative endeavors for all strata of society. At midcentury, the one-to-one model of much current practice no longer suffices for a public health–mental health approach to the social problems of mental health and illness.

Overview

Ultimate implementation of the third revolution depends on productive harnessing of information, effectively using the knowledge we have. As the first in a potential series on *International Trends in Mental Health*, this volume focuses on a world view of needs and resources, the evolving utilization of community centers, the growing relationship of mental health and education, and diverse approaches to the social problems of emotional disturbance in children, retardation, and juvenile delinquency. A final section includes WHO-recommended priorities for research, information on stipends and grants, suggestions on the use of films, a guide to more than 300 pocketbooks, and selected post-1960 references to trends in mental health programs in seventy-three countries. Each part, except the last, concludes with an integrative commentary.

Of the thirty chapters, nearly one-half are original papers. Of the thirty-three individual contributors, eleven are identified with Canada and the United States, ten with Europe, and seven with international organizations; the remaining five come from Africa, the Middle East, Southeast Asia, and the Western Pacific.

Following this overview, Part Two, "A World View," offers a broad picture of mental health in international perspective. J. R. Rees considers the universal impact of major developments, including advances in treatment, training, and prevention. This chapter is followed by a survey of mental health resources, progress, and problems by the late E. E. Krapf and by Joy Moser, based on responses to a WHO questionnaire received from thirty-three countries. Included are data on mental health organization and administration, personnel and their availability, inpatient and outpatient psychiatric programs for children and adults, and information on duration of stay and costs. Next, Arie Querido summarizes WHO reports from forty-four governments on mental health programs and public health planning. After a definition of the subject area and consideration of the evolution of mental health provisions, there is a discussion of priorities in organization and administration and related aspects of training and research. The particular problems of developing countries are noted by Phon Sangsingkeo, with emphasis on the snowballing effects of extensive urbanization, rising economic expectations, and rapid population growth. The citizen responsibilities of the mental health professional in promoting public health–oriented activities and social action for the prevention of mental ill-health are movingly advocated by Leon Eisenberg in his call for the rededication of our energies to ensure future survival. Part Two concludes with an integrative overview by François Cloutier of international activities in mental health, citing the historic roots of the citizen movement and the complementary roles of WFMH and WHO in facilitating the growth and progress of mental health endeavors throughout the world.

Part Three on "Community Centers" reports on current programs in several countries. Kathleen Jones begins with a review of British experience in community mental health care, noting the essential attributes of diversity, flexibility, adequacy, and ability to facilitate social relationships. Particularly sobering are her remarks on the cyclical nature of mental health reforms and the probabilities of an eventual downward trend. Philippe Paumelle and Serge Lebovici describe the professional services for children and adults organized by the Mental Health Association of the Thirteenth Arrondissement, an administrative sector of Paris with a population of 165,000. There is close collaboration with local authorities and other public and private organizations. By coordinating facilities within a geographic area and demonstrating the practical effectiveness of a community mental health team, which retains responsibility for the patient from initial contact to eventual social reintegration, more may be learned about social conditions favorable to mental health and the prevention of incapacitating mental illness.

Administration of community mental health services in the United States is reviewed by Herbert Dörken, who focuses on the social forces generating a growing demand for community resources, essential factors in organization and finances, and professional standards. B. A. Lebedev describes the government-sponsored public health preventive program in mental hygiene in the Soviet Union, noting environmental efforts, general mental health measures, and the coordinated services of neuropsychiatric dispensaries. In Japan, the practice of psychiatry is interrelated with broader patterns of behavior in the general culture. William Caudill and L. Takeo Doi portray some aspects of the organization of psychiatric hospitals and patient care, indicating differences with Western approaches while observing important relationships to Japanese value orientations, emotions, and family patterns. The advantages and limitations of the Nigerian village system are delineated by T. Adeoye Lambo; this experiment in community psychiatry may well become a model for developing African countries. The major conclusions of Part Three are integrated by Louis Miller, who provides additional commentary on experiences in Israel. Particular emphasis is on the growing awareness of community social factors in the prevention of mental ill-health.

Part Four on "Children and Schools" considers the relationship of mental health to education. Samuel R. Laycock discusses the concept of school mental health and comments on the roles of discipline, teaching methods, and administrative policies. Jack H. Kahn and Jean P. Nursten present a comprehensive view of school phobia, including a review of the literature, community attitudes, and treatment. The difficulties in organizing and developing a community mental health program for children and the problems encountered in working with school personnel and the community at large are aptly described in terms of actual experience by Lewis B. Klebanoff and Arthur J. Bindman. A cross-cultural view is provided by Shmuel Nagler's clinical observations on kibbutz children. Points of stress specific to kibbutz society are noted, along with available mental health facilities. As a commentary, Donald F. Buckle offers a reaction to all the chapters. He suggests that schools be oriented toward undertaking preventive milieu therapy and that teachers be primarily milieu therapists and secondarily instructors. To justify such a change in orientation, he holds that the value given to academic knowledge in the early stages of school life be lessened, with a concomitant expectation that the result of this reorientation will be to increase the gains from independent initiative in learning. But, as Buckle observes, do mental health specialists have the right to impose their views on educators?

Diverse approaches to social problems, including emotional disturbance in children, retardation, and juvenile delinquency, are considered in Part Five. W. W. Lewis notes the history, program, and initial observations of Project Re-ED, a residential school conducted five days a week for emotionally disturbed children. There is particular emphasis on the role of the teacher-counselor and the model provided by education with its emphasis on health and teaching rather than illness and treatment. The WHO Seminar on the Inpatient Psychiatric Treatment of Children in Europe is summarized by Donald F. Buckle, Serge Lebovici, and J. Tizard. The public health approach is apparent in the broad representation, involving child psychiatrists, special educators, psychologists, nurses, and psychiatric social workers from twenty-one European countries. Discussion at the seminar included the extent of the problem, the kinds of residential facilities available, criteria for placement, treatment resources, staff roles, and research needs.

The description of The Hague's community program for retardates is an excerpt from the *Report of the Mission to the Netherlands* by the President's Panel on Mental Retardation. Of particular interest are the recognition and analysis of a range of specialized needs; provision is made for a continuing network of services directed by trained staff. The unique High-fields program of work and guided group interaction for delinquent boys is reported by Albert Elias, while Asger Hansen describes the pedagogical-psychological orientation of the Viby center for severely maladjusted girls. Both offer unusual approaches to the social malaise of delinquency, whose rise has been a source of apprehension in both established and rapidly industrializing countries. It is the major thesis of the integrative commentary that innovation and shared experience are essential ingredients in mental health progress, but that full fruition depends on communication and on effectively coping with resistance to change.

Part Six consists of several resource chapters. Suggested priorities for research are outlined in the 1964 *Summary Report* of the First WHO Scientific Group on Mental Health Research. Top rank was given to the promotion of epidemiologic studies on the distribution of mental disorders in different countries and on assessing the effectiveness of rehabilitative and preventive services. The essay on mental health grants reviews individual opportunities for study and training abroad, surveys the activities of American foundations and the United States government in supporting international research, and discusses the problems and pitfalls of preparing and evaluating grant applications. Thomas L. Pilkington notes the varieties and values of mental health films and offers suggestions on their presentation. Particularly useful is Benjamin Schlesinger's guide to more than 300 low-cost mental health pocket books. These are arranged in numerous topics and subtopics, including family life, psychiatry, psycho-analysis, psychology, sociology, and social work. The volume concludes with a list of selected post-1960 references on developing trends in mental health programs and psychiatric services in seventy-three countries, compiled in association with Hans J. Priester.

Summary

Intended for mental health practitioners, researchers, and administrators, as well as for students and the citizen participants so vital in the public decision-making process, this volume will, it is hoped, stimulate practice-oriented programs and reinforce the concept that in this shrinking world we all have something to learn from each other.

References

1. Albee, George W.: *Mental Health Manpower Trends*, Basic Books, Inc., Publishers, New York, 1959.
2. Collomb, Henri: "Psychiatric Teaching and Research in African Medical Schools," *Int. MH Res. Newsltr.*, 6(4): 11–15, 1964.
3. Hobbs, Nicholas: "Mental Health's Third Revolution," *Amer. J. Orthopsychiat.*, 34:822–833, 1964.

4. Klineberg, Otto: Foreword to H. P. David (ed.), *International Resources in Clinical Psychology*, McGraw-Hill Book Company, New York, 1964 .
5. *Mental Health in International Perspective*, World Federation for Mental Health, Geneva, 1961.
6. Riess, B.F.: Editorial, *Int. MH Res. Newsltr.*, 6(4): 1964.

part two

A World View

2. The World Community

J. R. Rees

In suggesting the title for the second of the Barton-Pope Lectures, I wanted to underline both the importance of research, training, and treatment in your own city of Adelaide and, at the same time, the fact that everything that you do (or fail to do) affects the quality of your contribution to the world community. I would remind you of the much-quoted sentence of John Donne: "No man is an island, entire of itself." This is true of individuals, and it is probably even more true of communities or countries. Today it seems especially true because of the rapid communications with which we are all so familiar, which could allow me to leave London eight days ago, have two days' consultations and discussions in Bombay, two days in Bangkok and the same time in Manila, and then be here in Adelaide tonight.

Since Lunik circled the moon, many of us have a feeling that perhaps even this world as we know it will not much longer be an island separated altogether from what we have hitherto regarded as outer space. That is problematical, but it is quite certain that neither Australia nor Adelaide itself can ignore that they are in fact part of the world community, with appropriate responsibility in their field of work and cultural life, along with our colleagues all over this world. We are indeed members of one another.

Advances in the Treatment of Mental Ill-health

The world's leading expert on virus diseases, Sir MacFarlane Burnet of Melbourne, writing a decade ago in the *Lancet* on "The Future of Medical Research," said:

Second Barton-Pope Lecture, delivered under the auspices of the South Australian Association for Mental Health, Inc., in Adelaide, Australia, Apr. 5, 1960; published in *Social Service*, 11 (6):3–14, 1960; adapted for this volume.

What are the major medical problems which have not been effectively dealt with? The first and most important is of course insanity and feeble-mindedness; probably the next is functional disease of the nervous system, with its manifestations in the psychoneuroses and psychosomatic disorders. It would be in line with modern thought to add that crime, delinquency, and general bad manners are hardly distinguishable from the medical manifestations. . . .[2]

This was striking perhaps because it came from someone whose special interests are not, presumably, in our field. He certainly is realistic. I hardly need to remind you of the magnitude of the problem of mental ill-health, which in countries as different as the United States of America and the People's Republic of China has often been said to constitute the first priority in the medical field.

Grossly neglected as mental ill-health has been by society and by the medical profession, there have been startling changes and improvements in the past twenty-five years. The introduction of psychological treatment and of the empirical methods of physical treatment have revolutionized the lot of those who suffer from serious mental breakdown. Electrical and surgical techniques have been followed by the use (and the misuse) of pharmacological preparations; and here one might say in passing that, properly used, these can all be of enormous value, but they also can be a menace insofar as they mask the symptoms of mental ill-health and distract us from the really necessary treatment of the individual as a person who must be respected, cared for, loved, and helped in many aspects of his illness to reestablish his proper relationship with society. Whereas the recovery rate from psychosis had not varied by more than a few decimal points for more than eighty years up to World War II, we now have a situation in which roughly 70 per cent of those who need in-patient care in mental hospitals are within three or four months fit to be back at work and with their families.

We have realized that patients can be treated but that those who are prisoners behind barred windows and locked doors cannot be treated so easily or successfully. We have rediscovered that day hospitals can produce the same therapeutic results for a very high proportion of patients as can be achieved by residence in a hospital and that the desocialization of institutional life is thus avoided, to say nothing of the considerable economic saving. Outpatient departments and the provision of beds in general hospitals have been further progressive steps all over the world, and in consequence the stigma attaching to mental illness has quite markedly diminished and will disappear. Psychiatry can be proud that at long last it has woken up and that it now produces therapeutic results which are at least as good as those attained by most other branches of medicine.

Let me emphasize again that, in my judgment, the primary operating factor in all this revolutionary achievement has been the improved care and respect for the individual patient, without which all these specific special methods which we use and which we shall still develop much further would be of much less value.

From many places, as for example the United States and the United Kingdom, there are reports that in the last year or two there has been a drop in the numbers of people having to be cared for in mental hospitals, and we may well ask ourselves: what is the relationship of this fact to the whole situation of mental illness and its opposite, mental health, in the world?

Because of my position with the World Federation for Mental Health I had the privilege of visiting a very great number of countries in every continent, and there is impressive indication (of which we still need statistical validation) of an increase in the stress and mental disturbance that are experienced. The good, well-trained psychiatrists in the countries all over the world who have been trained in the West and are now working in their own countries tell us that their general hunch is that there is no true increase in the psychoses (as, for example, the group of illnesses which we call the schizophrenias) and no difference in their quality, though of course the presenting symptoms are colored by the cultural patterns of any country. Such cases are, however, becoming more obvious, because hitherto they tended to be hidden by the joint-family organization or the tribal systems of any territory and now this is not so possible, so that they come to notice more often and the demand for their treatment increases. One of the long-term objectives which we have, along with the World Health Organization of the United Nations, is to carry out reliable and comparable studies of the actual incidence of mental illness in the total population.

Stress and Cultural Change

Whilst it is probably true that psychosis is not increasing, it is almost certainly true that stress, anxiety, and neurosis are on the increase in most countries. These are to some extent disorders of civilization.

You will remember, no doubt, the statement from the United Nations that some two-thirds of the total population of this world have never known anything but hunger. This situation will change very slowly, despite all the efforts of the Food and Agriculture Organization, of the United Nations Children's Fund (UNICEF), and other activities which are aimed at trying to nourish properly the ever-increasing population of the world.

Because people are poor, ill equipped, and hungry and because they now realize that this is not an inevitable part of life on earth, all the underprivileged countries of the world are struggling to raise their standards of living. Better communications and the mechanization of agriculture, along with industrialization, are being achieved by countries every-where, and in this extremely laudable effort they are being helped with technical assistance by the United Nations, the Colombo Plan, and the Agency for International Development of the United States.

There would appear, however, to be, alongside this, certain ill effects which result from the inevitable change in habits of living and in culture patterns in these countries. Tribal habits and the extended-family systems are breaking down. People are changing in many countries from a barter economy to a money economy, which in itself is a disturbing factor. The tempo of life is speeded up, there are rapid increases in education of many different sorts, and it is small wonder that many people get a sense of identity confusion (as Erik Erikson called it) and consequently suffer from anxiety. If for the first time you have the opportunity of earning money and buying food, you naturally become anxious about getting a job. Women may leave their homes and their children to do paid work. There comes the fear of not keeping the job; and as the abilities to live better increase, there comes inevitably the tendency to keep up with our neighbors, which again is an anxiety-producing matter, particularly if we don't seem to be as successful as we would like to be.

These, perhaps, are some of the causes of increased anxiety, through economic and social factors, and still more through questions of attitudes. So we have disease and poor mental health. And these are some of the reasons why we need to change both our medical and our social outlook; why we must urge better training in psychiatric principles and in psy-chology for all those who in medicine, nursing, education, social work, or other professions are concerned with human beings. It also explains why we need more and better research into the causes of the more everyday neurotic and psychosomatic troubles, as well as into the unsolved prob-lems of psychotic conditions like schizophrenia. In all these ways we over-privileged people must do everything we can with our facilities and our know-how for our own people and for our neighbors.

Training

Everywhere in the world, as far as I am aware, there are good mental hospitals, and they outnumber the bad ones. Nearly everywhere there are good psychiatrists, but they are in extremely short supply, and I would remind you that skilled professional people are infinitely more important than buildings and other physical facilities. I often say that three of the best mental hospitals that I have ever been in are in San José, Costa Rica, in Bangkok, Thailand, and in Barbados—human, happy, competent hos-pitals. In Ruanda-Urundi * for the past twelve years all psychotic patients have been cared for with completely open doors in the general hospital of Usumbura, with excellent results and no outstanding problems. We in the

* Since 1962, the separate independent countries of Rwanda and Burundi.

supposedly modern world can learn from many of the things that are going on, even in what used to be called "the white man's grave." The experience we gain from cross-national contacts is always a two-way traffic of information and stimulation.

On the other hand, you may find a country like the Sudan, with 20 million people, which has only one African psychiatrist. Certain parts of the British colonial system have no psychiatrists and deplorable facilities. We cannot hope in countries like these or, say, the People's Republic of China, with its 650 million people, to train sufficient doctors to meet their needs, to this add specialist training in psychiatry for a number of men and women, and visualize that they then could provide buildings and supply treatment for all who require it. If we are realistic, we must come to the conclusion that the longer-term policy of prevention is the one to be followed and that this must be designed rather in the way in which our colleagues in public health have operated. We perhaps shall never eradicate mental illness in the way that (hopefully) we may eradicate malaria, but we can go a very long way toward that goal. We don't even use all that we know, and through research we shall produce many new facts that will lead us on to educational and social action to diminish the appalling human, social, and economic burden of mental ill-health.

Figures compiled by a group of economists in the United States on the direct and indirect costs of mental ill-health show the annual cost to that great country to be some 3 billion dollars, and presumably this is some guide to the proportionate costs of such matters in other countries.[3] To spend more on personnel and prophylaxis in our field could well lead to a great saving and release funds to tackle the epidemic physical diseases of the world.

I go back now to two points which I mentioned earlier: (1) the urgent need for better training of members of all those professions which are concerned with human beings and (2) the necessity for additional research to produce data upon which preventive measures can be established.

It is probable, I think, that the future of preventive psychiatry will lie primarily in the hands of the family doctors and the public health nurses, since these are the people who have access to the home at all times, who can be most effectively concerned with the care and upbringing of children through friendly help given to parents. Most surgery is carried out by the family doctors, though clearly there is a need for surgical specialists and for the continuous improvement of surgical knowledge and technique.

The same is true in psychiatry. There will always be the need for well-trained psychiatrists, for research departments, and for the extension of their interests into the social field. It is the discovery and the validation of facts through research which have primary importance for devising preventive measures

We do not use nearly enough our clinical or practical experience, whether we are doctors or educationists, sociologists or parents, and the distillation of our experience, which would involve us in extra thought and work, can provide guidelines for preventive action through education or social change.

How, after this, do we move to tackle the prevention of mental ill-health? There have been very few satisfactory and acceptable definitions of mental health. One of the paraphrases which I appreciate most comes from Dr. Marie Jahoda, when she talks about improving the quality of living. Whether we are thinking of physical, mental, or social health, we clearly would all of us like to do this.

Our colleagues in child psychiatry have probably come nearest to prophylactic activity of anyone, because the team of psychiatrist, psychologist, and social worker which is usually employed does approach many of the varied causative factors which contribute to the ill-health or malaise of the child; since the parents and other members of the family have also to be helped, child psychiatry has become, happily, an activity which not only helps most of the actual child patients but tends to affect family life and the other children in that family and probably spreads its influence to the children next door and down the street.

Prevention and the Team

Whenever we think of the promotion of health as something positive, the building up of toughness and resistance to the stresses of life as well as the absence of abnormal attitudes or disease, and whether we are thinking of physical health or of mental health, we always come to realize the necessity for a team. It is true that psychiatrists, or doctors with a knowledge of psychiatry, are probably the backbone of mental health activity. To clothe the skeleton and give it life, however, we need a brain to produce ideas and limbs to execute them. We must have a team, therefore, which includes all those who are concerned with the development and life of human beings: psychologists, sociologists, anthropologists, and, of course, educators and clergy, as well as nurses and doctors. When we use this concept of the team, it is regrettable that sometimes those in the medical profession regard themselves as necessarily being at the head of the pecking order. In fact, "team" means that each member supplies something of value from his or her angle and that all have a contribution to make, although, according to the varying circumstances and the task in hand, someone from any particular profession or discipline may at that time be the leader of the team.

If all of us, whether doctors, teachers, or others, gave greater thought, in our contacts with people in difficulty, to the problem of "How did this person get ill, or become difficult as he did and when he did?" we could acquire a much better sense of the causative factors and should be on our way at any rate to outlining methods by which other individuals might be helped to avoid similar trouble.

In Britain, if you take any one of the less distinguished Sunday papers, you will find on the front page stories of loss of memeory, drunkenness, child neglect, industrial unrest, delinquency, sexual offenses, and many other things. These of course are social problems. Sometimes their causes may be partly economic. But every one of these problems has considerable psychological factors, and we need to understand these factors if we are to attempt to treat the causes and not just the symptom.

Israel has provided a rather stimulating experiment in preventive work. It was not initiated by the medical profession particularly but as the result of the observations of the Chief Children's Magistrate of Israel, who by training was a psychiatric social worker. Most of us who have worked with children know that when a child has been involved in a sexual assault, it tends to suffer later from anxiety and from guilt feelings, which in very many cases prevent the establishment of easy social contacts with the opposite sex and may lead to a frigid character structure and sexual frigidity in the adult. We also know that the necessity for the child to appear in court and be questioned by the defending counsel is often more harmful than the actual assault episode itself.

In Israel they decided, about a decade ago, to pass a new law in the Knesset (Parliament) that no child who had been so involved would appear in court. They appointed social workers of experience, one of whom interviews the child (and probably at that time does most of the therapy that is necessary) and then appears in court to give the child's story and answer questions. The lawyers naturally disliked this type of testimony, as being hearsay evidence, but now are convinced, since no complaint of injustice to the man concerned has yet been raised.

The follow-up of this work will probably demonstrate its value, but our own common sense can appreciate that this is a method of prevention of future trouble which must contribute to good mental health. This is just one instance of the way in which facts of which we are already aware could be utilized and lead to social action.

If some of you have been trained in public health, you will probably know the story of Dr. John Snow, one of the first distinguished anesthetists in London. Over 100 years ago, an epidemic of cholera was raging in London, and around what is now Piccadilly Circus in the parish of St. James's there had been 1,200 to 1,400 deaths in a period of two weeks. The parish council was meeting, and they were a group of very puzzled men. Dr. Snow, who was quite unknown to them, came to the meeting and asked if he might speak with them. He explained that he had had considerable interest in these epidemics and had come to the conclusion that they were due in some way to the contamination of drinking water by sewage. (You must remember that the organism which causes cholera was not discovered for many years after that.)

The councillors asked him what this added up to in the way of action that they might take, and he said: "Well, I think you should take the handle off the pump in Broad Street." They did. It was a most unpopular piece of social action, because housewives had to fetch water from distant pumps; but that particular cholera epidemic came to a very rapid end.

This was not fully scientific: it was a hunch based on observation. It seems to me that even in our day there may be some pumps whose handles should be removed, and we should learn something as a result of that.

As you know, I am sure, a great deal of work has been done in recent years on the insecurity and anxiety and depression in children under four years of age who feel themselves deprived of mother love, by absence in hospital or by the absence of the mother or her substitute. Not all children suffer in this way, but many do and both physiologically and psychologically may develop tendencies which it is very hard indeed to reverse. The publication of Bowlby's work on the effects of separation by the World Health Organization [1] has led to a marked alteration in the willingness to have parental visits at all sorts of times to the small child who has to be in hospital. This work has thrown much light on the tragic circumstances of unloving foster homes and orphanages and other institutions for children, and nearly all over the world people have been modifying their methods of care for children, something which must in the long run make an important contribution to better mental health.

Most of us can understand a physical disease like malaria, which is an infectious and killer disease, and so we can understand the efforts that are being made throughout the world totally to eradicate malaria by killing off mosquitoes and by sanitary engineering. It does not always occur to us, I think, that in our field we have similar problems which need to be tackled. There is one which we can quote, *prejudice*, which is very largely a problem of poor mental health and faulty attitudes, though there are many other aspects to it, such as political and economic problems. Prejudice is a killer disease too—it killed 6 million people in Europe not long ago. It is endemic; that is to say, it has always been present in every population group; and at times it is epidemic.

What do we do about it? Remarkably little. Legislation to make prejudice or discrimination punishable will never get very far, because it is only dealing with symptoms. It is like giving morphia for a pain in the abdomen when really it is the inflamed appendix which needs to be removed.

What causes prejudice? Why do small babies born without any trace of such feeling develop it as they grow up, acquiring it from their parents or from other children at school? How are we to give people a positive sense of their own proper place in society's scheme of things, so that they don't need to compare themselves with other people who have a different color, a different religion, or a different sex?

This is a problem which our own conduct, as members of families and as citizens, through the activities of everyone who teaches children, can undoubtedly influence. We do, however, need a great deal more work and study to learn some of the causative factors and try to find ingenious ways by which we can institute new procedures and new approaches in education that can remove the actual infective process which gives rise to this appalling set of false attitudes.

In concluding, let me turn to a different aspect of our concern for mental health: the problems which bedevil the world at the present time. I think your newspapers will inform you on any one day of tension and trouble in at least twenty areas of the world. We have not escaped the danger of world suicide with which the threat of the atomic bomb presents us. What are you and I, ordinary citizens, to do about these matters? How can our concept of better mental health be made operative?

Mental health begins at home, and there are tensions and stresses in your families, in the offices or other activities in which you work, in the committees on which you serve, in your local government, and in your national government. The attitude you take toward these, the degree of interest you give to the fundamental causation of such problems, is certainly going to do something for our understanding of how they can be solved. Discussions between knowledgeable people from various professions, with administrators, politicians, and your representatives in the international field, can certainly throw light on and help to clarify some of the issues at stake. Each one of us has to carry a full, man-sized load of responsibility for these great world problems. We cannot take refuge in relative isolation.

I very often quote a story which cheers me up when I sometimes feel oppressed by the magnitude of the problems of the world and the sense of individual impotence in dealing with them. In the seventeenth century the famous Chancellor of Sweden, Count Axel Oxenstierna by name, had a son who had been offered a post in diplomacy but had refused it, saying that he did not know enough about it. His father wrote him a charming letter, in which he said: "My boy, you have no idea with what little wisdom the world is governed." We as doctors, social scientists, teachers— whatever our job may be—certainly do not know the answers to the world's problems. Neither, I may add, do the economists or the politicians. Everything that you and I can do to bring about better mental health in our locality and our country will add something to the sum total of wisdom available for the direction of the affairs of mankind.

References

1. Bowlby, J.: *Maternal Care and Mental Health,* WHO Monograph Series, no. 2, Geneva, 1951.
2. Burnet, M.: "The Future of Medical Research," *Lancet,* Jan. 17, 1953, pp. 103–108.
3. Fein, R.: *Economics of Mental Illness,* Basic Books, Inc., Publishers, New York, 1958.

3. A Survey of Mental Health Resources

E. E. Krapf and Joy M. Moser

Introduction

During 1960 the Mental Health Unit of the World Health Organization circulated an inquiry to members of the WHO Expert Advisory Panel on Mental Health, requesting information on mental health progress, resources, plans, and priorities. Replies were received from thirty-three countries.* Although data from several countries where considerable progress has been made are missing from the report, it is believed that the material presented will give at least some indication of the international situation.

Administrative Structures for Mental Health Services

Reports on the existence of a mental health division or section at the national level were received from twenty countries. Practically all such divisions and sections are within ministries or departments of health and welfare or public health.

In England and Wales, "the Mental Health Division is integrated as fully as possible with the other medical services, both centrally at the Ministry of Health and in other regions." In the Union of Soviet Socialist

Excerpted and adapted from a paper originally published in *Mental Hygiene*, 46:163–191, 1962. Current information is continuously collected by the Mental Health Unit of the World Health Organization in Geneva, under the direction of Dr. P. A. H. Baan, who became Chief in October, 1963, following the retirement of Dr. E. E. Krapf (who died a few months thereafter).

* Australia, Austria, Brazil, Canada, Chile, China (Taiwan), Colombia, Costa Rica, El Salvador, Federal Republic of Germany, Finland, France, Guatemala, Honduras, Iran, Ireland, Israel, Japan, Lebanon, New Zealand, Pakistan, Peru, Portugal, Ruanda-Urundi (now Rwanda and Burundi), Sweden, Switzerland, Thailand, Union of South Africa (now Republic of South Africa), United Arab Republic (Egypt), United Kingdom, United States of America, Union of Soviet Socialist Republics, and Yugoslavia.

Republics, "there is a group of specialist psychiatrists dealing with problems of psychiatry which forms part of the department of special services of the Ministry of Health of the U.S.S.R. and the Ministries of the Union Republics." Respondents from seven countries reported that there was no such national department nor was any envisaged.

In some countries there are mental health offices below the national level. Ireland is divided into eighteen hospital districts, each with a mental hospital authority responsible for the distribution of mental health services. In the Union of Soviet Socialist Republics, a psychiatrist is attached to each oblast (regional) health department. Mental health services in Canada are administered by separate divisions in health departments of each of the ten provinces, the national authority being mainly advisory. Japan has a mental health section in the Tokyo Health Bureau, and one or more officials are engaged in mental health services in the other forty-five prefectural health departments.

In the United States of America, the National Institute of Mental Health has nine regional offices, and each state has a mental health or mental hospitals authority, or both. The respondent from New Zealand mentions two regional hospital boards with small psychiatric departments. In Israel, the Mental Health Division of the Ministry of Health has a Psychiatric Advisory Committee consisting of leading Israeli psychiatrists.

Regional Organization of Mental Health Services

In several countries there are ongoing or projected plans for improving the organization of mental health services so as to reach a higher percentage of the population. The report from France, for instance, states that organization of services by districts is being stressed at the ministerial level and that this will entail a widespread increase in day and night services, work therapy, and sheltered workshops.

According to a comprehensive plan for the reorganization of mental health services in Sweden, many small hospitals for mental patients would be built in close contact with general hospitals and provide extensive extramural services: it is a "plan for 'infiltration of society' with mental health attitudes in many activities."

A similar attitude toward the organization of services is shown in Canada, where some feel that "the small regional psychiatric hospital, closely affiliated with the general hospital closely attached to community resources, may prove to be the unit of the future." In one of the provinces, Saskatchewan, a 180-bed regional psychiatric hospital has been planned as part of the general hospital complex. "An effort will be made to make this the center of a community service involving public health resources, family doctors, etc., in striving to return all patients admitted to the community."

The Australian report also mentions an increasing degree of regionalization and of rural services, as money and psychiatrists become available. A plan for regionalization was incorporated into the 1952 Mental Health Act in Finland, and efforts are being made to carry this plan into effect. In the United Kingdom, there has also been a great increase in community services.

Psychiatrists' Work in Public Institutions and Private Practice

In a number of countries, 80 per cent or more of the psychiatrists are stated to work in public institutions. This is true of most of Canada, China (Taiwan), England and Wales, Finland, Ireland, Israel, Japan, New Zealand, Pakistan, Scotland, the Union of Soviet Socialist Republics and the United Arab Republic (Egypt). In several cases it is mentioned that these psychiatrists also see private patients. For instance, in the U.S.S.R., "some psychiatrists in addition to their work in state medical establishments also receive patients on a private basis, but the size of such private practice is negligible." In Finland most of the psychiatrists in public institutions also run private practices, but very few have full-time private practices. The report from Israel states: "Apart from psychoanalysts there are only a few psychatrists in the country who do private practice only, but there are a number of hospital doctors who devote some hours per week to private psychotherapy or to consultative practice."

A somewhat lower percentage of psychiatrists work in public institutions in the following countries: Switzerland, 70 per cent; Lebanon, about 60 per cent; Austria, 50 per cent (of whom one-third are in part-time private practice). From some countries information was received on the percentage of psychiatrists' time spent in public institutions, as follows: Costa Rica, 70 per cent of the time; Guatemala and Portugal, 40 per cent.

In British Columbia (Canada), Colombia, El Salvador, Iran, Peru, and Thailand, considerably more time is devoted to private than to public practice. This is true also of registered psychiatrists in South Africa. The report from the United States of America states that "according to the American Psychiatric Association, based on a study of a 10 per cent sample of their membership, two-thirds treat private patients, but only 15 per cent are solely in private practice; about 16 per cent are in hospitals only." In the Federal Republic of Germany, 64 per cent of the psychiatrists are solely in private practice, and 6 per cent have both hospital and private work.

Availability of Personnel

About three-quarters of the respondents point to shortages of all categories of personnel. The greatest difficulty seeems to be unevenness of distribution, general physicians and psychiatrists tending to prefer working in urban areas. (In the United States of America, for instance, "there is an average of one psychiatrist per 12,200 people in the ten most urban states, and an average of one psychiatrist per 43,800 people in the ten most rural states.")

Shortages are mentioned in all responses, even from countries having the highest ratios of psychiatrists to the population. A number of reasons are suggested, including a lack of interest in psychiatric specialization; poor quality of psychiatric courses in medical schools; the absence of psychiatric training facilities; and the difficulty of getting suitable candidates, who are also deterred in some cases by the prospects of low status, unattractive working conditions, and low salaries. The Swedish report mentions that new services and specialized facilities have been established too rapidly to be adequately staffed with available personnel.

It would appear from the report from the Union of Soviet Socialist Republics that shortages of personnel in that country are not felt to be acute: psychiatry is included in the list of "harmful" occupations, and consequently "all psychiatric personnel enjoy a shorter working day (six hours), longer holidays (one month), are given 15 per cent and 30 per cent additions to the general medical salaries, and enjoy certain other privileges."

The *First Report* of the WHO Expert Committee on Mental Health suggests that "in order to provide satisfactory treatment for all cases of psychological disorder . . . it is necessary for a community to have one psychiatrist per 20,000 of the population." This would mean fifty psychiatrists per 1 million population. Linked to this factor is the question of how the psychiatrists' time is used, and, as indicated above, in some of the countries with a comparatively low complement of psychiatrists considerably more time is devoted to private practice than to work in public institutions.

In the face of the shortage of psychiatrists, it is encouraging to note the increase in numbers of physicians in countries with low staffing levels. It appears that future mental health endeavors in such countries can be greatly strengthened by the expansion of the mental health and psychiatric content of the training of the general practitioner.

A number of countries are employing at least some psychiatric social workers. In Peru, with a relatively low proportion of psychiatrists to the population, there are stated to be 7½ times as many psychiatric social workers as psychiatrists. The highest number, seventy-five per 1 million population, was reported from Israel. The largest ratio of clinical psychologists was found in the United States. Shortages of trained psychiatric nursing personnel were noted nearly everywhere.

Medical Training

The number of medical schools increased by one to four during the decade preceding the survey in several countries: Canada, China (Taiwan), Colombia, Finland, Iran, Peru, South Africa, Sweden, Thailand,

and Yugoslavia. In the United States of America seven schools were added, but in more than half of the responding countries there was no increase. Figures showed an increase of about 25 to 30 per cent over the decade in Austria, Canada, Peru, Sweden, and the United States of America; they approximately doubled in Colombia, Finland, Guatemala, and South Africa; and they showed a threefold to fourfold increase in Iran and Thailand. In Japan, however, the figures in 1959 were only 50 per cent of those ten years earlier, when physicians had been trained in temporary wartime courses. Figures for Sweden and for England and Wales showed a slight decline over the decade preceding the survey. Nearly all the reporting countries showed the same number of chairs of psychiatry as of medical schools.

Psychiatric Facilities

While some countries have made notable advances, the reports suggest that overcrowding continues to be a serious problem. There has been a considerable increase in the number of psychiatric wards in general hospitals, but not every country has such services. Of the countries reporting day hospital facilities, Canada, China (Taiwan), and Portugal showed less than one place per 100,000 population; the United Kingdom, 2.5; and the U.S.S.R., three. In both France and Ireland, two such hospitals are being planned, and the United States of America has seventy-six. There was very little information on night hospitals. Correspondents from Portugal and the U.S.S.R. report about eight places per 100,000 population in working villages, while Israel noted twenty-nine. In Switzerland such villages are attached to psychiatric hospitals.

Halfway houses or sheltered workshops exist in all psychiatric hospitals and clinics in the U.S.S.R. There are sixty-four such facilities in the United States of America, and one in Brazil. Israel has about seventeen places in rehabilitation institutions and 0.5 in halfway houses per 100,000; Canada, about 0.4 places; and Australia, 0.3. There are at least one halfway house in France and a certain number in the United Kingdom.

The numbers of beds reported per 100,000 population in private psychiatric hospitals are roughly as follows: 0, Honduras, U.S.S.R.; 0.1 to 2, Brazil, Canada, China (Taiwan), Costa Rica, Finland, Guatemala, Peru, Portugal; 8 to 20, Iran, Japan, United Kingdom, United States of America; 35, Ireland; 75, Israel; 100, Lebanon.

Means of Admission

Entry to psychiatric establishments in the most recent year for which statistics were available was reported to be on a voluntary basis for 75 to 100 per cent of all patients for the following countries: China (Taiwan), Japan, Serbia (Yugoslavia), and the United Kingdom. Approximately the same percentage applied also to short-stay hospitals in Canada.

The percentage of voluntary admissions was 45 to 60 for Ireland, New Zealand, Portugal, and Sweden. Statistics from ten states in the United States of America showed that 25 per cent of first admissions were voluntary.

Admission by administrative or court order still seems to apply to about 50 per cent of the patients in Austria, Guatemala, Ireland, New Zealand, and Sweden, and to 95 per cent in the United Arab Republic. In the U.S.S.R., admission depends on medical decision.

Average Duration of Stay

As pointed out in a reply from the United Kingdom, "it would be better to know the average stay of the percentage that stay for less than one year, or the percentage that stay for more than one year," since "nearly 90 per cent of those discharged are discharged within one year." For the United States of America, statistics on "length of stay for patients discharged from psychiatric hospitals are not collected nationally. One reason is that discharge represents a legal or administrative act, and, as such, varies from state to state. Thus, a patient may be carried 'on the books' of a hospital while on convalescent care from periods ranging from three months to three years, or more, while awaiting discharge. . . . In addition . . . definitions may vary regarding first admissions, readmissions and whether the duration of stay is for the current admission or total time in mental hospitals." The median length of stay varied from 57 to 126 days in eight states for first admissions in 1958, and from 57 to 141 days for readmissions.

In France, the average length of stay was 226 days in 1958 (averages of 82 to 349 days for the different *départements*). These figures were obtained by dividing the number of days of hospitalization by the number of patients treated in the year (i.e., those in the hospital on January 1, plus those admitted during the year).

For other countries, average durations of stay of 30 to 763 days are reported. As compared with ten years earlier, such durations appear to have been shortened by about one-third or more.

Average Cost

The cost per patient per day in psychiatric hospitals was computed as a fraction of that per patient in general hospitals. Of nineteen countries from which reports were received, one showed costs of roughly three-quarters for psychiatric patients, seven showed costs of roughly one-half, and eleven showed costs of roughly one-quarter.

As stated in the reply from the United Kingdom, because of the large number of chronic patients, the cost per patient in psychiatric hospitals is much lower than in general hospitals. "It should be remembered that, although mental disorder needs between 40 and 50 per cent of all bed accommodation, it only deals with 3 per cent of the admissions to hospital."

Psychiatric Outpatient Departments

From the data received from most countries it is not possible to ascertain whether the number of clinics given includes those operated by psychiatric hospitals. For example, figures for Switzerland include psychiatric polyclinics and psychiatric hospitals with polyclinic consultations. Those for the U.S.S.R. include psychoneurologic sections in polyclinics but exclude consultation services and outpatient treatment by psychiatric hospitals. In the reply from the United States, psychiatric outpatient departments are defined as "mental health clinics with outpatient services and a psychiatrist in attendance at regularly scheduled hours who takes the medical responsibility for all clinic patients."

The number of psychiatric outpatient clinics reported per 1 million population ranged from 0.01 to 0.4 for Brazil, China (Taiwan), Colombia, Pakistan, Thailand, and the United Arab Republic to more than ten for France, Ireland, and Japan. The United Kingdom, the United States of America, and the U.S.S.R. indicated from 5.0 to 9.9 clinics per 1 million population. All reporting countries showed an increase in the number of units over the decade preceding the survey, several by 50 to 200 per cent.

The numbers of first consultations per year per 100,000 population varied from 24 (South Africa) to 520 (Japan) for the most recent year, and increases of 14 to 200 per cent were shown compared with ten years earlier. Numbers of total consultations per 100,000 population for the most recent year varied from 125 (South Africa) to 2,030 (Japan), increases over the preceding ten years ranging from 10 to 200 per cent.

It would appear that the shortage of other provisions for psychiatric care in certain countries is not counteracted by widespread outpatient services.

Children's Facilities

Not all the reporting countries have child guidance or parent education centers. The U.S.S.R. stated that "with regard to examination and guidance for children, one pediatrician-psychoneurologist in a medical district provides services for 4,000 healthy children." In France, nearly half of the total number of individual consultations in psychiatric outpatient clinics were given to children.

Student mental health services do not appear to be widespread. In the United Kingdom, "all universities, except Oxford, where medical services are linked with colleges, have student health services. Usually, one of the two or three student medical officers takes a special interest in the psychiatric aspects."

Most of the respondents mention facilities for children with psychiatric disorders either in special departments of psychiatric hospitals, in separate units, or in separate outpatient clinics. A comparison of available services between countries cannot be made because of the lack of detailed data. It is not always certain whether the services mentioned include or exclude services cited elsewhere in the inquiry.

Research

In response to a request for information on research institutions for the study of mental health problems, several countries—e.g., Canada, China (Taiwan), England and Wales, Finland, Scotland, and the U.S.S.R.—referred to research carried out through departments of psychiatry in the universities, frequently in cooperation with medical schools. Mention was made of research units in mental hospitals in Australia, England and Wales, and Scotland, and such units are known to exist in a number of other countries.

Japan and the United States of America each named its National Institute of Mental Health as the most important research and coordinating body, the latter country having also many other institutes and foundations devoted to mental health research. The Federal Republic of Germany has the German Research Institute for Psychiatry in Munich. Pakistan has an Institute of Mental Health which fosters some research. Thailand has three units carrying out research on specific problems. In France, psychiatric research comes under the aegis of the Centre National de Recherche Scientifique and the Institut National d'Hygiène. Research is sponsored by the Medical Research Council in England and Wales and in Ireland. The U.S.S.R. report enumerated the Institute of Psychiatry of the U.S.S.R. Academy of Medical Sciences, that of the Ministry of Health, and that of Georgia; psychoneurologic institutes in Leningrad (Bekhterev Institute), Kharkov, and Odessa; and the Serbski Institute of Forensic Psychiatry. In South Africa, the National Institute for Personnel Research carries out studies on mental health problems.

Throughout the field of mental health endeavor, an important increase in emphasis on the need for research has become apparent in the post-World War II period. It is widely realized that there is far more to be discovered in the etiology, treatment, and prevention of mental disorders than is known. The problem of means of promoting mental health is beginning to be attacked. Methods of organization of mental health facilities and services are being studied scientifically in a few areas.

The means and effects of mental health education are being investigated. Activities connected with the epidemiology of mental disorders have multiplied, and one of the initial difficulties, agreement on nomenclature and classification, is receiving increasing attention.

In each of these areas of research and investigation, great changes in approach have taken place in recent years. Scientific methods of planning and execution of research projects are being applied, and importance is attached to the evaluation of results. The necessity for multidisciplinary cooperation in many research activities is now understood.

The quest for information has led to the uncovering of a vast quantity of isolated facts. In an effort to integrate and coordinate this knowledge, important developments have occurred in the publication of findings, the indexing and sorting of information, the organization of seminars and conferences for the exchange of recent findings, and national and international travel for the comparison of results. These tasks have been assisted by the growth of national and international mental health societies and organizations.

There is no universal agreement on what constitutes mental health nor on what the mental health tasks are, but at least among those interested in the field it has become more clearly apparent that just as appreciable advances can be made in the physical health of a community through continuous endeavor, so it now seems probable that progress can be made in the public's mental health.

Summary

A survey of mental health progress and problems is presented, based on questionnaire responses received by the WHO Mental Health Unit from thirty-three countries. It is hoped that this consideration of facilities and resources will be useful in planning for future research and development. (See Chapter 26, "Mental Health Research: A Summary Report of Suggested Priorities.")

4. Mental Health Programs in Public Health Planning

Arie Querido

Introduction

Definition of the Subject

For the purpose of this chapter, mental hygiene or mental health care is conceived as the sum of activities, based on a body of scientific understanding, to promote, protect, maintain, and restore mental health in man. Mental health is an integral part of the general concept of health, as expressed in the preamble of the WHO Constitution.

The term "public health care" is used within the frame of the definition originating from Winslow [4] and amended by the Expert Committee on Public Health Administration in its *Fourth Report*.[15] The term is therefore used to designate care organized by community effort. In some countries, however, organized community effort includes medical care for the sick, which may encompass hospital care as well as the activities of the general practitioner.

Elsewhere, either the hospital or the general practitioner, or both, may be partly or entirely outside organized community effort. In some countries, organized community effort is limited to preventive activities; in others, curative activities are partly or entirely included. Public health care, therefore, refers to an organizational situation, and it remains uncertain, without further qualification, which activities the term covers. When it is desired to refer to all preventive and curative activities in a given area irrespective of organizational structure, the term "general health care" is used.

Based on reports received from forty-four governments and prepared as a working paper for the technical discussions at the Fifteenth World Health Organization Assembly (1962); previously published in the *Tijdschrift voor Sociale Geneeskunde*, Nov. 16, 30, 1962, and in *Mental Hygiene*, 46:626–654, 1962; adapted for this volume.

The subject matter requires frequent use of terms that might possibly lead to misinterpretation because of the different structure of health services and the organization of medical care in various countries. This difficulty is met whenever similar subjects are to be discussed and has been dealt with in various WHO publications.[7,11,15] No mention is made of problems concerning the mentally subnormal, since the implications of this topic are too far-reaching to be dealt with satisfactorily as a subsidiary item.

Since mental health care deals with the relations of man to others, it will be the concern of all those who, by reason of their role, position, or profession in society, influence these relations. The work of policy makers, legislators, administrators, educators, and mass-media experts has implications for the mental health of the population. Just as physical hygiene, however, could only develop as a science from the understanding of the pathologic, the scientific basis of mental health care took its origin from the experience gained in dealing with mental patients.

While in the field of mental health care it is possible to delineate the proper domain of the psychiatrist, i.e., the care and cure of those suffering from or theatened with mental illness, there are a number of areas where other experts and professionals bear the main responsibility, but where the psychiatrist can contribute from his experience until those experts have integrated mental hygiene principles in their own body of knowledge.

Therefore, for the present, it does not seem desirable to attempt to define the field too closely, including certain activities and excluding others. It seems more appropriate to follow the historical pattern of development with the psychiatric activities in the center, fanning out into adjoining areas.

Need to Bring Mental Health into Public Health Planning

At present a renaissance of medicine is being witnessed: the rediscovery of the patient as a human being and, by implication, the introduction of mental health thinking into general medicine.[5,6,10] The number of reports that have introduced this element in their argument is remarkable.

"Since people cannot be divided into physical beings and mental beings," states one report, "we are compelled to coordinate and integrate the goals and definitions of services and hence the services themselves." "Public health and mental health care services are so intimately interwoven that it would be difficult, and indeed harmful, to attempt a separation," remarks another.

A third report observes that "mental health deals with persons and their environment as well as public health does"; a fourth, that ". . . since 1950, a general tendency exists to make mental health care equivalent to general medical care"; and, to finish these quotations, "the public health approach to mental disorders is the same as the public health approach to other groups of illnesses: prevent what we know how to prevent; terminate and mitigate what we know how to terminate and mitigate; reduce disabilities resulting from illness."

While strong statements are to be found in the reports advocating the integration of mental health programs in public health activities, at the same time many point out that these activities often, or even always, touch on mental health problems, since they are concerned with people who frequently seek public health service because they are in a transitional or critical stage of their lives. These again are arguments for the closest possible cooperation, if not for the identification of mental health care as an aspect of general health care.

Many reports point out that no clear lines can be drawn between preventive and curative activity. If, for technical reasons, delineations must be made, the interaction between prevention and cure is so close that it is impossible to separate their effects.

The same point has been emphasized by Mackintosh,[2] who remarks that "it must be clearly stated, however, that preventive and curative medicine have reached the stage where they are no longer separable . . ." and "during the period following the second World War there has been a very strong tendency to move toward the further integration of health and medical care. It may be confidently predicted that this movement will gain in strength." The course of events in subsequent years, as well as the remarks in the reports on this point, have confirmed Mackintosh's prediction.

From the reports which express themselves on this point, it can be concluded that separation of cure and prevention in the mental health field is acceptable only when carried out for technical reasons. Assimilation of mental health care in general health care is highly desirable. It may be expected that this assimilation will increase the potentialities of both fields of endeavor and, of more specific pertinence to our subject, will bring the potentialities of modern mental health care to the population.

Feasibility of Modern Mental Health Care Programs

In the following pages a number of mental health care procedures and activities will be discussed as they were gathered from the various reports.[8,10,16] Many reports, however, also mention the impossibility of carrying out these activities for lack of expert personnel and adequate funds. Frequently the remark is made that programs advocating such activities are unrealistic in view of actual conditions, especially in developing countries. There is an unmistakable tendency to employ meager resources exclusively for the care of the most seriously deteriorated patients, who seem too often the most pressing or, indeed, the only problem. Several reports, while acknowledging the importance of other activities, postpone these to some later phase when it is hoped additional personnel and funds will be available. This means a perpetuation of the custodial mental hospital system for an indefinite period.

This attitude implies a danger, for without exception the reports make it clear that as long as the classical, i.e., custodial, mental hospital remains the main or the only remedy offered, the problems will keep on moving in a vicious circle. Since double or even triple overcrowding in mental hospitals is not uncommon, the creation of adequate space alone will cause intolerable burdening of the budget; lack of personnel renders the service so unrewarding that no new personnel can be induced to seek service and physicians feel no incentive to take posts in mental hospitals. Furthermore, it is well understood that an increase of mental hospital accommodations does not offer any real solution but will only result in a new accumulation of patients and new overcrowding.

It is not only developing countries that complain of lack of funds and personnel. The same complaint is heard in practically all reports.

While it may be a philosophical question whether it will ever be possible fully to satisfy mental health (and general health) needs, even in developed countries the provisions are often dramatically below what is considered a minimum requirement. One report from a highly developed country vividly describes the extraordinary difficulties—and failure—in making a radical change in the classical pattern of care for mental patients because of lack of funds and personnel.

The way the legislative and administrative base for the care of the mentally ill originated in many countries (custody and segregation being the main purpose) caused a development into patterns of procedure which, at present, cannot be regarded as adequate for the tasks of modern mental health care. In some countries these patterns have been changed; in others they are so rudimentary that they are no impediment to change. Elsewhere, and especially in many developed countries, they are most extensive, and replacement and rebuilding must be carried out while the everyday functions go on—a difficult problem for a building as well as for an organization.

It is well to bear in mind that the great majority of activities constituting modern mental health care programs are *functions* which are not necessarily identical with an equal number of specialists or with the existence of various specific institutions.[10,16] The expert worker can carry out, supervise, and advise on a number of different functions, each representing an item in the program, just as one building can have many varied activities going on under its roof. Obviously a limited number of personnel will limit both the extension and the depth of the proposed activities.

Both extensions and increases in depth (or sophistication) required additional personnel and money. As to extension, it is not inevitable that the number of specialists has to be increased correspondingly with the increasing scope of the service. The provision of specialists whose functions would be mainly consultative and advisory would enhance their effectiveness without increasing their number in the same ratio.

As to increased depth in mental health care, this is achieved by specialization and differentiation coordinated in the mental health team. The psychiatrist becomes a social psychiatrist, a psychotherapist, a child psychiatrist, etc. Undifferentiated auxiliary personnel become mental nurses, psychiatric social workers, occupational and recreational therapists, etc. The psychologist, pedagogue, and sociologist are brought in.

In the light of practical experience it would, however, seem a mistake to try to establish a broad differentiation at the start of any mental health program. Irrespective of whether the start is made in a developing or an advanced country, further increases in depth and further differentiation can only develop as the results of the interplay of given conditions and current activity.

"To plan the mental program in relation to the present situation and expand it as personnel becomes available and the situation warrants it is the essence of a sophisticated approach," as one report remarks. It might be well to examine at which strategic points the specialists should be placed and what could be regarded as the minimum requirements for the start of a mental health program.

Evolution of Mental Health Care Provisions

The Mental Hospital: Old and New Roles

Many reports condemn, sometimes in the strongest terms, the mental hospital as being detrimental to the well-being of the patients.[9] Frequently this detrimental influence is identified with the custodial functions of the mental hospital. It must, however, be accepted as an undeniable fact that it may be necessary to place a mental patient under custodial care, either in his own interest or in the interest of others; this fact is duly mentioned in several reports. On the other hand, it will be admitted— again, as numerous reports point out—that this is only necessary exceptionally, and the period during which the involuntary stay has to be enforced may be short. If some levity be permitted, it might be said that "you may have to lock up some patients sometime, but never all patients and never all the time."

It cannot be denied that deprivation of the patient's liberty may be detrimental to his condition and to his chances of recovery. The fact, however, that in some cases a stay has to be enforced does not obviate the necessity to provide treatment, and it is this treatment which is frequently reported as lacking. A similar deterioration of the inmates, which some reports vividly describe, can be observed in those children's and old people's homes where adequate care is lacking but where there is no question of custody.

The detrimental influence, so widely ascribed to the mental hospital, is not chiefly a result of its custodial function; rather, it results from the fact that apart from custody few or no adequate activities are carried out to promote the patients' well-being and cure. As one report remarks: "The difference in length of stay in various mental hospitals is determined by the therapeutic principles applied." In the light shed by other reports, it might be added "and by whether any therapeutic principles are applied at all."

Several reports remark that the population expects or demands that the mentally ill be segregated and secured in closed institutions. This attitude is understandable as long as the fear of the "madman" persists. It may be pointed out that this fear is chiefly fed by the image of the patient as it results from long years of inadequate care; this image is identified with the mentally ill, in general, and with the hopelessness of the psychiatric case. The mass media have done much to exploit this fear. As long as the mental hospital remains a horrible place, which, indeed, produces horrors, no other attitude can be hoped for. It is only when the mental hospital can point toward positive results that this attitude can be expected to change.

The "no-restraint" movements of the nineteenth century arose from the understanding that the insane should be kept in a place that was more a hospital than a prison; Esquirol's [1] ideas are still fully applicable today.

The systematic attempts to change the role of the mental hospital, based on an insight into normal and abnormal human behavior, are now almost fifty years old and yielded considerable results long before the discovery of the ataractic drugs.[9] The importance of these drugs as offering enormous support to psychotherapy and sociotherapy is generally recognized,[12] but they can offer only a partial solution to the therapeutic problem, since they deal with certain aspects of the patient only. There is even some danger that they will detract from the main therapeutic target, that is, the totality of the sick person.

The so-called "active therapy" (Simon van der Scheer, T. P. Rees, P. Sivadon, and others) was worked out during and after World War I and was assimilated in many mental hospitals. The essence of this method is the creation of a therapeutic community, a miniature society in which the patient can be made to experience and to enjoy being a member. He receives compensation for his labor, has responsibility, lives as an individual, and seeks recreation. The changes brought about by this regime in the mental hospital can only be called revolutionary. The revolting aspects of the mental hospital disappeared; the average length of stay decreased until it was counted in months instead of years. The interdependence with environment, not only of behavior but of symptoms which were generally regarded as inherent in the illness, was once more demonstrated, as had been done by Philippe Pinel more than a century before.

It may be recalled that changes in the old and often dismal wards—changes essential to create a comfortable and permissive environment—were often carried out by the most primitive means and by the patients themselves. Furthermore, as a rule, the change of regime was carried out by the old staff; it was usually sufficient when one staff member had really studied and grasped the philosophy of active therapy and was able to direct and inspire the others. It must not be forgotten that it was not only the patients but also the medical and nursing staff who had to be exposed to an intensive period of reorientation and reeducation. It is deeply to be regretted that the ravages wrought by World War II, in which mental hospitals and their patients suffered severely in many countries, destroyed much of this work. At present the world's mental hospitals seem to show all stages, from the pre-Pinel and the pre-Simon to the therapeutic community.

From the tenor of most of the reports, as well as from a number of explicit statements, the conclusion can be drawn that the old mental hospital concept is regarded, without reservation, as obsolete.

On the other hand, the mental hospital as a therapeutic community has to be considered as an essential link in the mental health care provisions of a community. A considerable number of patients require a procedure of reeducation, resocialization, and rehabilitation. This process may take months and often needs a combination of various forms of psychotherapy, drug therapy, and occupational, recreational, and social therapy. This principle is being further developed; the interaction of the patient with his group and with the hospital personnel has been formulated in the terminology of modern psychology. New concepts of group psycho-therapeutic mechanisms are being developed and tested.

In countries in which the readaptation will have to be made with a highly industrialized society, this will require institutions specially equipped with workshops, recreational facilities, and extensive grounds. Apart from a number of more or less specific medical provisions, this new mental hospital has chiefly the function of a rehabilitation center. Countries offering a more agricultural setting require a therapeutic community conforming more generally to their social pattern.

To educate and treat a patient by giving him trust and responsibility requires doing away with the locked door. Many reports mention that in some of the wards or part of the hospital the doors are open. This situation has to be distinguished from the "open ward" which in many countries is reported as a feature of the mental hospital. While the "open-door" system may be found in an institution which in itself is "closed" (the patient is legally committed in a hospital with an active therapeutic system), the open ward receives patients on a voluntary basis. The open ward is, therefore, a further step in what can be called the emancipation of the mental patient. There is considerable difference as to the frequency of these voluntary admissions and the proportion of open to closed wards. In a few countries no such facilities are reported; in others, the number of voluntary admissions may range from 10 to 85 per cent of all admissions. The extent to which the open-ward system is in use may be regarded as a fair measure of the level of psychiatric hospital care and of its acceptance by the population.

The Evolution of Extramural Mental Health Care

One of the results which follow logically from an active regime in the mental hospital is the need for closer contact with society.[8,10] Improved behavior and the disappearance of symptoms have to be followed by parole and discharge; the ties with the family must be maintained or strengthened; what the patient has been taught in the hospital must be applied outside.

Since the therapeutic community is an artificial society, it is possible to adjust the burden put by this society on its members according to what the patient is able to bear; this method, in fact, makes it a therapeutic instrument. To consolidate the gains of intramural therapy, it might be necessary, in a number of cases, to assist the patient's adaptation to society after his discharge by a device for adjusting the burden of society, within limits, according to the needs of the patient. The device is the *aftercare system*, which developed in several countries as a consequence of an improved mental hospital regime.

In its first stage, it extends certain intramural activities outside the hospital for the benefit of discharged patients. Guidance and support are given to the patient and his family by nurses, social workers, or doctors, or by all of them. Mediation with all kinds of social institutions on behalf of the patient is carried out. If return to the hospital should be necessary, this extended influence makes such a step easier for the patient to accept and less of a traumatic occurrence.

Gradually the tendency to project a greater number of activities from the hospital into society arises. If the patient does not require the extensive adjustments possible only in the artificial hospital society, there are great advantages in leaving him in his own environment and bringing the therapeutic facilities of the hospital to him. In this way he may profit from occupational and recreational therapy through the organization of sheltered workshops and clubs. Psychotherapy, chemotherapy, and group therapy may be found in day hospitals, outpatient clinics, etc.

As will be understood, when the possibilities reach this scope, they are no longer destined exclusively for patients discharged from mental hospitals but are also for patients who have never been admitted to a mental hospital. At this stage, aftercare activities begin to merge with preventive activities and other curative activities in the mental health field—early diagnosis and treatment, marriage counseling, child guidance, vocational guidance—while public health activities are being approached, and important interaction may develop with other agencies.

Special mention has to be made of *outpatient services* (polyclinics, dispensaries, etc.). Their development may, in some instances, be a result of the orientation of the mental hospital toward society: an aftercare service may become the center of ambulatory psychiatric treatment in the community. Frequently the outpatient department develops independently of the mental hospital. In that case, it is a concomitant of medical specialization, which requires high-level ambulatory treatment, backed by such hospital facilities as laboratories, X-ray installations, etc. The psychiatric outpatient department offers early diagnosis and treatment in close cooperation with other medical specialties. Especially when linked with clinical wards on the one side and with a social service on the other, it may become a very important instrument for primary and secondary prevention.

Extramural activities are often brought together in a comprehensive mental health care service or at least in some focus of activity, such as the mental health clinic, the outpatient service, or the psychiatric hospital service. In this way the sociopsychiatric service comes into being, conceived as an organization coordinating a number of facilities that will ensure prevention, early detection, referral for adequate treatment, rehabilitation, and follow-up in the mental health field. It is designed to give psychiatric care a dynamic character by fitting it to the requirements and potentialities of the patient at each stage of his illness and by exploiting the possibilities of the community to the utmost. Rural areas may profit from these activities by means of mobile teams based on a central organization.

Psychiatric Wards in General Hospitals

It has become clear from the reports that psychiatric wards have been in general hospitals in several countries for many years. In other countries the introduction has been made more recently; in some, the possibility is under consideration, and in a very few the reaction is negative. Among the advantages may be mentioned the fact that the length of hospitalization is usually short and no commitment is involved, so that there is less social disruption for the patient and his family. Early diagnosis and intensive treatment may eliminate the necessity for transfer to long-stay institutions. The presence of the psychiatrist may lead to consultation with other specialists and improve medical services throughout the hospital.

One report mentions as a possible disadvantage that the staffs of mental hospitals would be depleted and that only chronic patients would be sent to mental hospitals. On the other hand, the establishment of psychiatric wards in general hospitals might increase psychiatric manpower by attracting psychiatrists in private practice and by using these wards as teaching centers for medical nursing students.

It is generally agreed in the reports that psychiatric units in general hospitals should not become too large and that the patients should be selectively admitted (acute cases and psychoneurotic conditions as a result or complication of physical illness).

It may be remarked that in countries with very few psychiatrists there seems to be little point in admitting psychiatric patients to outlying hospitals, which can only infrequently be visited by psychiatrists.

When the total organization of mental health care shows enough differentiation to allow some choice, it becomes important to establish a *screening center* in which the patient can be observed and examined and a course of treatment and rehabilitation worked out. Such a screening center can be of great importance to the efficiency of the entire mental health care apparatus. To neglect this screening procedure enlarges the risk that the illness will be unduly prolonged or that the patient will be reduced to permanent invalidism. Apart from the human suffering that can be prevented in this way, the costs involved are only a fraction of what has to be spent later on the care of those initially neglected patients.

It is not possible to give a generally valid ratio of inpatients to outpatients in such a center; much depends on its relationship to other facilities. But as a general requirement it can be stated that, to fulfill its function, the center must be able to make use of the full aid of specialist consultation and laboratory facilities of modern medicine. To erect such a center as a separate hospital would be a costly duplication of a general hospital, and the same would be true if such a center were attached to a mental hospital. The most effective way seems to be to incorporate it into a general hospital or to associate the two very closely.

Under favorable circumstances this center can become the strong point of the mental health care organization. It may function as a teaching unit for future specialist personnel, medical undergraduates, and general nursing personnel. Its outpatient department may function as a sociopsychiatric service for the region; it may form the basis of a psychiatric emergency service. It can contribute enormously to the assimilation of mental health practice into the general hospital and into the public health and social services of the community.

Mental Health Implications in Other Fields

As mentioned previously, mental health care has no monopoly of dealing with interhuman relations and their disturbances. These are also the concern of many other agencies working in the community, such as the educational organization, public assistance, and the agencies dealing with juvenile and adult delinquency, with prostitution, and with special groups such as migrants and foreign laborers. It is, or at least has been, a general complaint that these activities are locked in watertight compartments and that no interchange of experience, information, or ideas takes place. A mental health service may often be instrumental in breaking through these compartments to mutual advantage.

It is often necessary, in order to make the existing possibilities in the community available to the patient, to arrange contact with social agencies, public and private organizations, and the public health services. This contact may lead to two results. In the first place, it may be discovered that the other agency has problems in connection with clients who turn out to be mentally disturbed but were not recognized as such. This contact may prove an important means of case detection. In the second place, further contact may lead to an understanding of mutual procedures that can be most instructive. In this way, there may arise a consulting activity which originally was more or less accidental and informal but which may result in a diffusion of mental health principles at strategic points in the community.

Recapitulation

In the Introduction it was argued that the development of modern medicine renders it imperative to bring preventive and curative activities together and to recognize mental health care as an aspect of general health care. In the section on "Evolution of Mental Health Care Provisions" it was shown that mental health care at present has evolved in such a way that it can provide a program of comprehensive care in its own field. Public health care in its content has many mental health elements, while mental health care in its structure and in its aims has become more and more an aspect of general health care. It would seem that the time is ripe to increase and expedite attempts that will lead to a merging, assimilation, or integration of mental health programs in public health planning, resulting in a comprehensive activity of general health care.

The following sections of this chapter will be devoted to the examination of the question of how this aim is to be achieved. It is realized that no single answer is possible and that in the final analysis each country will have to find its own solution. It can, however, be assumed that the longer the history of the various provisions in a given country and the more complex the current state of development of these provisions, the greater the difficulties that will be met in achieving this merging. Countries which still have to build the major part of their health organization have, in this respect, a great advantage.

When analyzing the reports received, one is impressed by the fact that fundamentally there is very little difference in the problems to be faced, irrespective of the state of development of the country. This may seem hardly credible in view of the vast differences in resources and in sophistication of organization. It would appear, however, that the similarity of problems to be solved and the way to solve them largely overrides the differences, which are more a matter of quantity than of principle.

Organization, Training, and Research

General

These subjects are interdependent and so closely interwoven that they are brought under one heading, although a systematic treatment of each will be attempted. Research is used to include epidemiologic and other surveys and deliberate studies undertaken to provide information for the planning or evaluation of services.

Ideally, first should come surveys to determine the nature and extent of needs. This procedure would offer the possibility of drafting an organizational scheme that would answer the questions of functions and facilities required and the strength of the necessary personnel. This would lead in turn to the establishment of a quantitative and qualitative training schedule from which a timetable could be drawn to show when the organization could be expected to become operative.

Next to a quantitative study of needs, a study of population attitudes is necessary to determine the measure of tolerance of the community in regard to the mentally ill, which, of course, will be an important factor in establishing the extent and the nature of the resources actually to be provided. Furthermore, the study of population attitudes may be the basis for the educational and informative campaign that will be necessary to gain the cooperation of the public in regard to the proposed facilities.[13] In practice, this procedure is seldom strictly and fully followed. Apart from the fact that the type of research needed is lengthy and costly and that manifest needs will press for action, it is very difficult to carry this procedure out before some organization has been established. Facilities may stimulate demands which were not present, and shortages of personnel and difficulties of recruitment may make it necessary to postpone the execution of plans.

In the light of past experience it may be stated that well-planned preliminary research, even if it would postpone action and absorb funds that seem so urgently needed for the alleviation of manifest needs, will make it possible to avoid costly mistakes and will result in higher efficiency of the established services.

In the reports it is unanimously stated that *training of personnel must have priority over organization of services;* the fallacy of having services which cannot be manned is pointed out. This signifies that it is the general opinion that the scope of services is determined by the strength of personnel available. This conclusion may seem to be an undeniable fact, but it requires qualification, as will be shown below.

As is pointed out in one report, in various countries considerable differences will be found in the need of personnel to be trained for carrying out mental health programs. In one country the most urgent need may be to have additional social psychiatrists or child psychiatrists; in another the need for social workers or home visitors may be more pressing. Therefore, it does not seem enough to give training priority over organization: the question of the level of the personnel trained has also to be considered. It would appear that here is raised a point of primary importance which requires further examination. What are the organizational factors determining the level and strength of personnel required?

Organizational Considerations

The usual way of starting a mental health activity, in developing as well as in advanced countries, is by the establishment of a nucleus, activated by some inspired person or group, by a pilot study or a demonstration project. It is expected—and in many instances the expectation has proved to be justified—that the example established in this way will cause a chain reaction, which in due time will extend the activity both in scope and in depth. This is how mental health activities have been established in most countries.

As a rule these activities were started with a view to individual needs, and no quantitative considerations concerning the needs of the total population were taken into account. Indeed, the initiative did not have this purpose; it was taken to ascertain whether the activity was workable in a given setting and not to provide a service for the entire population, as for instance would be the aim in establishing an organization to combat a widespread infectious disease.

From many reports, especially those originating from developing countries, the impression is gained that numerous projects initiated as nuclei or pilot studies fail to cause the desired chain reaction. Since they do not propagate, it turns out to be impossible to extend the activities, and this is ascribed to lack of personnel.

At the same time, advanced countries, in which mental health provisions have been operating for some time, begin to relate existing provisions to the needs of the population as a whole, and they come to the conclusion that a wide gap exists between available provisions and estimated needs, a gap which again results from the lack of expert personnel. A study of the figures shows that in most instances it will not be possible to fill this gap in the foreseeable future. Taking the highest current figures of plus or minus 1,000 physicians per 1 million population, of whom plus or minus 50 are psychiatrists, and using, furthermore, the generally accepted estimate that in the same countries 5 to 10 per cent of the population is in need of some psychiatric care, we find that even in the most advanced countries this number of psychiatrists would have to be increased between five and ten times, equaling half the total number of physicians, to give every patient one hour's time a month. Obviously this is not a realistic goal.

Fundamentally this problem is the same for developing countries as for developed countries, although the even greater gap existing in the former may necessitate different practical solutions.

The problem which is met here can be formulated as follows: the purpose of any health service is to make the full range of medical knowledge existing in a given field available to the entire population or population group deemed in need of that service. Ideally this would mean that each member of the population should have access to the specialists and provisions in that field. In a very few, albeit important, instances this ideal seems on the way to being realized; in the vast majority of countries the reality is far from the ideal state, certainly in the mental health field.

This being the case, it has to be asked: what is the highest level of the health organization at which the personnel is in sufficient numerical strength to provide total or optimal coverage in the field in question—in this case, in the field of mental health care?

The answer will vary according to the country. In the majority of developed countries, coverage can be provided by the general practitioners; there are sufficient general practitioners to be reached directly by any member of the population. In developing countries this is often not the case; here the highest level to give optimal coverage may be provided by nurses or again, when sufficient trained nurses are not available, by a body of health workers with a simpler training. However thin the lower level may be spread, it will always give greater coverage than any higher level and, since training is shorter, an increase will be more rapidly achieved.

If the highest level of skill is numerically not strong enough to provide the desired coverage, the skill has to be made available to the population by encompassing its permeation into the lower level where there are many professional workers.

If this principle could be accepted, the scope of a service would not remain limited by the strength of its highest expert personnel, as at present is often the case in mental health services, but by the way the required levels of skill are distributed in the service and the lines of communication between these levels. It will be understood that the level of skill may not be determined by a single specialist activity, such as psychiatry, mental health nursing, psychiatric social work, etc., but by the combined activities of a group of specialists, who make up a mental health team.

The problems which are faced when further development of mental health activities is contemplated may be seen in the light of maldistribution of specialist potential. It may be that echelon formation, as outlined above, could offer some solutions; in that case the problem is simplified when it is also possible to channel mental health programs through public health activities.

Since the public health workers are *eo ipso* concerned with the mental health aspects of their activities, the training necessary to establish a mental health echelon at their level will not imply an extension of their allotted task but a rounding off of this task itself. The same may be true of workers in such allied fields as education, social work, etc.

What has been the single level of activity would become at least two or perhaps even three levels. The first contact, initial screening, and dealing with cases of the average type will have to be entrusted to personnel working at levels which give greater coverage to the population. In the advanced countries this will be the general practitioners and the personnel of such public health services as mother-and-child care, school health, industrial health care, and care for the aged. It may be possible to establish a more advanced echelon by making use of the teaching staffs of schools and social workers in various allied fields.

The specialists themselves will have to be placed at a level at which the specificity of their aptitudes can be fully used to the advantage of lower-echelon workers: by providing advice, consultation, supervision, and teaching, and by dealing with special cases. Usually the specialists will be working in a team—the mental health team—consisting of psychiatrist, social worker, psychologist, or other or more subspecialized workers. It is characteristic of the mental health team that each member carries his own responsibility in regard to the case at issue. If it is deemed necessary, in order to increase effectiveness, to move the specialist to a more consultative and advisory level, the team should be regarded as a unit that has to be moved as a whole. It may be possible to organize an intermediate level at which persons are trained to perform therapeutic activities without having had the training of the physician. It does not seem desirable to state dogmatically where the proposed expert level should be placed within the organization as a whole. Here various countries will require different solutions. If a screening center should have been developed in the sense of the central point in a comprehensive mental health organization, this would seem the logical place. This place may, however, also be in the mental health department of a comprehensive health service or in the psychiatric department (provided it gives clinical, social, and outpatient care) of a large general or teaching hospital.

Countries which still have to develop their mental health programs must start with nucleus or pilot projects as before, but this does not detract from the necessity of establishing representation at the administrative level, as will be discussed later.

It is of the greatest importance for future success that the place of this nucleus in the existing or proposed health organization be chosen with regard to its strategic value, for, assuming that this nucleus will be run by experts, they will be the very few experts available in the country for an appreciable period. Their initial position in the organizational frame determines the level from which they will operate. If the level chosen is too low, the same difficulties that are experienced in advanced countries will be felt, but they will come sooner and be more serious.

Although the choice of operating level of the initial project and of the experts is most important, here again dogmatic pronouncements must be avoided. A good place would seem to be a hospital in which the teaching of medical undergraduates and general nursing personnel is carried out. A psychiatric ward in such a teaching hospital might form a center from which outpatient activities and the mental health care in the area the hospital is serving could be developed and directed.

It might also be possible to use as nucleus a new-style mental hospital with outpatient facilities from which cooperation with general hospitals and the other existing health facilities might be developed. The importance of training future specialists, general practitioners, and public health personnel at all levels should be kept in mind.

The two initiatives mentioned above are based on either general or specialist hospitals. It may, however, be argued (as has notably been done in the Sudan, for example) that a first principle of mental health care is to maintain the links and the affinities of the patient with his family and his group. The initial structure and the backbone of a mental health program might consist of outpatient services, with hospitalization taking second place. This concept seems to be very important and worthy of discussion. It must be remarked, however, that a system of outpatient services can be established only if a certain number of specialists are available; it may be possible to limit this number by placing the outpatient units in echelons, but obviously a minimum of specialist staff will be required to make the system workable.

It would seem—but this may be a point of discussion—that it is not possible to carry out all psychiatric teaching in an outpatient service, although the possibilities are larger than is generally assumed. Some clinical teaching will be necessary, if only to integrate psychiatry with other branches of medicine. The outpatient service (which might be part of the public health service) should be combined with a psychiatric clinical teaching unit, preferably, as has been remarked, in a general teaching hospital.

There can be little doubt that the echelon providing the greatest coverage in these countries will be the first line of public health workers, albeit this line itself needs further development. In these countries the vast reservoir provided by the exponents of local health customs must be taken into account as a preformed channel to bring mental health care to the population.

Training

It will be understood that the carrying out of echelon formation and the channeling of mental health programs in public health services, as suggested in the preceding paragraphs, will have implications for training. Many of these implications are discussed in the report of the WHO Expert Committee on Mental Health dealing with the role of public health officers and general practitioners in mental health care.[3] Furthermore, many reports received show clear awareness of the fact that an integration of public health and mental health activities will have consequences for the training curricula of both groups of workers.

While the conclusion is drawn that public health workers need to receive training in principles of mental health thinking for carrying out their task, training in public health will become necessary for mental health experts as mental health programs become more closely associated with public health services. It need hardly be emphasized, after what has been said before, that this training will have to be undertaken for all personnel, irrespective of the level at which they are working. If one group should be omitted, it would immediately cause a weak link in the chain of provisions.

Many reports refer to the various methods by which mental health training is introduced, and most methods of modern teaching are mentioned. Emphasis is put on refresher courses and on the importance of in-service training with guidance and supervision. From the reports it would seem advisable to limit training in other cultures as much as possible and for the country to be served to develop training centers of its own culture as soon as feasible.

There is a relation between the responsibilities attached to a given function, the general level of education of the person carrying it out, and the teaching material to be offered to him. On the other hand, it may be stated that the same mental health principles will have to be taught at all functional levels, the difference lying in the way the material is treated and the scope it is given. So any public health worker will have to be taught the principles of human motivation and behavior and the way in which they develop in relation to family, school, and society. For the first-echelon fieldworker with the same cultural background as the people to be served, this teaching may consist in giving him a systematized awareness of his own experiences. For the physician, this training will deal with sociology, psychology and psychopathology, psychiatry, and cultural anthropology.

In the second place the training has to be relative to the functions the trainee is expected to carry out, i.e., to the place of his echelon in the organization. The content of the training is highly dependent on the organizational structure. The thinner the coverage, the more the workers in the first line will have to be "all-purpose"; the weaker the higher echelons are numerically, the more they must be relieved by the activities of the lower.

Apart from the overall requirement to teach the basic principles of mental health thinking, in some settings it may suffice if the first-line personnel are able to recognize disturbances and to effect adequate referral; in others they must be able to differentiate between situations which they will be able to handle themselves or not, and again, under other conditions, they must be able to carry out part or parts of the specialist's task.

This policy would require an analysis of the specialist's activities with the purpose of distinguishing between tasks which absolutely require the full range of his training and experience as directly applied to the patients' problems and tasks which could be delegated to properly trained personnel without decreasing their value or effectiveness.

As one report remarks, a ward of 200 mental patients with one physician allows the doctor very little time for each patient, but it may be asked whether it is really necessary for the various therapeutic activities to be carried out by the physician himself. It would seem that quite a number of these—occupational, social, and recreational therapy—can be carried out by personnel trained for these tasks, as is already practiced in many institutions.

A number of diagnostic activities are carried out by such nonmedical personnel as laboratory staff and psychologists. It might be asked whether the same procedure can be followed for psychotherapy, the physician remaining the supervisor and adviser. In many organizations the (psychiatric) social worker has a therapeutic task to fulfill. In these instances the required number of specialists would not depend on the number of patients he is able to handle but on the number of co-workers he is able to supervise.

In advanced countries, mental health training will have to be carried out where medical, nursing, and public health personnel are trained. This will be in medical schools, schools for public health, nursing schools, training centers for social workers, teachers, etc. In developing countries it would seem of great advantage to establish a teaching center, which logically would be affiliated with the mental health care project. In this training center the expert nucleus would provide the training for future specialists and for medical students and would train the trainers for the lower echelons. The relation with the mental health care organization would ensure that clinical and social teaching materials were available.

Research

There is no report which does not emphasize the importance of research in the mental health field, and each report mentions the difficulties arising in this regard.[16] In public health, *epidemiologic research* is rightly regarded as basic for planning. Epidemiologic problems in the mental health field are, however, complicated; the more so because terminology and classifications are far from uniform. Much has been said in this respect in the Eighth Report of the Expert Committee on Mental Health.[14]

For the purpose of planning, data on the movement of patients—admissions, discharges from various institutions, visits paid to outpatient arrangements, etc.—remain basic but should be related to the factors of the total social setting before being applied to or compared with others.

The reports leave no doubt that *clinical research* is regarded as essential. It is pointed out that new methods may be evolved as the result of clinical research, which may requires new provisions or procedures in mental health care or result in radical changes of the existing ones. This again may influence the design, extent, organization, and requirements of the overall service. Many developments have been effected or supported by clinical research. To mention only two examples: the development of drug therapy and the control of general paralysis are typical clinical achievements, and the planning of a mental health service is seldom based on well-established evidence of quantified needs. As a rule this evidence begins to be gathered after an initial period of activity. Furthermore, even if the original plan has been based on previous research, it has to be continuously tested against the actual needs evolving in the course of time. Very often when, for scientific or practical planning purposes, questions are asked about the functioning of a provision in society or within the organizational frame, it becomes apparent that these questions cannot be answered without lengthy and costly *ad hoc* investigations. The means of evaluating a service should, therefore, be foreseen and designed as part of the organization.

Administration

General

According to the general tenor of the reports, integration of mental health and other health services is advocated. Most reports recognize the need to achieve integration in the administrations concerned, while some reports state that this integration has already been carried out at some or all administrative levels of the country. On the other hand, reservations are made.

In one report doubt is expressed as to whether mental health activities will have a better opportunity to develop when they are administered as part of public health activities. In this situation they may suffer from the "competition" of public health care, because the latter is older, more firmly established, and more extensive. This danger would not occur with a separate administration for mental health care. This is similar to the remark made by Mackintosh in his introductory paper on the function of the hospital,[2] where he mentions the possible difficulties arising from an integration of curative and preventive care, in which preventive care might suffer from the same kind of competition. It would seem that the reality of this situation has to be recognized. On the other hand, it can be argued that this competition—if it may be so called and if it indeed exists—will be found in any administrative pattern.

General health care and mental health care cannot be regarded as competitors for public funds or interest when it is realized that their aims are identical and that it is to their material advantage to use, as much as possible, identical means to reach these aims. Only when this is recognized will adequate and balanced distribution of funds and interest be achieved. It would seem that the chances of creating this situation are better when administrative integration exists. "A mental health division separated from the public health activities—for instance by departmental boundaries— will be in great danger of becoming isolated from the main stream of medical development," as is remarked in one report. "Separated" is here the operative word.

National Level

About half of the reports mention adequate representation of mental health care in the top administrative level of the country. Either mental health is represented as a department of the health ministry, or some mental experts are officials in the health department. In the latter case they are usually, but not always, hierarchically placed under the highest official for general health in this department.

At the national level, there should be one person or organization responsible for programs, one for training, and one for evaluation of programs and results. On this basis it would be possible to determine national policy. In a number of countries these tasks are divided between governmental and private organizations. In those cases this pattern is also found at lower levels. This division, arising from historical reasons and the structuring of public affairs in the various countries, does not preclude the need for top coordination and representation of mental health activities. Close cooperation between governmental and private organizations is necessary.

In many reports from less highly developed countries, it is remarked that expert representation at the national level is recognized as desirable but cannot be achieved because of lack of expert personnel. Here again we meet the question of the strategic placing of specialists. Not everybody, not every physician and not every psychiatrist or mental hygienist, has the aptitude or the inclination to work at high administrative levels.

On the other hand, it is a very important question whether, when only very few specialists are available, it is most efficient to use all their skill at the level of treatment and small-scale organization. It may be very tempting and, under the pressure of urgent needs, almost unavoidable to charge the few available specialists with the task of setting up a good mental hospital, or reorganizing one, or arranging clinical and outpatient facilities. Those facilities, in that case, will be established with a view to more extensve coverage.

It may be that the experts concerned will be fully absorbed by their tasks and will take no initiative to increase coverage. It may also be that they are conscious of this need but do not get satisfactory response and cooperation from higher administrative levels because there is nobody to understand them. On the other hand, an expert in the national administration would be able to review the whole field in regard to coverage and the steps necessary to increase this. It would seem at least a point of consideration whether, even when few experts are available, it would not be of long-term advantage to place one at the highest administrative level.

In a number of countries a national institute for mental health is established. Other countries are contemplating its establishment, according to the reports. Sometimes it forms part of a national institute for health; sometimes it is independent. Such an institute, as a rule allied to the institutes of higher learning of the country, may serve to carry out research in the mental health field, to coordinate research, and to advise the government in national mental health problems. It therefore has a unifying and coordinating function at the national level.

Intermediate and Local Levels

The reports make it clear that integration has generally advanced further at lower administrative levels than at the national level. Serious difficulties have been encountered and are not always overcome, however, because the administrative origins of the various measures may be widely divergent.

Usually the mental hospitals are originally under different administrative bodies, often at a different level, from public health activities and the general hospital. Each may develop facilities in the mental health field: the mental hospital, an aftercare service; the general hospital, an outpatient service; the public health service, a domiciliary care program or an emergency service. For administrative reasons, these activities will initally be isolated from each other, although they may deal with the same problems and often with the same patients. Integration starts from the bottom, i.e., by the mutual contact of the workers, and may proceed upward.

As several reports show, this lower-level integration may, in its turn, promote integration at higher levels. When it is proposed to carry out closer cooperation as a matter of policy, administrative integration becomes a preliminary necessity. When channeling of mental health activities through public health services is contemplated, an administrative merging will have to come first.

Mental Health Advisers

There is no divergence of opinion about the need to make use of the counsel of mental health experts in public health activities. "In all problems of social medicine, general hygiene and other problems of the protection of public health, counselors and experts in mental health must be taken into account"—to give one quotation.

It has been pointed out that in many other fields of public service, mental health elements are present and may require the advice of the expert. Here again a shortage of experts may limit the possibilities of calling them in, although it may be remarked that it certainly is a task of the expert to make workers in other fields conscious of the mental health problems they have to meet. A strategic placing of the expert may increase his possibilities both for serving as an adviser and for giving enlightenment to others. Calling in an adviser may often be the first step to future coordination or integration. To use a specialist mainly working on the administrative level might be a temporary solution of the problems offered by a shortage of experts and the urgency of manifest needs.

Summary

Based on reports from forty-four governments, varied aspects of mental health programs in public health planning are surveyed. Following a definition of the subject area, there are discussions and suggestions regarding the need to bring mental health into public health planning, the feasibility of modern mental health care programs and the evolution of hospital and extramural developments, priorities in organization, training, and research, and administrative considerations. Observations from World Health Organization technical reports are included.

References

1. Esquirol, J. E. D.: *Mémoire statistique et hygiénique sur la folie*, Paris, 1882.
2. Mackintosh, J. M.: "Role of the Hospital in the Public Health Program," *WHO Technical Discussion Report*, World Health Assembly, Geneva, 1957.
3. *The Role of the Public Health Officer and General Practitioner in Mental Health Care*, WHO Expert Committee on Mental Health Report No. 11, Geneva, 1962.
4. Winslow, C. E. A.: *The Evolution and Significance of the Modern Public Health Campaign*, Yale University Press, New Haven, Conn., 1923.
5. World Health Organization Technical Report Series, no. 9, Geneva, 1950.
6. World Health Organization Technical Report Series, no. 31, Geneva, 1951.
7. World Health Organization Technical Report Series, no. 55, Geneva, 1952.
8. World Health Organization Technical Report Series, no. 73, Geneva, 1953.
9. World Health Organization Technical Report Series, no. 90, Geneva, 1955.
10. World Health Organization Technical Report Series, no. 134, Geneva, 1957.
11. World Health Organization Technical Report Series, no. 140, Geneva, 1957.

12. World Health Organization Technical Report Series, no. 152, Geneva, 1958.
13. World Health Organization Technical Report Series, no. 183, Geneva, 1959.
14. World Health Organization Technical Report Series, no. 185, Geneva, 1960.
15. World Health Organization Technical Report Series, no. 215, Geneva, 1961.
16. World Health Organization Technical Report Series, no. 223, Geneva, 1961.

5. Mental Health in Developing Countries

Phon Sangsingkeo

Introduction

It is to be recalled that at the concluding session of the 1960 Annual Meeting of the World Federation for Mental Health in Edinburgh, Dr. A. Lamarche, the distinguished delegate from France, expressed his deep concern about mental health in underdeveloped societies. He said that as agricultural countries would be seriously affected by rapid changes in the socioeconomic environment resulting from mechanization and other "benefits" of Western culture, attention should be given to these areas while they were still in the stage of transition. I think his proposal should be supported by all those who are concerned with the mental health problems of the world. I think this not because I am from a region where the impact of technological change on family life and its disruption of old patterns of living are acutely felt, but because the problem of social and cultural changes, especially those brought about by industrialization and automation, is now recognized as one of the most urgent in current mental health work.

Under modern conditions the world cannot long remain divided into a few prosperous islands and a vast sea of human misery. In our crusade toward better mental health of mankind and harmonious relationships among all peoples of the world, it is our responsibility to take an active interest in the mental health problems of developing societies, as well as those of highly developed societies. It is with this conviction in mind that I selected "Mental Health in Developing Countries" as the title of my address.

Presidential address, Sixteenth Annual Meeting, World Federation for Mental Health, Amsterdam, the Netherlands, August, 1963; published in *World Mental Health,* 15:125–134, 1963; adapted for this volume.

Struggle for Economic Progress

Today we are witnessing the struggle of a number of developing countries to achieve economic growth and stability. They need essentially everything in order to provide their rapidly growing populations with food, housing, schools, health services, transportation, communication, and industries. These goods and services are all needed quickly in response to rising expectations, and there is pressure against acceptance of the gradual process of exchange and evolution characteristic of the England of the Industrial Revolution and the United States of 100 years ago. Today things move so fast and the rate of change is so rapid that those who delay fear that they will only fall further behind. With the resources of modern technology, plus outside help in the form of foreign assistance, the industrial revolution in these countries will be compressed into a relatively short period; but the rapid pace, however desirable economically, may have dangerous psychological, social, and political consequences. Let us not forget that the endogenous industrialization of the West was prepared for by a cumulative historical development starting at least with the Renaissance and including the rise of individualism, rationalism, empiricism, and science, the fall of feudalism, and numerous other changes which led to the attitudes associated with successful industrialization. The sudden introduction of an alien economic system without historical preparation is a far more difficult and dangerous operation. It is unavoidable by now, but we must be prepared for undesirable side effects. The social and psychological complications will be experienced by the developing countries in an even more acute form than they were elsewhere, and I feel that an attempt should be made to anticipate them.

The Danger of Rapid Urbanization

With the development of urbanization, which has accelerated at such a rapid pace in Asian countries, for example, the traditional extended family tends to be dissolved. The migrants to the great urban conglomerations are for the most part young men and women who have to make a swift adaptation to city life, for which they are usually unequipped. They may maintain contact with their families in the rural areas for a time, but the influence of the patriarchal head or the tribal chief or senior members of the family may decline, and there may be no other factor controlling conduct to take its place. Thus values and patterns of behavior are threatened. Meanwhile, as a result of this draining off of the young men to the cities, certain rural areas are left to the women and the aged, and productivity there may sink to low levels.

In Thailand, for example, a large number of young men and women from rural areas in the northeast are drifting into the cities in the more prosperous central plain to look for jobs as laborers, factory workers, and household employees. Some of them, faced with the frustrations of city life, may return home after a short while, and some may go back temporarily to help their families during the harvest season; but most will settle down in the city, although they have to struggle so hard and earn so little. Eventually they will lose contact with the old folks back home. Family ties are broken, and poor mental health results. As a visitor to my people in the rural areas in northeastern Thailand, I used to be confronted with the problem of the aged woman who would come to meet me, demanding: "Bring back my children to me. Don't take them to Bangkok away from me. I am lonesome. Nobody loves me, nobody cares to take me to the monasteries for temple services, and I feel isolated." It is not very pleasant to witness an old father who, after traveling a long way to the capital city for the first time in his life and having great trouble in locating his young daughter, finally fails to persuade her to go home to take care of her ailing mother. Tragic as it is, this kind of thing is happening to thousands of rural families in Thailand.

Societies have a threshold of tolerance for the rate of change which, if exceeded, must lead to some measure of social disorganization. Past experience has shown how great an effect industrial and technological changes may have on mental health, through their impact on family life and their disruption of tradition, customs, and old patterns of living. Where mental health is concerned, it is the effect of technological change on interpersonal relations in the smallest unit of society, the family. The importance of the family, both as a social force and as the basis for healthy personality development, is consistently stressed. As it has become more and more apparent that, in developing countries, family cohesion is being seriously disturbed by the social and cultural changes following industrialization and urbanization, the perils to the mental good health of their populations must not be neglected.

In developing countries, much of the investment required is what economists call "infrastructural," e.g., roads, education, public health, and mental health. The economic returns on this sort of investment are slow. Yet, without it, other, faster-paying investments do not go far. The economically most rational investments are the politically least rewarding and potentially dangerous ones. Most of the developing countries can be helped significantly by the introduction of more efficient agricultural practices, but this would bring into the open the hidden rural unemployment which now exists. Further, efficient present-day agricultural practices in many cases would disrupt age-old customs, institutions, and power distributions. The surge of large numbers of unskilled migrants into the cities of Asia and Africa and the ensuing complications in terms of alcoholism, delinquency, and other manifestations of social or mental disorder on the one hand and, on the other, the impoverished old people left behind in the country who are suddenly deprived of care within the family are different facets of the same social process. Although the data concerning the incidence of mental illness among the aged in developing countries are very limited, certain investigations conducted in Asia suggest that, for the more serious forms of mental illness in the aged, the developing countries are as vulnerable, even at the present time, as the highly developed countries. Things ought to be planned and organized for these human resources from the outset.

The Problem of Rising Expectations

There are still deeper sources of political danger in economic development. Dissatisfaction, unfortunately, is not bred by poverty, as many have believed. Rather, one's dissatisfaction is in direct proportion to the distance between one's ambition and one's achievement. The greater that distance, the greater one's resentment. Now, clearly, the distance between ambition or expectation and achievement is a function of both; hence, dissatisfaction may grow as achievement does; or, if ambition grows faster than achievement, as it will during the process of industrial development, dissatisfaction will rise despite an increase in material welfare. "Relative deprivation," as sociologists now call dissatisfaction, is likely to be intensified by education, by communication, by urbanization—in short, by the widening of horizons which industrialization must bring about. The more frequent the contacts the people of developing countries have with those of developed countries and the more familiar they become with Western ways of living exemplified by foreigners, the more severely deprived they are likely to feel relative to the foreign "reference groups"—the experts, technicians, businessmen, and educators who have come to help them. Thus, even if the economic gap between the developing and the developed countries were not widening, the distance between the expectations and the achievements of the developing countries still would be lengthening, and therewith the feeling of relative deprivation and the resentment directed against the developed nations.

Material progress in the form of roads, ultramodern buildings, ostentatious industrial plants, etc., can be achieved in a short time by the substantial investment of available financial resources, but it requires much greater effort and a much longer time to raise significantly the living standards of the rural population. Moreover, there is always a wide gap between technical knowledge and the ability of the villagers to accept and utilize it, especially when some of the end products of Western industrialization are prematurely introduced into rural communities. Here there is evidence of want of balance. Where all needed technical advances are developed together and kept in proper balance with respect to one another, the chances are that the economy and the culture will also have grown with them. In the artificial situation of a technical aid program, however, there is not only a risk but almost a certainty of upsetting the preexisting balance. For example, to free a large population area, in a period of two years, of the malaria that for centuries has decimated it and kept its vitality at a low level is certainly to ask for social problems, unless provision is also made to feed, to educate, to accommodate, and to employ the increased and changed population that will almost immediately result. Here we have a situation in which the order of things is more or less reversed. In the desire of developing nations to move rapidly toward the social and economic advantages of an industrial economy, there is a possibility that the forced-draft telescoping of changes may lead to a state of social confusion and mental ill-health. It must be recognized that in many parts of the world today steps are being taken that are of the greatest concern to the world mental health of tomorrow and that the tempo of social change has become accelerated to a degree never reached before.

Training of Personnel

From the foregoing paragraph, it is clear that the success of a community development program depends not only on technological progress but also on the adaptability of the villagers to changed environments. Investment in roads, health, and welfare will yield nothing if the villagers are not prepared to adapt themselves to the social and cultural changes brought about by modern technological advance.

As social disintegration has already taken place in many developing countries, our immediate task is to find out more about the effects, prevention, and control of this undesirable phenomenon and the reactions of individuals and groups to rapidly changing circumstances. It may even be that the best hope lies in training young people to come to terms with social insecurity. The damage in industrial urbanized societies is already largely done, but in developing countries it may, perhaps, be forestalled. This process may be started by helping people to accept responsibility for social action, because such a role may not have been, in the past, a part of their customs. The public must be taught to develop attitudes of acceptance and satisfaction in adaptation. Recognizing the importance of the human element as the vital key to the success of any economic development program, we should continue efforts to train all categories of personnel participating in health and welfare work so that they can create satisfactory interpersonal relationships and can work smoothly with the public. Undergraduate and postgraduate training courses in psychiatry and mental health promotion for doctors, nurses, and public health nurses should also be encouraged and strengthened. Of first priority is a nucleus of well-trained psychiatrists to give service, to assist in training other physicians and allied personnel, and to act as consultants to other professional groups.

Attention should also be given to the selection and training of international personnel for service among peoples whose cultures and customs differ from their own. Past experience has shown that lack of tolerance and failure to adapt oneself to international and intercultural living have, in many cases, considerably retarded the progress of foreign-assisted projects in developing countries. In this respect, it must be kept in mind that many developing nations, like individuals, resent outside help and are vulnerable to any act of superiority exhibited by the "giver." Therefore it would be good policy if these international personnel could be oriented to the culture, customs, way of living, and emotional background of the population among whom they are assigned to work.

Implications of Rapid Population Growth

To the student of population, the field of public health presents a curious paradox: its very successes, in some parts of the world, have been self-defeating. Today, in many of the developing countries, the introduction of Western medical and public health technology has, in fact, brought about marked reductions in mortality, unaccompanied by comparable reductions in the birthrate. As of the present moment, the more thoughtful leaders among these nations are becoming gravely concerned over the threat of excessive population growth unattended by the social growth that a slower evolutionary process would have permitted. Public health measures, in reducing the death rates, have vastly multiplied social problems by creating new mouths to feed, new organisms to care for, and new demands on struggling economies. Wherever a population grows much faster than its economy—and this is frequently the case in the present-day world—starvation, sickness, poverty, and mental ill-health are specters on the horizon.

The present rate of population growth experienced in a large number of developing countries is unprecedented in the history of mankind. While the world population after World War I was around 1.8 billion people, it now exceeds three billion, and before the end of the century it is expected to exceed six billion. More than half of the world's population is now concentrated in a land area of only 16 per cent of the world total, and 56 per cent of the world's population, living in Asia, has only 13 per cent of the world gross national product.

The present population trends in the developing countries have important economic and social implications which will affect the struggle against hunger and poverty in the world. Substantial economic progress has been made in developing countries in recent years, but the rapid population increase has, in most cases, absorbed the greater part of it. Consequently, major improvements in levels of living have barely been made in these countries in recent years, in spite of many vigorous plans for economic and social development and foreign and international assistance. A large share of the resources for development in these countries is now devoted to the maintenance of an increasing population, leaving very little to improve living conditions. Many new schools, many more teachers, many more health centers and hospitals, many more houses, tools, machines, and means of communication must be provided at an increasing rate merely to maintain the *status quo*.

The problem facing these countries is readily understood if their age structure is kept in mind. Because of the high level of fertility prevailing in the developing countries, no less than 45 per cent of the total population is under fifteen years of age. For the individual breadwinner and for the community as a whole, the support of large families is a drain on resources of food, housing, education, etc. Very often both parents have to work outside the family to support their children, who are too many to be adequately fed and clothed. Frequent absence of both parents from the home, deprivation of parental love and care, lack of recreation, unfavorable home environments, etc., are harmful to the mental and emotional development of children. Under such circumstances, feelings of insecurity, resentment, and hostility toward the parents or the society as a whole will eventually lead to behavioral problems and juvenile delinquency. The situation will be worse if the child is unwanted and unplanned for. He may be rejected by one or both parents or by the whole family, to his great ultimate detriment. As the family is a basic institution for personality development, these implications of rapid population increase will seriously affect the mental health status of our younger generation.

Although the economically less highly developed countries have a very youthful population at the present time, a continuing fall in birthrates and decline in mortality are likely to increase the proportion of individuals in older age groups within the next few decades. The difficulties are not essentially those of the proportions in various chronological age groups but of the pressures created when the proportion of the feeble, infirm, dependent, chronically sick, and isolated rises above a certain level.

The effects of rapid population growth are today apparent in several other fields of economic and social development. Housing conditions are steadily deteriorating in cities in recent years because of the heavy influx of people from the countryside. Spectacular progress has been made in the field of education, but the fact remains that, according to recent population censuses, there are larger numbers of illiterate persons in many developing countries today than there were ten to fifteen years ago. It is also worth mentioning that urbanization and unsanitary conditions associated with population growth will probably increase the likelihood of such infections as contagious respiratory and contact diseases.

It should be recognized that not only the number of consumers but also the number of producers is increasing rapidly. A major part of the labor force in the developing countries is unskilled, however, and is to a considerable extent underemployed. Productive employment of labor requires equipment and other forms of capital which are scarce in most developing countries. The same is the case with unused land resources. Considerable investments are required to turn such resources into productive use. Therefore it can be anticipated that poverty and hunger will be more widespread in developing countries than ever before.

Briefly speaking, rapid population growth has created excessive demands on economic, social, and medical resources, all of which are proving inadequate in developing countries. Changes are generating new fears and new threats to the mental health of individuals and communities. It is therefore the responsibility of all workers in the field of mental health to dedicate themselves to the continuation of their tasks, to alleviate dangers arising from the population explosion, and to create better mental health all over the world, particularly in developing countries.

6. Preventive Psychiatry: If Not Now, When?

Leon Eisenberg

Introduction

The final report of the (United States) Joint Commission on Mental Illness and Health, *Action for Mental Health*,[1] is a singular document. It represents a significant advance in public psychiatric planning. The mental health professions, for the first time as a body, have acknowledged the social responsibility that accompanies specialized knowledge. We have, in force, entered the political arena as spokesmen for the disenfranchised: the mentally ill of today and those destined, in the absence of effective public action, for illness tomorrow. And yet this report, despite some excellent proposals for action, is peculiarly representative of the conceptual shortcomings that have restricted our vision in the past. It gives but fleeting recognition to children; it cavalierly dismisses the possibilities for prevention; it bypasses the mentally retarded.

In this address, I shall attempt to remedy these failings. But let me, at the outset, salute the crusading ethical spirit of *Action for Mental Health*. Knowledge confers upon scientists a clear moral responsibility: to disseminate that knowledge in order to provide their fellow citizens with a sound basis for rational decision making and effective social action.[56] It is in this spirit that I would have us consider the following questions: Is the prevention of mental illness possible in any meaningful sense? If, as I shall contend, it is, why have we been so inert and ineffective as advocates of preventive psychiatry? What need we do to reorient our efforts to the

Delivered at the 1962 Presidential Session and copyrighted by the American Orthopsychiatric Association, Inc.; previously published in the *American Journal of Orthopsychiatry*, 32:781–793, 1962, and in *World Mental Health*, 15:48–64, 1963; also issued in English and French as Supplement 36 to *Canada's Mental Health*, April, 1963; adapted for this volume.

end that we accept our full responsibility to promote social as well as professional action for mental health?

Prevention

In the green years of the mental hygiene movement, dedicated enthusiasts proclaimed that mental illness could be abolished through the application of psychological rules for hygienic living. Some decades later, the millennium has notably failed to arrive despite the proselytizers for psychological rearmament. Let us grant them that universal acceptance of their precepts has never been fully forthcoming. But, as *Action for Mental Health* notes, there is literally no evidence of even modest success from a multitude of earnest educational efforts.[42] Indeed, the one clear result has been derision of the very notion of mental hygiene. Critics with a paranoid bent warn the public that we intend nothing less than to remake them in our own troubled image—a gratuitous warning in view of the absence of any demonstrated effect. Cynics call gleeful attention to contradictions in our theories and chide us to put our own house in order before we offer panaceas to a gullible public.

Some of our colleagues have been undeterred by criticism, whether based on fact or on fancy; preempting the mantle of mental hygiene, they continue to dispense the same tried and untrue bromides of an earlier era. Other colleagues, chastened and troubled, counsel perfection. Lest we further confound our public "image," they urge that we stick to our last, which they take to be individual case management. After all, they ask, must we not admit that our ignorance is considerable?

Agreed, but is not knowing all to be equated with knowing nothing? If what has passed for mental hygiene has been little more than pious platitudes, it does not follow that the infant, preventive psychiatry, born of what is known with reasonable certainty,[18] must be thrown out along with the bath water of glittering generalities. Yet in effect this is what *Action for Mental Health* has done. It is all the more regrettable that in so doing it exemplifies a widely held attitude.

Part of the confusion about mental hygiene lies in loose use of global terms, part in an overemphasis upon individual psychology to the exclusion of the social and biological determinants of behavior.

What are the goals of prevention? Programs for mental hygiene all too often imply, when they do not explicitly state, an objective of "eliminating mental illness." But this, on the face of it, is absurd. It is not simply that we do not know enough to do so now. There is no entity "mental illness" that can be prevented; there is, rather, a variety of psychiatric disorders, each with causes, mechanisms, and outcomes. The task for mental hygiene is to devise specific methods for preventing particular disorders, certain of which may yield to scientific attack at a given time.

Beyond this matter of illness in particular versus illness in general is to be found a more fundamental question in the philosophy of medicine. Can *all* mental illness, any more than *all* disease, be eliminated, either now or in the foreseeable future?

What we call disease is the result of maladaptation between the human organism and his environment. When, in order to counteract disease on a wide scale, we alter the dynamic equilibrium between organism and environment, we set into action a train of interrelated events whose final steady state we can predict only imperfectly. Antibiotic treatment has been accompanied by the multiplication of resistant microorganisms that constitute a new challenge to health. Medical salvage of the victims of hereditary diseases increases the carrier rates for deleterious genes. Prolongation of longevity adds to the burden of degenerative diseases and materially augments population pressures, particularly in underdeveloped nations.[10]

Must we not anticipate like effects from psychiatric treatment maneuvers? Reduced mortality from prematurity portends morbidity in the form of brain syndromes among survivors. *If* schizophrenia is hereditary, then effective treatment, by restoring patients to the community and thus enhancing the likelihood of marriage and procreation, may add to the transmissible gene pool. *If* patients previously hospitalized are now kept afloat in the community, although psychologically impaired, may there not be a potential for damage to children reared by disturbed parents? With medical progress reducing the inexorable, cruel, but nonetheless self-correcting biological population pressures, we become increasingly dependent upon a high degree of control over ourselves and over an environment whose contingencies cannot be completely known.

Note that this is *not* a counsel of despair. No reasonable assessment of the intended good, and unintended evil, effects of medical treatment would lead to the conclusion that we should abandon scientific progress. Clearly, there has been a net gain of very considerable proportions in human lives and human happiness. But these complexities remind us that the goals of medicine are modest as well as noble: the diminution of suffering from disease, the enhancement of the capacity of man to cope successfully with stress, and not the unattainable goal of the total elimination of disease and stress. Unless we specify our goals in restricted terms, we condemn ourselves to repeat the self-defeating cycle of grand promise and paltry accomplishment that breeds doubt and despair.

If we foreswear the illusory goal of "total mental health," of "universal happiness," what can we hope to accomplish in the prevention of particular neuropsychiatric disorders in the light of current knowledge?

Manifestly, no comprehensive treatment of this topic is possible or entirely appropriate within the confines of this address; I have attempted such statements elsewhere.[14,15,18] Let me, instead, set out the features of one endemic psychiatric disorder that can serve as a paradigm for preventive psychiatry. This disorder is quantitatively one of the most frequent we face; in its qualitative features it presents aspects discernible in other psychiatric disturbances; its solution will require the mobilization of community-wide efforts. The disorder to which I refer is the syndrome of deprivation.

Clinically, the "deprivation syndrome" is, in varying degree, a complex of intellectual retardation, personality defect, and social maladaptation, observable in children who may or may not exhibit a substratum of detectable central-nervous-system impairment. The designation "deprivation" posits an etiology: the unavailability to the child of the biosocial necessaries for normal growth and development, usually as a consequence of gross social pathology. It has been customary to employ the term "maternal deprivation" for this syndrome.[5] This terminology is too restrictive. It singles out of an etiologic complex one aspect, albeit a central one; other elements are thus too easily overlooked and the finger of blame pointed at the mother, who is no less a victim of this tragedy than is her child. Moreover, it directs attention to "mothering" as though it were a suprascientific mystique, not reducible, as it is, to observable transactional processes.[49] Hypothetical "critical periods" for its effect have been invoked in disregard of the chronicity of the traumatic factors that afflict these children from before birth through adolescence.[17] The broader designation deprivation syndrome requires of us that we specify what it is that the child has been denied: food, protection, stimulation, consistent and predictable interpersonal contacts, ordering of the environment, and so on.[23] The term maternal deprivation is best employed to separate out of the larger class of cases those instances in which pathologic mothering has been the noxious agent despite relative adequacy in other aspects of the infant's world.

What is the pathogenesis of the deprivation syndrome? When does it begin? I would suggest that it *can* begin before conception in maternal ill-health that impairs normal pregnancy and in parental unreadiness for child rearing. Many of its victims have an unintended beginning that might have ben averted by the wider availability of birth-control information and access to better birth-control methods.

The next assault occurs during pregnancy. Pasamanick and his co-workers [30,36,46,47,52] have provided convincing evidence of the continuum of reproductive casualty (extending from cerebral palsy, mental defect, and epilepsy through behavioral disorder and reading disability) that is associated with abnormalities of pregnancy and parturition. There is a significant association between the incidence of maternal complications and socioeconomic status. Mothers at high risk are the poor, the migrant, the unmarried, and, especially, the Negro.[7,43,44,45] Similarly, prematurity, which carries with it a significant risk for neuropsychiatric sequelae,[33] is found at higher rates in lower social classes.[51] As the result of malnutrition,[27] poor prenatal care, and, possibly, psychological stress,[59] there are born a significant number of defective children whose crippling disease is unnecessary in the sense that it could have been prevented with available methods, had we but the determination to apply them.

Even after birth, the biologic hazard is operative. Severe malnutrition,[55] as well as specific nutritional deficiencies,[20] have been shown to be associated with mental defect. Accidents and infections, which may impair central-nervous-system function, show differential distributions by social class. Again, we have identified preventable disruptions of normal development whose amelioration waits not upon the acquisition of new knowledge but upon the social use of available knowledge.

These disorders, let it be noted, are not limited to the lower social classes; they have an appreciable incidence among the privileged. We have no right to assume that even with the best of care such disorders can be eliminated altogether. What can be altered is the social-class rate differential, with both rates lowered to some minimum value not further reducible by present techniques. This would result in significant salvage of children otherwise destined for chronic handicap.

The neuropathologic sequelae of maldevelopment, malnutrition, injury, and infection already noted are no more fateful than the psychopathologic sequelae of the intellectual understimulation, noxious interpersonal experiences, and social psychopathy to which these children are exposed. Positive correlations between intelligence-test scores, academic performance, and social-class membership have by now been documented beyond need of further repetition. Developmental studies of white and Negro infants indicate a similarity of performance early in life which changes with time to a superiority for the white as cultural influences manifest their effects.[34] In contrast, environmental enrichment has been shown to lead to improvement in intelligence-test performance among previously understimulated children, including those who are grossly defective.[8,9,31,37,38,39,40,50]

Many studies have indicated the personality defects and delinquent behavioral patterns to be found among deprived children.[5,17,23,24,25,60] These youngsters receive little intellectual stimulation at home; they come to school poorly motivated; they attend overcrowded, understaffed, and unattractive schools, when they attend school at all. They live in decaying neighborhoods, rich only in opportunities for trouble and characterized by value systems opposed to those of the dominant culture. Rates for parental disease, death, and desertion are high, with the result that these children experience multiple losses and a multiplicity of living situations. Some of them, in tribute to the resiliency of the human organism, manage somehow to grow into functioning adults. Far too many contribute to statistics on delinquency and disease; they become premature and inadequate parents themselves, fated to repeat for a succeeding generation the cycle of deprivation.[17]

Perhaps the single most disconcerting feature of this squalid nightmare is that many children experience deprivation after they are known to community agencies and receive from them what is euphemistically termed "assistance".[11] There are in the United States well over 2 million children [58] supported by aid to dependent children at levels barely sufficient to glue body and soul together.[53] Another quarter million are in foster care; [41] recent studies suggest the dismaying possibility that an appreciable number of foster children may in fact continue to deteriorate while in care.[4,23,41] The reasons are not far to seek: miserly board rates; absurd wages for professional workers, with consequent staff shortages and rapid turnover; and morale-busting assaults by pettifogging politicians behind the rallying cry: "Economy, yes! Children, no!" But where, *where* have we been in the fight to better their condition?

Many of these children come to rest with the "diagnostic" label of "familial" or "garden-variety" mental retardation (if familial, then no more so than tuberculosis; if a garden, how unlovely does it grow, choked by social weeds). For all the real satisfaction we may take in the recent biochemical and genetic advances in oligophrenia,[13,16] metabolic disorders constitute but a limited part of the total problem of mental deficiency. The largest category of intellectual retardation results from failures in social metabolism which can be corrected only by infusions of the social enzymes and substrates necessary for normal development.

I trust that I have marshaled sufficient evidence for my thesis: effective (though not total) primary prevention of certain mental disorders [15,18] is possible with what we know *now* if we but have the will to apply it. The ingredients have been mentioned: family planning; good health care and decent housing; adequate unemployment compensation and job training for displaced workers; casework services to minimize family breakdown; effective substitute care for homeless children; and enriched school programs, recreational facilities, vocational training, and other social services.

We can agree that these remedies are far from simple to apply; nor is the task ours alone. Our nation faces a staggering shortage of professional workers which only a massive recruitment and education program will alter.[2] We shall have to become considerably more expert in rehabilitating multiple-problem families and in remotivating youngsters who have given up on our social institutions.[6] The very question of foster care must be reexamined: can it be maintained in the face of the contemporary urban revolution in family life? Must we not become more creative in the use of group homes staffed by well-paid and properly respected foster care workers? [12] All these measures presuppose the transformation of an anachronistic system of state and local funding; only a federal tax base can provide the requisite funds, an issue justly emphasized in *Action for Mental Health*.

Central to these proposals is the recognition that human resources are the precious capital of a democratic society. Our nation must be prepared to invest its material substance, to an extent far beyond present conceptions, in the cultivation of people.[22] This will require a major change in the value orientation of our citizens and of the representatives they elect, a change that will not come about overnight or indeed through our efforts alone. But we, as physicians, social workers, and psychologists, have a vital contribution to make in the political arena, precisely because of what we know about the needs of children.

All of this may go far afield from what is conventionally labeled "mental hygiene"; there will be those who will contend that it is not our business to go beyond the clinic and the consulting room. But is it at any less our business than a contaminated water system is the business of a microbiologist, than a reservoir of uninoculated children is the business of a virologist, than interior lead-containing paints are the business of a pediatrician, than nuclear fallout is the business of a physicist? As the experts in behavioral science, we must join those already in the front line: public health doctors and nurses, pediatricians, teachers, housing experts, welfare workers, and others, in order to stop the epidemic of socially induced psychopathology at its source.

The Responsibility of the Mental Health Professions

If my argument is correct, then we must face an uncomfortable question: Why have we been so inert and ineffective as public advocates for preventive psychiatry? Why have our energies been dissipated in moral sermons on the royal road to the happy family via breast-feeding, proper toilet training, sex education, and the like, desiderata in themselves perhaps, but quite unsubstantiated as guarantors of mental health?

The answer, I submit, is to be found in the mode of practice which, if not in fact customary for all of us, nonetheless represents the ultimate in prestige: the one-to-one psychotherapeutic interview conducted in a well-appointed office, carefully insulated from the sights, sounds, and smells of society. It is this that has given birth to theories of behavior embedded in individual instincts, constrained perhaps but not basically altered by social experience. It is this that we hold up before our trainees as *the* method of therapeutic efficacy. For only this, we tell them, will bring about recovery with insight, i.e., a *real* cure; anything less is "superficial," and its practitioners are rather dull chaps, needed of course and all that, but not admitted to the fellowship of the sanctified.

You will reply that I exaggerate. If we take adherence to psychoanalysis as an index of preoccupation with individual psychotherapy, the American Psychiatric Association reports that only 10 per cent of its members belong to analytic societies.³ Let me remind you that, according to the same source, more than half of the chairmen of departments of psychiatry hold membership in such associations.³ This may be a tribute to the caliber of analysts, but it also says something of prevailing interests in the field. I have no figures for social workers and psychologists; I can only report my dismay at the growing numbers who forsake their heritage to function as quasi-psychiatrists, often complete with couch and fifty-minute hour. I am not aware of any evidence that they are any less effective as psychotherapists, but I see no compelling reason to suppose that they are any better. By their defection from their proper calling, we suffer an intolerable loss of professionals who have a contribution to make in their own right.

The prestige-laden psychiatric residencies are, in general, those offered at university centers. Many provide little or no experience in the state hospital and clinic, where the public mental health problem is to be found. Typically, they focus upon the intensive psychotherapy of selected (i.e., articulate) patients under close individual supervision by privately practicing senior psychiatrists. Whatever the ostensible goals of the department, this pattern of apprenticeship, frequently the major learning opportunity in the residency, provides the trainee with a model for professional identification that weighs heavily in determining his career choice.

In some centers all, or almost all, the residents enter personal analysis. Let us for a moment agree that this may be a useful experience for some. But pause to consider how a personal analysis tends to mold a resident's professional career. For one thing, it restricts his geographic mobility for three, four, five, n years. For another, its cost may necessitate a search for supplementary income from after-hours private practice, a step officially frowned upon but often tacitly encouraged; if he manages somehow without it, he may complete his training so heavily in debt that the lure of a lucrative private practice is difficult to resist. Most significantly of all, the didactic analysis, together with time-consuming courses in the institute, prepares him for a psychiatric technique obviously inapplicable in the state hospital and usually considered unsuitable for outpatients of lower social class.²⁹ Is it at all reasonable to expect him to cast aside what he has so painfully and so expensively acquired, particularly when its pursuit promises him a perfectly honorable and comfortable career?

The problem is far greater than the number of young people who choose to seek psychoanalytic training. Severalfold more, who never become full-fledged psychoanalysts, follow a mode of training which places a quite similar premium on individual psychotherapy. Again, they are isolated from public service except for an occasional consultancy or half-day teaching stint. Many are effectively lost to medicine itself since what they do borrows least from their medical training and emphasizes most what there is every reason to believe they could have done equally well without the time and expense of attending medical school. They, together with adherents of acknowledged analytic schools, contribute to a hierarchy of values that molds their successors in the same frame. Thus, the problem of recruitment and training of the psychiatrists needed for public health is qualitative as well as quantitative: *how* we train, as well as how many.

Now, I do not doubt that psychological influences have a potent impact on human behavior or that psychotherapists bring relief to those suffering from emotional disorders.[21] Indeed, with the very best efforts at prevention, there will remain a multitude of patients for whom psychotherapeutic methods represent the treatments of choice. There is no implication here that we should abandon such patients in our emphasis on prevention but rather that we disperse our forces more rationally than we do at present. From any scientific vantage point, what is remarkable is the preoccupation with intensive individual psychotherapy. After some five decades of its advocacy as the preferred method for the treatment of emotional disorders, we still do not know how to measure its effectiveness; we have no evidence that any one way of doing it is better than any other [21] or that long-term is superior to brief psychotherapy.[14] Confronted with this distressing state of affairs, some will perhaps reply that psychoanalysis was never really intended as a method of treatment but as a research tool for the investigation of the personality. But this is hardly any more credible, at least in its present form, since the "research" method seems to follow none of the accepted scientific principles of prediction, design, control, and quantification. The fault is far more general than that of psychoanalysis; research training is an uncommon feature of residency training programs anywhere.

I am not impugning the integrity of those who practice psychoanalysis and intensive psychotherapy. I do not doubt their sincerity, intelligence, or competence. Indeed, my regret is the greater that, in my observation, it has been the bright and not the incompetent, the curious and not the unimaginative, residents who have been attracted to psychoanalysis and thus lost to research, university teaching, and public service. What I am suggesting is that methods of long-term individual psychotherapy offer no promise for public health psychiatry and that their practice inescapably molds theory so as to make it sterile for the larger problem, whatever relevance it may have for a restricted group of patients.

A meaningful final evaluation of the role of psychoanalysis and its derivatives in the history of psychiatry is a task for the historiographer of our specialty. We can grant its germinal role in reawakening interest in the meaning of symptoms as distorted communications. We can recognize the intellectual brilliance of its founder, whose literary tour de force was instrumental in my own decision to enter the field, as surely it must have been for many of you. The history of science, however, is replete with instances in which an initially liberating conceptualization, once institutionalized, became a barrier to progress. Whether this moment has arrived for psychiatry or not, we must recognize that, whatever present psychodynamic theory can contribute to our "understanding" [57] of individual aberrations, it is largely irrelevant to social pathology. Society is more than the mere aggregate of its individual members: if it is, in one sense, the product of their dreams, it also shapes those dreams. When systems in the social organism go awry, it is as absurd to attempt their correction by medicating the individuals whose aberrations are second- and third-order consequences of the basic lesion as it would be to treat the white count in meningitis rather than to eradicate the offending meningococci.

Revisions of Training

If there is any substance to the thesis of this address, it then follows that major revisions in the content and methods of psychiatric training will be necessary to meet the mental health challenge.

No residency program should be considered adequate that does not provide substantial experience in community and public hospital psychiatry. In part this can be met by integrating university and state hospital programs to ensure residents' rotation through both services, in part by having the university hospital take greater responsibility for the management of psychiatric emergencies and for the diagnosis and treatment of patients who live in its community.[35] This would not only enhance the quality of academic residency training but also diminish the overload on the municipal hospital and thus improve its teaching potential. The development of community clinic programs, staffed by residents, is a promising measure to provide responsibility for the care of patients in low-income groups.[32]

The all too common practice in child guidance clinics of denying service to patients with brain syndromes, mental retardation, or both, while perhaps the prerogative of the private clinic, cannot be accepted in a center that purports to provide training for child psychiatrists. The methods and theories of intensive psychotherapy should indeed be taught and perhaps even emphasized in clinics so oriented; but we should not certify for training a program that provides a resident with no more than eight to ten intensively treated cases a year with no further experience in diagnosis, other modes of treatment, or work with community agencies.

We must invest a far larger proportion of our professional resources in the development of research competence.[26,48] The limitations of present therapeutic methods doom us to training caretakers at a rate that ever lags behind the growing legions of the ill, unless we strike out successfully in new directions in the search for cause and treatment. Trainees must be imbued with critical skepticism toward what we teach; they must be encouraged to demand that each proposition be evaluated by scientific criteria. Whatever our theoretical biases, we as teachers should demand of ourselves that our students be familiarized with the evidence for and against what we say and not merely taught by rote what has our fancy.

The physiological and biochemical as well as the sociological determinants of behavior merit greater emphasis than they have been given. The most obvious justification for this proposal lies in the striking increase in mental disorders of the senium, the one class of psychiatric diseases for which we have unequivocal statistical evidence of an increase over the past century. And we appear to be on the threshold of major advances in the neurochemistry and neurophysiology of aberrant behavior. There is, as I see it, no contradiction in this call for an increase in our biological skills at the same time that we emphasize sociological expertness. The deprivation syndromes have biological consequences; the biological disorders of old age occur in a social nexus. Can geriatric psychiatry be effective without concern for the necessity of providing good medical care for the aged?

Those of us who are physicians must relate our practice to its roots in medicine as once we did and as surely we shall do again.[19] In all of what we attempt the touchstone must be the relief of suffering and the prevention of disease in order to fulfill our socially prescribed role as guardians of the public health.

This is no brochure for a training program. How to spell out the detailed application of these general principles remains a considerable task; important aspects of training have not been discussed in this brief survey. Nor would I argue for a single curriculum for all training centers. Each can profitably emphasize that in which it excels but must at the same time provide more than a minimum of competence in the other areas in which a psychiatrist is called upon to exercise judgment. Diversity enriches and provides best for a future whose outlines are uncertain. But society can ill afford today's precious overspecialization, in which trainees may learn one method even superbly well, but a method that ever lags behind the demands placed upon it, while they remain abysmally unaware of the problems besetting the bulk of the mentally ill.

A Call for a Rededication

This conception of the action necessary for mental health has emphasized the social roots and the social responsibilities of orthopsychiatry. Two threads have been woven into the fabric of the argument: the role of the mental health professional *as professional* and *as citizen*.

As professionals, we must expend our therapeutic energies more generously in the public domain: hospital, clinic, welfare agency, school, health department; we must support a higher level of professional work in these therapeutic centers with critical evaluation of present performance and imaginative enterprise in future efforts; we must modify our training programs to emphasize the public health aspects of orthopsychiatry; we must secure federal support for a much broadened system of higher education to produce the mental health workers our nation will need.

As citizens, we bear a moral responsibility, because of our specialized knowledge, for political action to prevent socially induced psychiatric illness. This implies fighting for decent subsistence levels in public assistance programs, good housing, health care, education, and the right to work for all. Advocacy of these causes may not make us popular; but neither was the task of a Philippe Pinel, a William Tuke, or a Dorothea Dix in unchaining the mentally ill an easy one. I am confident we shall not flinch at the challenge.

I cannot forbear to mention, as I conclude, one overriding issue thus far unstated. Ours is a world so shrunk by technology that men half the globe away must become our brothers or they will become our executioners and we theirs. Decisions to test nuclear weapons, taken by one nation, spell radiation damage to unborn generations in all others, whether they be friends or foes. If men cannot respond rationally to a world radically transformed by science, the very existence of life on earth may no longer be tenable. The plea of the American Association for the Advancement of Science for a "science of survival," [54] a science we do not now possess but must find the means to create, is a call for the dedication of our energies at this eleventh hour that there may be a future. And this, I hope, will yet become a cause to which we will devote ourselves.

Two thousand years ago, Hillel addressed three questions to mankind: "If I am not for myself, who is for me? And if I am for myself [alone], what am I? And if not now, when?" [28] His words remind us that if we are to improve our human condition, we must act for ourselves; that if we are to achieve full humanity, we must regard others as not less than ourselves; that, life being brief at best (and today altogether uncertain), we must act now, for there may be no tomorrow. This is a heavy charge indeed, but one that we cannot escape.

References

1. *Action for Mental Health: Final Report of the Joint Commission on Mental Illness and Health*, Basic Books, Inc., Publishers, New York, 1961.
2. Albee, G. W. *Mental Health Manpower Trends*, Basic Books, Inc., Publishers, New York, 1959.
3. *A.P.A. Newsletter*, vol. 14, no. 5, American Psychiatric Association, Washington, D.C., January, 1962.
4. Boehm, B.: *Deterrents to the Adoption of Children in Foster Care*, Child Welfare League of America, New York, 1958.
5. Bowlby, J.: *Maternal Care and Mental Health*, WHO Monograph Series, no. 2, Geneva, 1951.

6. Buell, B., et al.: "Reorganizing to Prevent and Control Disordered Behavior," *Ment. Hyg.*, 42:155–194, 1958.
7. "Children in Migrant Families," *Child Welf.*, 41:82–83, 1962.
8. Clarke, A. M., and A. D. B. Clarke: *Mental Deficiency: The Changing Outlook*, The Free Press of Glencoe, New York, 1958.
9. ——— and ———: "Some Recent Advances in the Study of Early Deprivation," *J. Child Psychol. Psychiat.*, 1:26–36, 1960.
10. Dorn, H. F.: "World Population Growth: An International Dilemma," *Science*, 135:283–290, 1962.
11. Eisenberg, L.: "The Challenge of Change," *Child Welf.*, 39:11, 1960.
12. ———: "The Family in the Mid-twentieth Century," *The Social Welfare Forum, 1960*, Columbia University Press, New York, 1960, pp. 98–112.
13. ———: "Review of Mental Deficiency," *Amer. J. Psychiat.*, 116:606–608, 1960.
14. ———: "The Strategic Deployment of the Child Psychiatrist in Preventive Psychiatry," *J. Child Psychol. Psychiat.*, 2:229–241, 1961.
15. ———: "Preventive Psychiatry," *Ann. Rev. Med.*, 31:343–360, 1962.
16. ———: "Review of Mental Deficiency," *Amer. J. Psychiat.*, 118:602–604, 1962.
17. ———: "The Sins of the Fathers: Urban Decay and Social Pathology," *Amer. J. Orthopsychiat.*, 32:5–17, 1962.
18. ——— and E. M. Gruenberg: "The Current Status of Secondary Prevention in Child Psychiatry," *Amer. J. Orthopsychiat.*, 31:355–367, 1961.
19. Felix, R. H.: "Psychiatrist, Medicinae Doctor," *Amer. J. Psychiat.*, 118:1–9, 1961.
20. Finberg, L., and H. E. Harrison: "Hypernatremia in Infants," *Pediatrics*, 16:1–14, 1955.
21. Frank, J.: *Persuasion and Healing*, The John Hopkins Press, Baltimore, 1961.
22. Galbraith, J. K.: *The Affluent Society*, Houghton Mifflin Company, Boston, 1958.
23. Glaser, K., and L. Eisenberg: "Maternal Deprivation," *Pediatrics*, 18:626–642, 1956.
24. Glueck, S., and E. T. Glueck: *Delinquents in the Making: Paths to Prevention*, Harper & Row, Publishers, Incorporated, New York, 1952.
25. Goldfarb, W.: "Emotional and Intellectual Consequences of Psychologic Deprivation in Infancy," in P. H. Hoch and J. Zubin (eds.), *Psychopathology of Childhood*, Grune & Stratton, Inc., New York, 1955.
26. Hamburg, D. A.: "Recent Trends in Psychiatric Research Training," *Arch. Gen. Psychiat.*, 4:215–224, 1961.
27. Harrell, R. F., et al.: "Influence of Vitamin Supplementation of Diets of Pregnant and Lactating Women on Intelligence of Their Offspring," *Metabolism: Clin. & Exp.*, 5:555–562, 1956.
28. Herford, R. T. (ed.): *Pirke Aboth: The Tractate "Fathers" from the Mishnah, Commonly Called "Sayings of the Fathers,"* Jewish Institute of Religion Press, New York, 1930, p. 34.
29. Hollingshead, A. B., and F. C. Redlich: *Social Class and Mental Illness: A Community Study*, John Wiley & Sons, Inc., New York, 1958.
30. Kawi, A. A., and B. Pasamanick: "Prenatal and Perinatal Factors in the Development of Childhood Reading Disorders," *Mgr. Soc. Child Develpm.*, 24(4):73, 1959.
31. Kellmer Pringle, M. L., and V. Bossio: "Early Prolonged Separation and Emotional Maladjustment," *J. Child Psychol. Psychiat.*, 1:37–48, 1960.
32. Kern, H. M., and C. A. Chandler: "The Cultivation of Community Mental Hygiene Leadership Ability as a Part of a Psychiatric Resident's Training," *Amer. J. Psychiat.*, 117:346–347, 1960.
33. Knobloch, H., et al.: "The Neuropsychiatric Sequelae of Prematurity," *J.A.M.A.*, 161:581–585, 1956.

34. Knobloch, H., and B. Pasamanick: "Some Thoughts on the Inheritance of Intelligence," *Amer. J. Orthopsychiat.*, 31:454–473, 1961.
35. Kolb, L. C.: "The Metropolis and Social Psychiatry," paper read at the New York Regional Meeting of the American Psychiatric Association, 1961.
36. Lilienfeld, A. M., and B. Pasamanick: "The Association of Maternal and Fetal Factors with the Development of Cerebral Palsy and Epilepsy," *Amer. J. Obstet. Gynecol.*, 70:93–101, 1955.
37. Lyle, J. G.: "The Effect of an Institution Environment upon the Verbal Development of Imbecile Children: I. Verbal Intelligence," *J. Ment. Defic. Res.*, 3:122–128, 1959.
38. ———: "The Effect of an Institution Environment upon the Verbal Development of Imbecile Children: II. Speech and Language," *J. Ment. Defic. Res.*, 4:1–13, 1960.
39. ———: "The Effect of an Institution Environment upon the Verbal Development of Imbecile Children: III. The Brooklands Residential Family Unit," *J. Ment. Defic. Res.*, 4:14–22, 1960.
40. ———: "Some Factors Affecting the Speech Development of Imbecile Children in an Institution," *J. Child Psychol. Psychiat.*, 1:121–129, 1960.
41. Maas, H. S., and R. H. Engler: *Children in Need of Parents,* Columbia University Press, New York, 1959.
42. *Mental Health Education: A Critique,* Pennsylvania Mental Health, Inc., Philadelphia, 1960.
43. Pakter, J., et al.: "A Study of Out-of-wedlock Births in New York City," *Amer. J. Publ. Hlth.*, 51:683, 1961.
44. ———: "A Study of Out-of-wedlock Births in New York City: Part II, Medical Aspects," *Amer. J. Publ. Hlth.*, 51:846–865, 1961.
45. Pasamanick, B., et al.: "Socioeconomic Status: Some Precursors of Neuropsychiatric Disorder," *Amer. J. Orthopsychiat.*, 26:594–601, 1956.
46. Pasamanick, B., and A. M. Lilienfeld: "The Association of Maternal and Fetal Factors with the Development of Mental Deficiency," *J.A.M.A.*, 159:155–160, 1955.
47. ——— and ———: "Maternal and Fetal Factors in the Development of Epilepsy," *Neurology*, 5:77–83, 1955.
48. Redlich, F.: "Research Atmosphere in Departments of Psychiatry," *Arch. Gen. Psychiat.*, 4:225–236, 1961.
49. Rheingold, H. L.: "The Measurement of Maternal Care," *Child Develpm.*, 31:565–575, 1960.
50. Richmond, J. B.: "The Role of the Pediatrician in Early Mother-Child Relationships," *Clin. Proc. Children's Hosp.*, 15:101–117, 1959.
51. Rider, R. V., et al.: "Associations between Premature Birth and Socioeconomic Status," *Amer. J. Publ. Hlth.*, 45: 1022–1028, 1955.
52. Rogers, M. E., et al.: "Prenatal and Perinatal Factors in the Development of Childhood Behavior Disorders," *Acta Psychiat. Neurol. Scand.*, vol. 102, 1955, Supplement.
53. Schorr, A. L.: "A.D.C.–What Direction?" *Child Welf.*, 41:72–78, 1962.
54. "Science and Human Survival," *Science*, 134:2080–2083, 1961.
55. Scrimshaw, N. S., and M. Behar: "Protein Malnutrition in Young Children," *Science*, 133:2039–2047, 1961.
56. Snow, C. P.: "The Moral Un-neutrality of Science," *Science,* 133:255–259, 1961.
57. Whitehorn, J. C.: "The Concepts of 'Meaning' and 'Cause' in Psychodynamics," *Amer. J. Psychiat.*, 104:289–292, 1947.
58. Wiltse, K. T.: "Aid to Dependent Children: The Nation's Basic Family and

Child Welfare Program," *The Social Welfare Forum, 1960,* Columbia University Press, New York, 1960, pp. 218–232.

59. Wortis, H., and A. M. Freedman: "Maternal Stress and Premature Delivery," paper read at the Annual Meeting of the American Public Health Association, October, 1959.

60. Yarrow, L. J.: "Maternal Deprivation: Toward an Empirical and Conceptual Reevaluation," *Psychol. Bull.,* 58: 459–490, 1961.

7. International Activities: An Integrative Overview

François Cloutier

Introduction

Whether it is at all possible to write an integrative overview of mental health activities is debatable. The mental health movement—and this is true of its national as well as its international aspect—encompasses so many different activities, sometimes with little in common but goodwill, that it escapes definition. Any attempt to reduce it to a given set of principles or to describe it in terms of one philosophy or one program is bound to fail.

The five preceding chapters of this "World View," which in their diversity all deal with some facets of international mental health, are illustrative of this point of view. This, however, should not prevent us from discussing the activities usually ascribed to the mental health movement. It might be useful for our purpose to begin with a brief historical sketch. Such an approach will lead to some comments on the movement's nature and aims, followed by a critical appraisal.

Historical Aspects

There have always been people concerned with the welfare of the mentally ill. It would be quite easy to list most of the efforts, reaching back to antiquity, that have been made in this connection. This, however, would be a purely academic exercise and one beyond the scope of this chapter. Strictly speaking, a "movement" refers to an organized structure. If one accepts this definition, the origin of the mental health movement can be ascribed to the founding of the Connecticut Society for Mental Hygiene by Clifford Whittingham Beers. The date is 1908, and the place the United States of America. At approximately the same period, a

Especially prepared for this volume.

few similar groups began in several European countries. The main characteristic of Beers's initiative, which rightly earned him the title of founder of the mental health movement, was that it was not a professional association, as were most of the groups elsewhere. It was truly a citizen movement, a movement of laymen.

Soon after the organization of the Connecticut Society, a National Committee for Mental Hygiene, which later became the National Association for Mental Health, started to work. In other countries, organizations patterned more or less along the same lines came into being. Finland in 1917, Canada in 1918, and South Africa in 1919 organized national bodies. The European League for Mental Hygiene, an important grouping of national societies, was formed in 1920. There are now national mental health associations in more than fifty countries all over the world.

Clifford Beers, dreaming of an international movement, favored the organization of new societies outside the United States and traveled extensively for this purpose. His most important initiative, however, was the formation in 1919 of an International Committee for Mental Hygiene; this Committee, whose foundation marked the beginning of international activities, sponsored three congresses: in Washington (1930), Paris (1937), and London (1948). It was at the London Congress that the Committee reorganized itself by creating the World Federation for Mental Health (WFMH), the only body truly representative of the movement until today.

The World Federation, although it succeeded the older International Committee, was quite different. While the Committee was mostly psychiatric, the WFMH aimed from the outset to be interprofessional and multidisciplinary. Its membership was not restricted to national mental health associations but was open to any society active in improving mental health. This is one reason why the membership grew rapidly, from 22 founder members to more than 150 member associations in 1964. The first president and director was Dr. J. R. Rees of the United Kingdom.

The World Federation for Mental Health was given consultative status with the United Nations and several of its specialized agencies, particularly the United Nations Educational, Scientific and Cultural Organization (UNESCO) and the World Health Organization (WHO). The last-named body, under the leadership of the Canadian psychiatrist Brock Chisholm (who later became president of the WFMH), created a Mental Health Unit in 1949. The unit, first headed by Dr. Ronald Hargreaves (United Kingdom), then by Dr. Eduardo E. Krapf (Argentina), and now by Dr. Pieter A. H. Baan (Netherlands), became another influencing force in the field of international mental health.

More recently, two other international bodies were founded: the World Psychiatric Association and the International Committee against Mental Illness. The World Psychiatric Association was organized during the Third

World Congress of Psychiatry in Montreal in 1961. It succeeded a committee whose main purpose was to organize psychiatric congresses. The
Association is a professional organization, representing psychiatric societies. The International Committee against Mental Illness is a smaller
body, which has been establishing treatment clinics in several developing
countries.

There are, of course, many other international bodies, some very
important, which concern themselves directly or indirectly with mental
health activities. As a matter of fact, very few associations which deal
with social and human problems can be considered outside the scope of
mental health. But we are discussing a movement, and we can certainly
state that, in its organized form, it is the World Federation for Mental
Health which represents the movement in the nongovernmental sector,
while the Mental Health Unit of WHO represents it in the governmental
sector.

Aims and Activities

In the beginning, the stated aim of the mental health movement was
the improvement of the living conditions and treatment of the mentally
ill. This concern grew out of the appalling conditions in mental institutions all over the world and, of course, out of Beers's own experience as a
patient. The newly formed organizations were acting, more or less, as
"pressure groups" in the hope of mobilizing public opinion and bringing
about changes. On this platform, there is no doubt that the mental health
movement has been extremely successful. The revolution in psychiatric
organization witnessed over the years is the direct result of such activity.
This is particularly true of the national movements in the various countries. The national associations were almost by definition involved in the
challenge to help the mental patient by influencing legislative and administrative structures.

At the international level, such direct action was hardly possible. This
must have been the reason why the International Committee for Mental
Hygiene thought of organizing congresses to disseminate information
about mental health and to create goodwill. This role, recaptured by the
WFMH, was expanded while a new program was developed. It seems that
the mental health movement shifted its emphasis from a main concern
with improving the lot of the mentally ill to an increasing preoccupation
with preventive goals. The movement became more and more sociological,
mental health becoming a cultural value and taking on much wider connotations.

This social trend is apparent in the statement produced by the prepara-
tory commission which was to propose the founding of the WFMH. This
statement, by its very title, "Mental Health and World Citizenship," gave
a dimension to the concept of mental health. It attempted an analysis of

the mental health situation as this was then seen and made many useful recommendations. It is interesting to note that most of these recommendations were subsequently implemented by governmental and nongovernmental agencies.

Taking this into account, the Executive Board of the WFMH reviewed this statement in 1961, and the document *Mental Health in International Perspective* was produced. Coming after so many great changes in the world situation and in the field of mental health, this document emphasized trends in the treatment and prevention of mental illness. It also made an attempt to describe the role and scope of mental health activities, particularly those in the voluntary sector. Cooperation with governmental organizations and promotional informational activities were stressed.

The contribution of J. R. Rees to "A World View" illustrates this point. The problem of prevention is discussed at some length, as is the question of training. Concern is shown for the effects of cultural changes. It is interesting to note that Phon Sangsingkeo's chapter makes the same observation. In an address given in his capacity as president of the WFMH in 1962–1963, Dr. Sangsingkeo adopts the point of view of developing countries facing rapid urbanization and industrialization. The impact of technological and cultural changes on family life and the disruption of customary patterns of living are presented as mental health problems.

It is also interesting to compare these two papers with the one by E. E. Krapf and Joy Moser of the WHO Mental Health Unit. Theirs is an attempt to describe the results attained over a period of twelve years, based largely on data collected by the unit. It illustrates one of the WHO functions which appear, so to speak, more technical than social. Since 1949, the Mental Health Unit, through its numerous expert committees, has developed a solid body of knowledge in the field. Almost all aspects of mental health have been considered at some time or other, and guidance has been made available all over the world.

It would be an oversimplification to assert that the World Federation for Mental Health has adopted the social approach, while the World Health Organization has confined itself to the technical one. In terms of trends, however, there might be some truth in this statement. Between the two organizations there has been throughout a process of cross-fertilization, WHO always being actively represented at WFMH meetings and WFMH board members serving on many WHO expert committees. There can be little doubt that these activities have been complementary.

Appraisal

Over the years, some circles have become increasingly preoccupied with appraising the value of mental health activities. Doubts have been expressed about the possibilities of real prevention, the impact of mental health education, and so on. The lack of valid criteria of mental health

and our ignorance of epidemiology make these criticisms quite understandable.

These shortcomings are very well illustrated by Leon Eisenberg's chapter. He asks: "Is prevention of mental illness possible in any meaningful
sense?" It is a real question indeed. Of course, Eisenberg refers to primary
prevention, where the basic problem lies. Secondary and tertiary prevention can be better understood in terms of public health. They make sense
because definite techniques can be used and, to a certain extent, results
can be measured.

Eisenberg's answer to the question is quite encouraging: he comes to the
conclusion that certain mental disorders could be prevented. While his
evidence cannot always be substantiated, it is convincing enough. This
does not come as a surprise, of course, to the mental health expert. The
importance of this chapter is that, after having had the courage to express
certain doubts, the author does not discourage action.

Can we, in this light, endeavor to appraise international mental health
activities? In such an attempt, I believe that the balance sheet would be
positive. The mental health movement may at times have oversold itself
through the enthusiasm of some of its proponents. An anthology of un-
validated, even wild statements would not be difficult to compile. Mental
health has occasionally been presented as a panacea. Uncritical hopes
have been expressed, and sometimes faith has played a greater part than
facts. Despite these shortcomings, the movement has succeeded in creating an extraordinary interest, which is at the bottom of the psychiatric
revolution that our generation has been experiencing. It has stimulated
action not only in organization but also in training and research. It has
disseminated information by creating an international forum and by
bringing people together above frontiers and languages. It has given and
is still giving inspiration all over the world.

I do not deplore, personally, that the mental health movement at the
international level has adopted a sociological approach. Even if certain
claims are exaggerated, there is little doubt that there are mental health
implications in most problems in which human beings are involved. Even
if the supporters of the movement cannot and should not try to propose
solutions in all instances, the simple fact that they emphasize the mental
health dimension is already useful. It is also noteworthy that the interdisciplinary approach, now so widespread in psychiatry, evolved in part
from the movement.

What was impossible just a few years ago is now happening daily. One
psychiatrist from the Sudan or from Thailand meets another psychiatrist
from Chile or from the United Kingdom, and they speak the same language. This achievement has taken less than a generation, and it is an
achievement indeed. It means that thousands of people have learned to
think along the same lines, to exchange their knowledge and their experi-

ences, and to implement ideas that can be tested against reality. The interest in mental health has spread also to the public health professions: one only has to attend a few international meetings or to travel a little to discover it. This is one direct consequence of the activities of the international bodies working in the field of mental health.

Is it at all possible to foresee the future? Maybe. It seems that the WHO Mental Health Unit, after having sponsored so many expert committees, will be thinking more generally in terms of research. This is a very interesting development, because only a well-planned research program, with the right priorities, will give us the answers we need to carry on. As far as the World Federation is concerned, it seems that it will give greater attention to its member bodies in terms of guidance and that it will make an attempt to regionalize its different activities. If this materializes, the mental health movement will be continuing stronger than ever.

part three

Community Centers

8. British Experience in Community Care

Kathleen Jones

When the history of the world mental health movement comes to be written—and there is a task here worthy of a new Arnold Toynbee or a future Max Weber—one of the fundamental themes must be the development of the concept of community care. By a long process of evolution and a few imaginative leaps in the dark, we have progressed from a belief in a limited and somewhat monolithic mental hospital service to a vision of a flexible and diversified service which will represent society's changing response to the changing needs of psychiatric patients. Stereotyped habits of thought have been replaced by fresh, empirical thinking about clinical care, about administrative methods, and about the basic philosophy which underlies both.

In this field, the Dutch are the acknowledged pioneers, and it is particularly fitting that we should be discussing this subject in Amsterdam, where Prof. Arie Querido's work and that of his colleagues has been an inspiration to psychiatrists and administrators from so many countries. Perhaps the most impressive characteristic of this work has been the humility of approach: the insistence on starting from an actual situation and investigating it in depth by means of a variety of research techniques.

Professor Querido's recent book *The Efficiency of Medical Care* [6] illustrates this view by its careful and scholarly refusal to theorize about the situation until detailed investigations have shown its nature and characteristics. I should like to proceed with similar caution, by first outlining the present situation in Britain and then discussing some of its problems and potentialities. Some of our problems will be relevant to those of other countries, and some may be international problems in the true sense, that is, problems common to all countries; but in the present state of our

Presented at the Sixteenth Annual Meeting, World Federation for Mental Health, Amsterdam, the Netherlands, August, 1963; especially prepared for this volume.

knowledge it would probably be unwise to try to distinguish these in any detail.

In Britain, the view that the institution was the right place for the mentally disordered, both for their own protection and for that of society, was dominant right through the nineteenth century. Mental hospitals were constructed in three great waves of building development, following the County Asylums Act of 1808, the Lunatics Act of 1845, and the Lunacy Act of 1890. They were usually sited several miles distant from the town which formed their main catchment area, partly because rural land was cheaper than town land and partly because there was a rejection mechanism at work, the patients being literally as well as metaphorically rejected by the society from which they came.

Until 1913, the law made no clear distinction between the mentally ill and the subnormal; but when a separate service was instituted for subnormal patients, a new principle emerged. Hospitals, or "colonies," as they were then called, were to care for the low-grade patients and for those whose home background had been found unsuitable; but there were provisions for the care and supervision of patients who remained in their own homes. The care of the mentally ill and that of the subnormal were administratively separated, and there was nothing equivalent to the new system for the mentally ill.

In the 1920s, however, outpatient clinics began to develop. This was a major breakthrough: the first means of treating patients without committing them to the mental hospital under certification. In 1930, mental hospitals were empowered to take voluntary patients. The huge chronic populations remained, but a new category of short-stay patients appeared and the question of aftercare became an urgent one. Hospitals began to appoint social workers, and the nucleus of a hospital-based psychiatric service developed.

After World War II, the institution of the "welfare state" brought radical changes. A variety of locally based services for the care of under-privileged or handicapped groups in the community developed. Mental health departments were organized as subsections of local public health departments.

The development of these new services was inevitably uneven. Some local authorities were quick to grasp the implications of their new position and began to experiment with community services. Others did very little apart from their statutory duties: the supervision of subnormals in the community and the conveyance of the mentally ill to the mental hospital. In a few cases (Worthing is probably the best known) the hospital took the initiative in providing a community service; but the relation between the role of the local authority and that of the hospital was obscure, and quite often the work went by default, neither body taking the initiative.

The Mental Health Act of 1959 changed the situation decisively. This act was the result of a royal commission which saw a great and expanding future for community care and a dwindling role for the hospital. Even while its discussions were taking place, there were new developments: the day hospital movement began to spread; mental hospitals, realizing the dangers of "institutional neurosis" so ably described by Dr. W. Russell Barton,[2] began to experiment with the idea of the "therapeutic community" and to open their doors; and local authorities began to test the potentialities of hostels for those who had no settled homes and sheltered workshops for those who could not be fully absorbed into industry.

By 1959, the idea of a diversified system of care was widely accepted, though the place of the inpatient hospital was (and still is) the subject of much debate. The official policy of the Ministry of Health [3] since 1961 has been based on a statistical projection from trends in the years from 1954 to 1959 which suggested a possible reduction in inpatient beds from 3.3 to 1.8 per 1,000 population within fifteen years. This policy has been criticized on the following grounds:

1. A long-term projection cannot be adequately based on a short-term trend.

2. The decline in mental hospital populations between 1954 and 1959 was marginal and is unlikely to continue indefinitely of its own momentum.

3. This decline resulted from a change in administrative policy rather than from a clinical advance.

4. There is a need for local variation in provision according to local need.

5. Any decision about the future of the mental hospital population is premature until the potentialities and limitations of community care have been more thoroughly explored.[4,5]

In recent months, the argument concerning institutional or community care has widened to include other forms of provision—homes for old people and epileptic colonies, for instance—and two main points of view have emerged. One is that the institution is a relic of custodialism, necessary enough when other services were not available but now outmoded. The second view is that although the institution is now only one among a number of means of social care, it still possesses a useful function for people whose disabilities are so great that they need a sheltered environment.

The argument is very largely one of degree, for very few people are prepared to push either view to its logical extremes by contending that all institutions should be abolished or that all patients now in institutions should stay there. The question is how many can be rehabilitated by modern methods of care and under what circumstances. A preliminary and necessary step is to ascertain what kinds of patients are at present in the institutions under review and to assess how far they would be capable of rehabilitation under existing conditions of community care. As Professor Querido has shown, such arguments need to be tied to what is possible and practicable now if they are to retain any contact with reality.

With these considerations in mind, a patient census of 10,000 psychiatric beds in the Leeds region has been mounted as a result of cooperation between the regional hospital board and the University of Manchester. We hope that the first results of our analysis will be available in the near future.

This controversy concerning institutional or community care may be a peculiarly British one, but the basic question underlying it is one of *balance* between the different parts of a diversified service. It seems likely that other countries will have encountered this question, though possibly framed in different terms, according to local tradition and needs. It is allied to two other questions, those of dimension and finance.

The problem of *dimension* arises from the fact that psychiatric need is difficult to estimate or delimit. Epidemiologic work is an urgent necessity; but while there is little argument about the extent of the field in other areas of epidemiology (we can establish clearly who suffers from typhus or smallpox), the need for psychiatric care must always be based on a multiple assessment. It is a matter not simply of disease or handicap but of disease or handicap plus social factors: no home, a poor home background, relatives who cannot cope with the patient, inability to hold down a job, and so on.

Mental disorder is still to some extent a submerged problem. We can measure the number of patients who come forward for treatment and construct incidence rates and prevalence rates, but we have no way of knowing how many more would come forward if the conditions of treatment were more acceptable. British experience is that increased provision has always resulted in increased demand. In the early days of outpatient clinics, it was thought that they would reduce the need for inpatient beds, but in fact they provided a supplementary service rather than an alternative one. Day hospitals have similarly tended to draw greater numbers of people into the orbit of the mental health services rather than providing a new means of catering for those already under care. The size of the problem is conditioned by the services we are prepared to offer. Presumably there is a limit to this process somewhere, but it is doubtful whether any country has yet made sufficient psychiatric provision to reach it. As Prof. P. Sivadon said recently, where mental health is concerned, all countries are "developing" countries.[7]

There is thus no clear answer to the problems of dimension. If one asks "How good a mental health service must we provide?" the answer must be "the best one we can afford."

The question of *finance* is basically one of allocating scarce resources among apparently bottomless needs. It seems to be a fundamental law of any society that this allocation will favor those who serve society best. Thus primitive societies have been known to abandon the old or expose the sick in time of famine or attack, concentrating food supplies on the working and fighting population (who guarantee the present survival of the group) and the children (who guarantee its future survival). It seems likely that this law holds good in more complex societies also. It is much easier to get money and equipment for a social service which will restore workers to productive employment or benefit children than to obtain these things for the mentally ill, the subnormal, or the old.

It seems likely that those who administer the mental health services will always have difficulty in securing the share of the national resources which social justice demands. The proper care of psychiatric patients costs a good deal of money, and it is difficult to demonstrate an adequate return on investments. A proportion of mental health work is, and perhaps always must be, economically unproductive.

Much of the opposition to adequate financing is not rationally expressed. If it were, it would be easier to combat, but it takes the form of agreeing that provision is necessary sometime and then putting it off indefinitely; or claiming that it will be sufficient to enlarge an existing building, when the real need is for another building elsewhere; or expecting one psychiatrist "temporarily" to do the work of two, or one nurse or social worker to do the work of four; or arguing that it is "good for the patient" to receive only minimal care, when the real benefit is to the taxpayer's pocket.

There are, of course, times when financial saving and therapeutic advantage do genuinely go hand in hand—when an authority can save money and at the same time produce a better service; but the occasions when this is possible are probably rarer than we care to think. An expensive service is no guarantee of quality, because the money can be spent unwisely, but a cheap service is rarely anything but an indication of inferior standards.

It is often claimed that day hospitals and other community care agencies can provide a cheaper service than that of the mental hospital. This may be so, but there is an urgent need for a full-scale costing study to prove it. The claims which are made for day hospitals sometimes ignore four important points:

1. The difference between capital and maintenance cost. A day hospital is cheaper to build but might be more expensive to maintain if it required a higher staff ratio.

2. The difference between marginal cost and average cost. Calculations are sometimes based on the additional cost of the day unit to the

cost of a parent inpatient unit. This is marginal costing. To give a reasonable figure, the cost of facilities used jointly by the day hospital and the inpatient hospital should be split between them.

3. Transferred cost. Day hospitals may be dependent on services paid for by some other authority—e.g., in England, ambulance and social work services, which are paid for by local authorities. These costs should be included.

4. Submerged cost. Day hospital care might result in a longer average stay than inpatient care or in a higher relapse rate.

Psychiatrists sometimes feel impatient at the mention of cost and financing, arguing that cost does not matter as long as the patient gets the best possible service. I think this is unrealistic. Just because it is difficult to get a fair share of the community's resources for psychiatric patients, it is important that psychiatrists should give consideration to these issues and put their claims in terms which politicians and government servants can understand. For instance, a study of mental hospital costs in the north of England [4] showed that, of three hospitals studied, the one with the highest weekly cost and the most intensive medical care actually had the lowest cost per case, because patients were discharged more quickly and did not relapse more often. Good care may be cheaper than minimal care in the long run. I think facts of this kind are worth demonstrating. Certainly studies in efficiency, whether linked to cost or organized on some other basis, may be crucial to development.

A further problem raised by the advent of community care is that of *selection of service*. When the traditional mental hospital was the only means of treatment, the question was simply whether the patient should enter the hospital or stay at home. When there is a diversified service, a day hospital, an outpatient clinic, a halfway house, and an inpatient ward all offer different types of care at different levels of intensity, appropriate for different needs. Each has a distinct function, and they are not necessarily interchangeable. From a whole range of services, the doctor must choose the one appropriate to his patient's needs. This involves a skilled assessment, based on two kinds of knowledge: (1) knowledge of the patient's condition and his environment; and (2) knowledge of the varied resources of the community, so that needs and resources can be matched. The kind of administrative knowledge necessary for an assessment of resources has rarely been included in medical curricula, but several British universities are now including some teaching (whether described as "social administration" or "social psychiatry") for medical students or postgraduate students in psychiatry.

Where some of the newer agencies for community care are concerned, the question of *function* is still being debated. Five years ago, we were arguing about the function of the day hospital. Did it provide the first stage in aftercare for those who had had inpatient treatment? Did it provide alternative care—a means of reducing the inpatient population? Did it provide supplementary care, drawing on a new and hitherto untreated population? The answer seems to lie somewhere between the three views, but there are still many local differences. We may use the same term "day hospital" for agencies serving different and even mutually exclusive purposes.

Since the Mental Health Act envisaged the development of hostel facilities, there has been a corresponding debate on the function of the hostel. Should it be of the halfway house type for patients in the process of rehabilitation? Should it provide a home for the chronic patient with no family who no longer needs the full resources of the mental hospital? Should it provide for patients who can go out to work on a full-time basis or those who cannot work at all? Should it mix patients with different needs and, if so, in what proportions? Doubtless some large authorities will be able to provide specialized hostels for different types of patients, but for the smaller towns and the rural areas the solution is not so easy. Some local authorities appear to be constructing hostels because this is official policy, with no clear idea of what patients they would like to take but with a strong suspicion that, whatever their preferences, they will eventually have to deal with unemployable, elderly, and chronic patients.

This would be very undesirable. Hostel accommodation for patients who stay only a few weeks or who are out all day may be quite satisfactory; but we have as yet few trained hostel staff, and hostels cannot provide all the facilities for socialization which a mental hospital has: the workshops, the sports fields, the cinema shows and entertainments, the libraries, the education classes. Such facilities could not be provided economically for ten or twenty patients. It is not community care to take an elderly and chronic patient away from the active social life of the hospital he knows and to place him in strange surroundings (however modern and near the shops) where he has nothing to do all day.

Perhaps we should think seriously about defining "community care," because it is evident that the phrase is being used in many different ways. In fact, it is seldom defined at all; it is usually denoted: "Community care means day hospitals, night hospitals, outpatient clinics, day hospitals, and so on." It is much more difficult to describe its attributes.

It is, of course, possible to define community care negatively, by saying that it means any kind of care apart from that provided by the institution, the mental hospital; but this may be a false dichotomy. A good mental hospital is part of the community, anxious to keep its patients in touch with community life and to be "a flowing stream rather than a stagnant lake." It is no longer in most cases what it was in the nineteenth century: an isolated, forbidding institution for society's rejects.

I suggest the following attributes as being essential to a reasonable standard of community care:

1. *Diversity*—there must be several different types of care.
2. *Flexibility*—the system must fit the patients, and not vice versa. Transfer from one type of agency to another should be as easy as possible.
3. *Adequacy*—the care offered must be at least as adequate as that offered by the traditional type of psychiatric hospital service. It is not community care to send an old man out of the hospital to live alone or in unfriendly lodgings, with only an occasional visit from a harassed general practitioner or a social worker. It is not community care to send a severely subnormal girl back to a family which neither understands nor wants her unless someone has the time to foster supportive family attitudes.
4. *Ability to facilitate social relationships*—the patient should have at least as active a social life as in the psychiatric hospital.

It is on factors such as these, rather than on the size of the unit or its siting, that community care depends.

Good community care is expensive. It is probably more expensive in running costs (though not in capital outlay) than good hospital care, because the services which the hospital would concentrate have to be diffused over an area. Even in England, where roads are reasonably good and the distances involved in traveling to outpatient clinics or domiciliary visits in the catchment area are rarely more than twenty or thirty miles, traveling time and mileage costs may be considerable.

In other spheres, we take it for granted that concentration is more efficient than dispersal. We do not expect the general practitioner to visit all his patients in their own homes, because it is more economical in time and effort for the patients to come to the doctor. We concentrate children in schools, students in laboratories and lecture rooms, and workers in factories for the same reason. If we disperse our resources for the treatment of mental disorder—and this is what community care means—we need more money, more workers, and more equipment than would be necessary for a centralized service. Community care may be better for many patients, but it is not a cheap alternative. The capital costs are lower than those of building new modern mental hospitals; the maintenance costs will almost inevitably be higher unless there is a drop in standards.

If I lay stress on the importance of maintaining standards, it is because they are very easily lowered, with often the best of intentions and the finest of descriptive phrases. Reform in the British mental health services has a curious cyclical movement: progress never follows a straight line, and the downward trend often seems to start from the moment of greatest success. There was a great step forward at the beginning of the nineteenth century, when the system of "moral management" used at the York

Retreat by the Tuke family became well known.[3] The new county asylums provided a fresh start in care and treatment, and it was common practice for their staff to be sent to study the new methods at the retreat before taking up their appointments; yet the county asylums settled into an institutional mold, and the system of moral management was never widely applied.

In 1845, a burst of optimism followed the passing of Lord Shaftesbury's Lunatics Act and the introduction of the "nonrestraint system" by John Conolly and Gardiner Hill. Conolly realized that the abolition of restraint was not enough in itself and that the corollaries of this reform were the improvement of standards among nurses and new forms of activity for patients; yet his plans for a nurses' training school and a school for patients were frustrated by a parsimonious committee. Half a century of neglect and indifference followed.

Such examples could be multiplied to show that the bright promise of one decade may be the lost cause of the next. It seems likely that this is not a specifically British phenomenon, for the American report *Action for Mental Health*[1] comments on a similar pattern in the United States. The report speaks of reform as coming in waves and adds that each wave is "quickly followed by apathy, loss of momentum and professional backsliding." It would be interesting to know if historians in other countries had found a similar movement, because this may be a pattern conditioned by the community's attitude to mental health problems.

Here is one explanation: the community at large is highly ambivalent to mental disorder. The general public will readily assent to the proposition that the mental health services should be improved or that psychiatric patients should be treated with kindness, but lip service does not lead to action. Intellect pulls one way; emotion, the other. This is where the stigma of mental disorder begins. Fear of becoming abnormal, of losing the power of responsible action and rational judgment, supersedes rational assent. Fear may be projected in the form of aggression against those who provoke it: the patient, the therapist, the institution. Sometimes laughter and ridicule take the place of open aggression. Thus, in the eighteenth century, young dandies in London paid twopence to see the lunatics in Bedlam; today, when we are too polite to laugh at the patients, there are plenty of jokes about psychiatrists and mental hospitals. Sometimes the reaction is a mental block: the whole problem is pushed out of the conscious mind as if it did not exist; hence the "conspiracy of silence."

May I suggest one more escape route? It is also possible to deal with this fear by becoming overarticulate about the problem. Catchphrases— "community care," "supportive therapy," "public tolerance," and the rest —can become almost a defense against the reality if used often enough, a kind of incantation. We define the problems of the day hospital when we ought to be building one or urging other people to build one. The case conference, instead of being a spur to action, becomes an excuse for a little dilettante speculation. Perhaps those of us who work in universities are particularly prone to taking refuge in verbalization, to thinking that we have dealt with a problem when we have merely described or defined it.

To sum up, I have tried to indicate some of the main problem areas in the community care field in the light of British experience: the questions of balance, dimension, finance and efficiency, selection, and function. I have suggested a definition of community care based on four attributes: diversity, flexibility, adequacy, and ability to facilitate social relationships; and I have offered a few comments on the cyclical nature of mental health reform as observed in England and the United States, with the sobering thought that the downward trend could happen again.

Perhaps I ought to end by saying, like Thomas Carlyle, "Brothers, I am sorry, but I have got no Morrison's Pill for curing the maladies of society." I suppose Morrison's Pill was some nineteenth-century panacea, some cure-all which failed to fulfill all the claims made for it. It is up to us to see that community care does not suffer the same fate.

References

1. *Action for Mental Health: Final Report of the Joint Commission on Mental Illness and Health,* Basic Books, Inc., Publishers, New York, 1961.
2. Barton, W. Russell: *Institutional Neurosis,* John Wright and Sons, Bristol, England, 1959.
3. Jones, K.: *Lunacy: Law and Conscience, 1744–1845,* Routledge & Kegan Paul, Ltd., London, 1962.
4. ———— and R. Sidebotham: *Mental Hospitals at Work,* Routledge & Kegan Paul, Ltd., London, 1962.
5. *Psychiatric Services in 1975,* P.E.P. (Political and Economic Planning), London, 1963.
6. Querido, A.: *The Efficiency of Medical Care,* H. V. Kroeser, Leiden, 1963.
7. Sivadon, P.: Address to the Annual Conference of the International Hospital Federation, Paris, June, 1963.
8. Tooth, G. C., and E. M. Brooke: "Trends in the Mental Hospital Population and Their Effects on Future Planning," *Lancet,* 1:710, 1961.

9. An Experience with Sectorization in Paris

Philippe Paumelle and Serge Lebovici

Introduction

It is the purpose of this chapter to report on the professional services of the Mental Health Association of the Thirteenth Arrondissement, an administrative section of Paris with a population of 165,000. Privately operated, it is supported by public funds and philanthropic gifts in its endeavor to provide for the inhabitants of the arrondissement an integrated mental health service, including neuropsychiatric facilities for children and adults, a program for the prevention and treatment of alcoholism, and a coordinated effort in mental health education. Because of its emphasis on serving a specific geographic area or sector, the work of the Mental Health Association of the Thirteenth Arrondissement has become known as a sectorization project.

While the residents of the arrondissement have always had public mental health services available to them, these were seldom sufficient to meet the need and were rarely coordinated to provide optimal results. Specialized residential or outpatient facilities were frequently located at a geographic distance, had limited communication with referring clinics, and had little contact with rehabilitation centers. Hospital stays were unduly prolonged by the difficulty of coordinating social readaptation. All too often, essential family ties were loosened or broken, thus retarding the reintegration of the patient in the community.

It is the aim of the Thirteenth Arrondissement Plan to create a whole range of extramural facilities with clearly organized and defined roles, all centering around the community Mental Health Center and each entrusted to a specialized team. In this way, patients can be served in the reality of their home environment, and professional workers motivated toward the goal of prevention. Toward these ends the Association de

Especially prepared for this volume.

Santé Mentale et de Lutte contre l'Alcoolisme dans le XIIIe Arrondissement worked in close partnership with authorities, practitioners, and the
general public.

With the program outlined in the Ministry of Public Health memoran-
dum of March 15, 1960, it became possible to coordinate mental health
services provided by hospital, day hospital, aftercare centers, and workshops. The way in which this was developed in the Thirteenth Arrondissement, as well as plans for the future, will be delineated in the following
sections. Throughout the emphasis is on a coordinated and continuing
mental health approach, with the same team assuming and retaining
responsibility for a patient once an initial contact has been made. The
team is part of a multiple-service organization, recommending whatever
treatment may be most appropriate and available at a specific moment,
given the patient's particular problems and circumstances. The dangers of
passing a patient from one isolated agency to another, without adequate
consultation or follow-up, are avoided. By further focusing on key organizations and contacts, an extensive mental health education effort is
mobilized, facilitating the concepts of prevention and early diagnosis and
treatment.

The Thirteenth Arrondissement

Situated on the river Seine, the Thirteenth Arrondissement is the
equivalent of a large French town with a population of about 165,000. It
may be considered a complete urban unit, taking the Place d'Italie as its
geographic and spiritual center.

Like all Paris arrondissements, the section is subdivided into four administrative districts. Of these, the two to the south are economically less
well endowed. The two northern ones, comprising the big railway network of the Gare d'Austerlitz and the large hospitals of la Salpétrière and
La Pitié are less densely populated, their inhabitants enjoying a higher
socioeconomic standard.

The two southern districts differ slightly from each other. The south-
west area, that of Maison Blanche, has a standard of living which is
slightly superior to that of the southeast, known as the station quarter,
where the automobile plants of Panhard and the aviation works of
Snecma are surrounded by the homes of workers and their families,
including a large number of North Africans. There are also small precision
industries with workmen who still take pride in their traditional skills.

On the whole, the arrondissement is a reflection of the poorest parts of
Paris with a sufficiently typical population composition, e.g., workers and
minor employees, foremen, a few executives, some professional people,
and comfortable shopkeepers. Because of lack of services and overcrowding, housing conditions have been, and often still are, very poor.

The 1954 Paris census reflects the unfavorable ecological factors in the

Thirteenth Arrondissement; conditions of life might be termed "pathogenic." Sociological reports on the arrondissement record a greater number of deaths due to tuberculosis, more frequent behavioral disturbances in children, and the highest figures for juvenile delinquency. These conditions may change, for the arrondissement is due for reconstruction. Important industries will move elsewhere, and the resident population is likely to increase by 10,000 to 15,000 within the next few years. This will probably effect changes in the social character of the population, and the newcomers are likely to introduce fresh aspects for future ecological studies.

The Alfred Binet Center

The Alfred Binet Center for Child Guidance is organized into four teams under the expert guidance of a director and a social assistant director. Each team is responsible for a geographic area of the arrondissement and is composed of a number of psychiatrists, psychologists, and social workers, together with secretaries and various professional assistants (psychoanalytic psychotherapists, psychomotor therapists, remedial teachers, etc.). Teamwork among the psychiatrists has produced highly dynamic aspects: theory as well as practical treatment is applied to every case. All the professionals work constantly at every level in the field of psychotherapeutic action from the moment of undertaking responsibility for a patient. Specialized psychotherapeutic treatment includes psychoanalysis, individual and group therapy, and psychodrama.

Every team directs its clinical and intermediary action as seems most appropriate, but for both theoretical and practical reasons it speedily became evident that the leader of each team could undertake an additional form of service. Thus, one of our number has organized an extensive facility for the study and treatment of speech difficulties, while another is the professional adviser to the Day Hospital for Children (described below).

Placement of a center for child psychiatry in a clearly defined geographical sector has immense advantages. Disturbances treated are so closely involved with reaction toward home surroundings and family circumstances that realization of the ecological dimension is important, particularly in an area like the Thirteenth Arrondissement. The children we examine and treat are preselected by means of constantly improving cooperation between, for example, school social workers and the center's social psychiatric assistants. By coordinating our plans, the waiting list can be shortened to reasonable proportions. Similarly, time spent on patients who suddenly arrive or are brought for consultation can be reduced if it is realized that today's noisiest cases will not necessarily be tomorrow's gravest problems and that the "best-behaved" children may be harboring serious inhibitions of a neurotic or psychotic nature.

Continuity of treatment, vital in mental health work, is assured at the Alfred Binet Center, since the team responsible for a case keeps that responsibility throughout the period of treatment and aftercare. The role of the social worker who follows the family's progress is particularly important; the "key contacts" at her disposal in the arrondissement facilitate follow-up at critical moments in the near or distant future. This continuity adds a longitudinal dimension to the center's services, as noted by the return of families at times of crisis.

The whole staff of the Alfred Binet Center is engaged in a series of research endeavors, with current emphasis on epidemiologic studies, involving the detailed recording of cases, including psychosocial, diagnostic, prognostic, and therapeutic indications noted in the course of treatment, all under the expert guidance of a member of the French National Institute of Health. Extensive reports are made on each patient at intervals of one, three, and five years after admission to the center or earlier in the case of discharge or discontinuation of treatment for other reasons. It is, of course, impossible in this brief space to give details on the approximately five hundred new cases treated every year. The majority are children aged from six to fifteen. The fact that preschool children and adolescents are rarely brought for treatment indicates the importance of cooperating with the school services in the area. The referral of patients by family social workers, vocational guidance counselors, police, court authorities, and other key contact organizations provides practical proof of our success in integrating the center with the neighborhood. Research studies indicate that the great majority of children sent for examination come from reasonably secure social and economic backgrounds and are generally members of natural, adopted, or foster families; factors of apparent psychosocial etiologic importance may, however, be elicited. It is evident, for example, that among the lower social classes pathogenic tendencies are encouraged by overly large families and overcrowded housing conditions. We hope to utilize our research for effective preventive care in relevant areas and are particularly interested in studying the structural, plastic, and social aspects of what may be seen as a single unit from a dynamic point of view—structural diagnosis and prognosis.

Coordination between the Alfred Binet Center and the Mental Health Center for Adults is of additional assistance in certain difficult cases, as, for instance, when parents of a child are themselves known mental patients or psychopaths. In addition, we hope eventually to establish a well-equipped specialized facility for adolescents, to which patients may come of their own accord.

Perhaps the ultimate advantage of our community system is the emphasis placed on the utilization of intermediary bodies, whether in a technical or a theoretical sense. The inevitable discrepancy between the ever more urgent needs and the sadly slow and limited development of services makes it imperative to distribute the implementation of psychiatric action, thus creating the most hopeful conditions for the prevention of mental illness in the new generation. Use can and must be made of key contacts for the practical promotion of mental health in all phases of prevention, case finding, and early treatment. Frequently key contact persons possess knowledge of the circumstances which, with the aid of practical discussion or of informal but productive seminars, enable them to take charge of cases that are less complicated or in which their action is more acceptable than perceived interference by a psychiatrist. One example of an important key contact is a pediatrician who sees the parents of very young children. We are also endeavoring to extend counseling for social workers in pediatric, school, family, educational, and leisure-time fields and for educators interested in the prevention of delinquency.

Intermediary action demands new methods of approach. At the Alfred Binet Center, we have found particularly productive the utilization of group-dynamic techniques and, at times, psychodrama. Many other approaches may be pertinent. Over the last two years, under the auspices of the center's section on speech therapy, case-finding efforts have been conducted in some local schools. The ultimate goal is to provide remedial teaching for children unable to read, write, or draw, without transferring them to a special school. This is intended particularly for children who come from families that are not oriented materially or culturally to the needs and difficulties of scholastic educational achievement and are unlikely to welcome special schooling for their children. The development of these services in the schools also provides further opportunities for the counseling of teachers.

Another helpful collaborator in problems of child development is the visiting psychiatrist, appointed by the Mental Health Center to the various welfare stations for mothers and children in the arrondissement. Would-be assistants in this field could tell a long story of their efforts to gain a local foothold. At first the consultant psychiatrist was overwhelmed by the task of treating obviously hopeless cases; valuable time was lost before a number of pediatricians and their colleagues realized the necessity for coordinated efforts and a team approach. Only now has an effective atmosphere been created for counseling with kindergarten and primary school teachers, as well as with psychologists.

The Alfred Binet Center welcomes trainees seeking experience in a variety of fields. Participation is provided in the daily program, plus supervised responsibility for individual cases. Trainees also assist in keeping up to date the coordination of our numerous personnel and the organization of the variety of services to be provided; these include not only case conferences but also staff meetings from all specialized facilities and interprofessional scientific and technical discussion groups.

Other Children's Services

The *Day Hospital for Children* was instituted as an extension of the Alfred Binet Center. Supported by the Rothschild Foundation, it provides services in temporary buildings, to which the children are transported by bus. It is intended for treatment of severely neurotic or psychotic children of school age and serves approximately twenty-five patients. They receive schooling adapted to their various capacities, as well as suitable remedial teaching, planned along carefully thought-out lines of progression. Briefly, it is our aim to develop a therapeutic atmosphere in the Day Hospital, both by treatment and by introducing the children to work adjusted to individual requirements (e.g., in educational workshops). Parents are constantly seen by the center's social workers and are required to participate in group psychotherapeutic sessions. After leaving the Day Hospital, a child may be sent, if necessary, to the Alfred Binet Center for follow-up treatment. Roughly speaking, we can say that the annual turnover of children is about 50 per cent. The Day Hospital has now been in existence since 1960, and intensive follow-up studies are in progress.

We do not pretend that the Alfred Binet Center and its associated services can solve single-handed all the problems of child mental health in the Thirteenth Arrondissement. In our judgment, the most financially practicable plan is gradually to develop a variety of facilities, once the parent organism is fairly well established. By the time this chapter is published we expect to open a *family placement service for children,* to be coordinated with that projected for adult mental patients, in the neighborhood of the psychiatric hospital at Soisy-sur-Seine. The service would begin in a small way, dealing with temporary and urgent family placement cases. A few educators could take charge of a number of those children whose family conflicts would be assuaged by a separation of a few weeks; there would be no question of cutting a child off from his familiar surroundings, particularly important where school is concerned.

Establishment of a *day facility for severely oligophrenic children,* designed to combine various full-, half-, and part-time services, is in the planning stage. We also hope to initiate special classes, in cooperation with the consultations given by the Ligue Fraternelle des Enfants de France; these could constitute a particularly useful and necessary stepping-stone between the highly specialized pedagogic services of the Day Hospital and the ordinary schools attended by the children.

Finally, we have hopes of instituting, within the next few years, a *child neuropsychiatric center,* most probably located within the immediate neighborhood of the Soisy hospital for adult mental patients. This might be composed of a number of separate units, providing facilities for observation and hospital treatment along the lines of the medicopedagogic residential centers and psychotherapeutic clinics.

To complete the scope of these facilities, a *day hospital for adolescents* should be included among our projects, and also provisions for *specialized night services.* In our judgment, a careful review should be made of mental health resources for children, adults, and the aged, considering the future organization of the social centers which will inevitably follow in the wake of the large-scale building developments already under way in the Thirteenth Arrondissement.

The Mental Health Center for Adults

The child psychiatrist has come to realize the importance of the whole question of adaptation, its characteristics, and evolution in relation to family or school; similarly, yet with different aspects, the full importance of social rejection or alienation of the mental patient must be realized by the psychiatrist before he can hope positively to affect it. It should be remembered that the patient has often been excluded from the community of his fellowmen for years before he ever comes for treatment. His experiences probably range from isolation when he is quiet to police intervention and neighbors' fears if he becomes violent. He has met with more or less acute disappointment and degradation in his efforts to work and live and has finally been rejected. It becomes the task of specialized medical therapy to combat these disastrous social reactions, but it is no longer a question of the psychiatrist working alone. Technically, the psychiatrist is the leader of a team composed of a variety of professional associates to facilitate the necessary approaches, including social workers, psychologists, psychotherapists, rehabilitation workers, and nurses. All join in diagnostic and therapeutic efforts which go beyond "treating" the patient in the strictest sense of the term. The team seeks to attain an understanding of the patient's surroundings, background, family, and work conditions, that is, the milieu in which he lives.

To facilitate adult psychiatric services, the Thirteenth Arrondissement has been subdivided into three administrative areas, each of 50,000 to 60,000 inhabitants and each initially equipped with a medicosocial unit. Another unit is to be provided for each area, and together the teams will be expected to offer all required services. The hub of organization has been located in the Centre de Santé Mentale, 76 Rue de la Colonie. Facilities are being developed for consultation and for ambulatory, domiciliary, and emergency care. Consultations are timed preferably for the evening, after working hours, and are arranged beforehand in an attempt to allot adequate time (generally three-quarters of an hour for first, and half an hour for subsequent, consultations). All team members are available, thus facilitating cooperation and precise diagnosis for treatment. Taking into consideration the full circumstances of the patient's condition and difficulties before he comes, a welcoming atmosphere is seen as essential; the receptionists and social workers focus on this aspect, and team members' timetables are programmed to ensure constant availability.

Ambulatory care of all types is being developed to maximum capacity. Pharmacological treatment is dispensed by nurses. Psychomotor and relaxation therapy are provided in individual or group sessions. Many forms of psychotherapy are available to meet individual requirements, from psychoanalysis to supporting therapy. Special mention may also be made of our efforts to assist schizophrenics to avoid apparently inevitable hospitalization through intensive psychotherapy. A regular, psychotherapeutically oriented consultation has been developed to select appropriate therapeutic action for individual cases.

An occupational counselor is always available to advise team members on problems of rehabilitation and readaptation. His task is primarily to find work for patients, which involves information and contacts with prospective employers. He must also discover the best ways of reinserting patients into the productive life of the community, which requires observation and participation in the activities of the rehabilitation workshop.

The facility for domiciliary and emergency care was initiated in 1963. From a preventive and therapeutic point of view, it is essential to have immediate access to patients' homes, to step in at the first suggestion of an appeal for help, or perhaps even to investigate an ominous lack of communication. While physicians and social workers play an important role, primary responsibility rests with the team for domiciliary care. As of 1964, there were four nurses, who arrange between themselves to be constantly on call at the center, providing assistance for cases not actually requiring hospitalization; for example, senile patients with somatic disturbances, depressive conditions, anxiety disorders, etc. The nurse on duty is available to calm a troubled situation when an appeal is received from the patient's family, to accompany a patient for treatment, and so on. In some cases, domiciliary care of the severely mentally ill amounts to hospitalization within the home. Here, too, the contacts made by the nursing assistant in visits with the family and neighborhood are of extreme importance in the patient's ultimate social reintegration.

It is, of course, impossible to treat all sick persons at the center; the teams have not yet at their disposal a sufficient array of extramural facilities. So far, including the newly established rehabilitation workshop, we have the Day Hospital, established in 1959. This is intended for all instances in which consultation and domiciliary care are insufficient and especially for those persons who would formerly have been hospitalized, probably under committal. A fully integrated therapeutic and occupational program is planned for each patient and regularly discussed at weekly reviews of treatment progress.

A more distant project is the Club des Peupliers for former mental patients, envisaged as a social rehabilitation service with planned leisure-time programs. In close collaboration with the Élan Aftercare Center, we provide lodging and upkeep for convalescent patients in a sort of hostel, operated under medical and social supervision. This home is particularly oriented toward rehabilitation, and patients are, as a rule, reintegrated into normal occupational work. Plans have been drawn for an extensive chain of sheltered workshops and rehabilitation services for those patients whose readaptation to normal working conditions is likely to take a longer time. In these specialized facilities, the type of work and its remuneration must be considered with careful attention to detail, taking individual requirements into account insofar as possible. Patients especially affected include the retarded and those who have experienced long treatment processes, that is, the group which usually constitutes the "dead weight" in psychiatric hospitals, where their problems are often merely aggravated and rendered chronic.

Coordination of Services

The general plan of action for the various links in the chain of community services involves an initial contact between the patient and a team from the Mental Health Center. This contact is maintained throughout, the team following each patient's progress through the various facilities. Practical experience has shown how difficult it is for this program to run smoothly; constant meetings, discussions, and correspondence are necessary. It is of primary importance to help the patient, from the very first, to realize that he has not been thrust into a clinic where he knows nobody and nobody knows him (the classic situation), but that he is secure—a feeling even more important for the mentally ill person than for the physically sick. To achieve this ideal, each psychiatrist responsible for the general mental health of an area must also understand his responsibility as a functional leader of a service. In this capacity, he is no longer only a physician in charge of individual patients but the captain of a team, delegating the application of individual treatment to his colleagues. Considering the long-established, private, confidential nature of medical practice in France, leading only too often to successive treatments by isolated physicians, it becomes apparent that our team effort is breaking new and difficult ground in requiring everyone to coordinate his actions with all the others involved in the treatment process.

The physicians who administer the arrondissement's hospital at Soisy-sur-Seine (the Eau Vive) are also responsible for a medical sector team and are thus familiar with this type of cooperation. The Eau Vive operates on a small scale: 1 bed per 1,000 inhabitants, or a total of 175 beds when complete. These limitations of size impose conditions requiring intensive treatment over as brief a period of time as possible. To achieve maximum results we concentrate on continuity between services; the team continually surveys all patients. Since hospitalization is voluntary except in emergency or acute cases, we endeavor to stimulate active patient collaboration and adjust treatment to individual requirements. Patients progress positively, reaping the benefits of a varied daily timetable, adapted to their personal needs and leading away from completely isolated treatment to a social way of life opening onto the community.

Large-scale wards have been completely eliminated. Instead, the rooms vary in capacity from one to six beds. In addition, each section has its own functional aspects, ranging from facilities for patients in intensive treatment (where they may, if necessary, be completely cut off from noise, light, and normal social contacts) to the practically open areas, where men and women together may partake in a community life that, in its diversity, nearly resembles the outside world. After a conference with the architect, we also established for every section small units of a familial character, each containing seven beds, under the care of a nurse. These units facilitate temporary patient groupings of a therapeutic nature (as, for example, when their patterns of behavior are similar and they follow the same course of treatment). Feelings of human individuality and security are fostered, an important consideration usually impossible to attain when patients are crowded into vast wards.

It is hardly necessary to mention that the therapeutic goals of the hospital cannot be realized unless the number of qualified personnel is increased. We hope to achieve a ratio of one physician per twenty-eight patients and one nurse per seven patients, this being considered the absolute minimum requirement. Yearly we have to ask ourselves whether the per diem allowances should not also be raised.

Meanwhile, to the administrators and organizers of the responsible services, our projects and requirements are always new and often quite unprecedented. We must weigh in the balance human and financial responsibilities and the consequences of prolonged intramural care under conditions which, to say the least, often have little therapeutic effect. We are persuaded that our experience is well worthwhile on all counts if we can achieve the aims described: prevention of mental illness; treatment, primarily extramural, applied as early as possible; intramural treatment, continuously and intensively sustained; and, finally, social and professional rehabilitation of patients at appropriate levels of recovery.

Mental Health Education

In the centers for both child and adult mental health care, all workers hold to the principles previously described. As guardians of the mental health of the Thirteenth Arrondissement, we have come to realize the importance of screening candidates for treatment in the service facilities. It is our long-term aim gradually to orient key contact persons to an even greater awareness of mental hygiene and to bring them into ever-closer contact with the centers.

The various efforts to promote mental health in the sector's child and adult population come under the general supervision of the Mental Health Association of the Thirteenth Arrondissement. The association has organized a committee, under the direction of a social worker, which includes mental health advisers as well as representatives of the general public and individuals in useful positions and related professions.

The Club des Peupliers has among its members former patients from the Mental Health Center for Adults; it aims to provide assistance in leisure-time occupations and rehabilitation. Its executive committee is composed entirely of former patients, particularly those from the Day Hospital. The director of the Mental Health Service, a social worker, serves as professional adviser to the club and its sixty members. Twice a month, outings are arranged, including visits to theatres, day excursions, etc. For a number of former patients, the club provides their only link with the Mental Health Center, thus maintaining contact with the therapeutic community. Another useful function is that, by inviting individuals from the arrondissement to participate, we can gradually bring the general public to accept and understand behavioral symptoms of the mentally ill.

In the field of assistance to parents, the Mental Health Service has organized a film club. Meetings are held once a month in a community room in the arrondissement and are always attended by at least 150 parents. After the film presentation, difficulties of interpersonal relations within the family and educational problems are discussed.

The Mental Health Center also holds seminars for the educators of clubs for potential juvenile delinquents. At each meeting a specific problem of dynamic psychology is studied, information exchanged, and a case history reported by a staff member.

In considering the various mental health activities of the arrondissement, mention should be made of the educational coordinator, a psychologist who works on a half-time basis for the association, seeing both parents and schoolteachers. Using a schoolroom, she gives lectures for parents twice every term in each school in the arrondissement. Thus, a number of parents, unable or unwilling to discuss their problems at first, tend to do so more readily when the psychologist has become a familiar figure, either during the time for general discussion or at the close of the session. The psychologist tries to explain causes of children's behavioral problems (leading often to further discussion) and to help parents to adjust their attitudes.

More advanced educational activities are conducted by groups attached to various family associations. The same psychologist also directs group occupational facilities for young people. She is available for consultation as a staff member of the Alfred Binet Center and of the social assistance teams. A number of mothers ask for personal interviews to discuss their children's problems; for some, these individual consultations have become an excellent form of psychotherapeutic treatment.

Conclusions

In a practical sense, our endeavors to improve psychiatric assistance in the Thirteenth Arrondissement are still in their early stages, although we have followed the guiding lines of historic trends of development in France and, more specifically, in Paris. The Mental Health Association of the Thirteenth Arrondissement is a private organization, whose professional staff works in collaboration both with representatives of the population and with members of the administrative departments financing our efforts.

At this writing, a statistical research survey is in progress to determine results and direct future programs, with special emphasis on epidemiologic approaches. In addition, more specific research efforts have been initiated in an endeavor to understand the general characteristics of the arrondissement's "normal" population and plan for its future needs.

Because of its unique organization and services, the Mental Health Association frequently receives professional visitors from other parts of France or abroad. Some of these visitors, supported by grants from diverse agencies, stay with us for quite a long time, working or studying under our supervision. In the Mental Health Center for Adults, special provisions have been established for colleagues from abroad to learn about both hospital and community services.

Summary

A brief survey has been presented of the professional services and the preventive educational program for children and adults developed and implemented by the Mental Health Association of the Thirteenth Arrondissement of Paris, France, in collaboration with local administrative authorities and other public and private organizations. By coordinating facilities within a geographic area, serving 165,000 persons, and demonstrating the practical effectiveness of a community mental health team which retains responsibility for a patient from the moment of initial contact to social reintegration, it is hoped to learn more about the conditions favorable to mental health and the prevention of incapacitating mental illness.

10. Administration of Community Mental Health Services in the United States

Herbert Dörken

Introduction

The World Health Organization's philosophy is that health should be regarded not just as the absence of disease but as a positive state of well-being. This far-reaching concept was reflected in the activities and concerns of World Mental Health Year; it is reflected in the studies of the Joint Commission on Mental Illness and Health. Marie Jahoda's review, *Current Concepts of Positive Mental Health*,[12] points to the broad social orientation that is implicit in these new community mental health programs. Here then is the ultimate goal: the conservation, development, and full utilization of human resources.

Cast in these terms, the concept of community services emerges and is in line with public health philosophy. Public health, however, is concerned with the prevention of disease and the promotion of health through work primarily with the community rather than with the individual.[21] For mental health personnel, this is in essence a new type of social contract, involving the added dimensions of sound public relations and employer-employee accountability, since beyond the traditional diagnostic and treatment (clinical) services there lies a whole gamut of community services: consultation with agencies and professions in the community; collaboration and cooperation with them in the development of services; coordination and integration of related services; participation in community planning; provision of public and professional education; and emphasis on survey, evaluation, and research.[5] I might add that we especially need to learn more about using and developing the strengths and abilities of men,

Presented in part at the Third World Congress of Psychiatry, Montreal, Canada, 1961, and expanded with the support of Mental Health Project Grant OM-646; previously published in the *American Journal of Psychiatry*, 119:328–335, 1962; adapted for this volume.

instead of eternally studying their weaknesses and sicknesses. A concern with human assets is more in keeping with positive mental health than endless dwelling on the ramifications of psychopathology.

It is the involvement of society which is essential for developing public services. Mental health associations often provide the medium through which the public interest may become manifest. At critical stages in program development, it is advisable to involve in planning such key professional groups as the state psychiatric, psychological, social work, and medical associations. If the service is to become an integral part of the community, however, it is essential to have an active, balanced, and continuing participation of all the community's major segments—education, law, clergy, health, welfare, finance, industry, commerce—and not merely an initial advisory board. By providing broad constructive guidance, potential differences and difficulties may be resolved beforehand. Public support and professional participation are the cornerstones of a community mental health program. Nonetheless, social and professional aspects tend to be influenced by other, often overlooked factors, which I shall try to discuss in this chapter. The oversights, alas, are all too often due to the fact that the planning, advisory, or administrative bodies do not reflect or have wide community participation but are overrepresented or professionally biased groups. We should recall that the basic intent is the development of a community service.

Social Impact and Change

The increasing scope and expanding knowledge of mental health have led to increasing specialization and to a process of differentiation and upgrading.[16] Also, the complex cluster of interlocking bodies of knowledge and the growth of specialization are such that collaboration among a number of disciplines is required. Current trends appear likely to continue. Increasing emphasis on the psychological, social, and occupational factors in mental health suggests an expanding and more significant role for the behavioral sciences.

In terms of the American value system, the capacity of the individual to achieve is one of the fundamental conditions of the good society. Since mental health is one of the foundations of this capacity, its importance takes on a broader meaning. The gathering impetus of the mental health movement shows plainly that it is a developing social force.[19] People now consider that they have a right to a reasonable adjustment. They believe that science and mental health professions can improve their lot. As a result, communities are becoming increasingly active in demanding and organizing comprehensive mental health programs.

The needs, resources, and social groups in a society are in continuous change. Unless this change is reflected in appropriate program changes, there will be the equivalent of a cultural lag. Unfortunately, there is a tendency for professional roles and services to become stereotyped, if not biased.[22] Such professional expectancy leads to static patterns and narrow definitions which stifle creativity. A spirit of restlessness must be induced or maintained, for if progress is our aim, then programs must have a "growing edge" in search of new ideas, improved services, and better utilization of the full range of community resources.

We are overly prone to consider mental disorder as the prime factor leading to treatment or demand for mental health service, when, in many instances, the degree of community tolerance provides the basic impetus to seek professional assistance. There is a distinct relationship between social conditions and the ways in which mental disorder is dealt with by the community.[6] Mental illness in social terms is behavior deviant from the norm. Expectations within a particular society and the context of the action are factors bearing heavily on local attitude and determination, which in turn are related to need, demand, and utilization of service and ultimately serve to shape professional services and practice.

Taking the larger picture into consideration brings the total range of disordered behavior into focus. These ramifications are an integral part of society. To the extent they are overlooked, we fail to provide an effective community service. The professional staff, then, might be viewed as agents who would attempt to induce constructive social change in the community. We have only begun to explore the potential mental health effects of adverse social conditions. Certainly, failures in adjustment, shifts in values and cultural patterns, and social dysfunction, as well as disharmony within families, are hardly individual matters. The findings of research on group dynamics and communications, then, are quite germane and should become a part of our practice and program planning.

Prevalence and Incidence

Without proper survey and data we do not know the nature and extent of actual problems requiring attention; we do not know whether we need a particular mental health service. Certainly, it is not another "industry" to be attracted to town. Cursory surveys may magnify the problem by the use of prevalence statistics, but the number of active cases is not an appropriate basis for making probability statements, for which incidence rates (the number of new cases during a specified interval) are essential, though seldom obtained.[11] Each community has its backlog of cases with protracted mental disorder. If this backlog could be worked through at the case level by effective management, treatment, placement, or referral, the mental health center would begin to deal with the natural base rate or incidence of mental disorder in the community rather than its prevalence.

A related factor is the need for continuous program analysis; failure to evaluate past work and future needs critically results in errors and mistakes never becoming known and, presumably, never corrected. It is essential to take stock not only of the mental health services but of the major social, economic, and demographic community data as well; these data are in constant change, the urban population drift being merely one index. The everyday operations and concerns of community services are rife with intriguing and very practical research problems. Here again, pathetically little is being done.

Family Therapy-Agency Complex

Without trying to minimize the extent of the problem, several studies have shown [7] that a relatively small number of families and individuals keep producing the bulk of agency activity.[2] This activity by many agencies with the same family, the multiple-problem family, creates the impression of vast numbers when actually it is a symptom of uncoordinated activity, often with different facets of the same core problem. The need for an integrated system of discovery, identification, ambulatory treatment, and nursing home and hospital care is pressing. That multiple-problem families involve a small segment of the population suggests that it may be more feasible than many of us think to serve the total community, because problems of the large majority may be more amenable to assistance.

The history of the development of health and welfare services is replete with examples of rivalry, competition, duplication, and fragmentation. For the sake of clarity perhaps in the mental health field, attention has been focused mainly on the individual. Yet, in our society, the family is the basic social unit. Each family will have its unique patterns of interaction. Evaluaton and treatment, if geared to this natural social unit, would not only avoid many of the handicaps of partial or incomplete service; it would also facilitate the resolution of the emotional and social problems not just of the patient but of the other family members and lead to a realignment of family patterns of interaction, thereby facilitating progressively more favorable adjustment.

If service is to be comprehensive, it should be available to all within the community: all ages, all relevant disorders of behavior, all agencies and professions. Fragmented service may be easier to initiate (e.g., for children, for the retarded) but more difficult to sustain, since it depends more heavily on a specific interest group than on community-wide support. In order to gain the stability that comes from community-wide support and involvement, the service must be widely available and not the agent of any one group or profession (related service) or even identified in the public mind as such (restricted service). The location of the community mental health center often has a significant bearing in shaping the public image of its service. To illustrate, location in a welfare building, school, or hospital generally creates the assumption of service for the indigent, children, or the sick, respectively, thus impairing a community-wide orientation and service.

Center-Hospital Relationship

Considerable attention is paid to coordination between mental health centers and state hospitals, particularly in regard to aftercare. In some states such coordination may be the major function. By contrast, it is seldom thought that centers may be dealing with essentially different segments of the population. There appears to be a trend, however, for centers to refer progressively fewer patients to state hospitals. Recent statistics indicate that the centers deal with a population largely different from that of the mental hospitals and that they are reaching a large segment of the community having emotional, mental, and social disorders which, it may be assumed, was not previously reached.

Prevention and Control

Much lip service is given to the need for a preventive approach to mental illness, for programs of public and professional education, for co-ordination and consultation, for the concentrated development of additional community resources, and for research. Yet when a mental health center is established, there is often such an overwhelming demand for clinical services that program control and direction are basically lost.

In developing a service in response to a community need, there is usually the hope that it will help to control the problem and have a preventive impact, but such a development is often open-ended. While a progressively increasing amount of service is provided, responsibility for evaluating its effectiveness is evaded. It should be noted that service, by itself, rarely leads to prevention and almost never to the establishment of control. It is usually without focus or direction and, most important, seldom assumes responsibility for results.[3] It is essential to ask questions about problems and their proportions. How can these conditions be modified, controlled, or improved? Critical factors should be isolated to enhance the impact of services and techniques.

We must also consider the concept of accountability, a most challenging proposal,[20] though, generally, a most unwelcome and unpopular notion among clinicians who are prone to be ego-oriented rather than task-oriented. A statement of activities is not synonymous with accountability. Yet, without defined goals and accountability, control and direction are lost, and prevention fades into obscurity. Moreover, and this is seldom appreciated in the field, to the public official accountability is a reality of everyday, whether knowledge is incomplete, adequate, or even accurate; answers, often critical, must be given.

We have only begun to consider the potential of a reorientation of total community health and welfare services leading to a solution of the community problems stemming from disordered behavior. Rather than deal with symptoms of behavior, we must focus attention on the pathologic processes giving rise to social disorder. This need for service has been separately interpreted by each agency. Finally, the problems related to criminal and antisocial activity account for two-thirds of the annual incidence of disordered behavior; yet communities have generally ignored this area in planning services. Buell's findings [3] hold much promise and have tremendous implications.

Unfounded Claims

At times, some of us venture beyond the realm of our skills, and a "halo effect" may mask our inadequacies. At other times, overextended claims may be made for certain services. This can prove awkward later on, especially if no provision is made for the demonstration of results.

All too often, in the mental health field, our procedures are founded on unconfirmed hypotheses rather than valid explanations. Therapeutic zeal may militate against scientific determination, particularly in regard to the efficacy of psychological forms of treatment. Despite the high fashion and great investment of time over years in long-term, intensive, dynamic psychotherapy, there is no evidence that it is superior to less rigorous methods; in fact it would seem that methodology is being preserved for its own sake.[2,22] It is, of course, asking a great deal of many psychotherapists and analysts to cooperate in trying to find out whether they may be deceiving themselves as to the usefulness of their life's work.[13] Rogers [18] and others, however, have made some definite progress in their attempts to isolate (or insulate?) the factors necessary for therapeutic personality change.

Location and Distance

Service, to be provided, must be available. Logical planning would fix its location at the hub of the professional and medical community for the area and at the center of trade and transportation. Such logical sociological planning may be set aside by local prejudice, political considerations, and chamber-of-commerce activity. Witness state and provincial hospital programs, the majority of such hospitals in North America being located in towns of under 10,000 population,[17] in the shadow of isolation, with resultant removal from the sphere of related services essential to programming.

The growth factor of organizations perhaps has led to the development of overly large mental health services responsible for vast geographical areas, the patient, alas, fading into insignificance. The lesson for future community mental health planning is that small centers, well dispersed, will render better service—a service more dependent on individual skill than on organizational size or structure. The natural geographical boundaries will vary from place to place. In Minnesota, with its relatively low population density, a radius of sixty miles was found to be the effective limit,[10] about an hour's drive by car. Adequate coverage at a greater distance could only be achieved by regular staff travel into the outlying area.

Distance, while it has a very direct relation to frequency or use of clinical service (diagnosis and treatment), also has a qualitative effect: the greater the distance, the more serious the disorder and the more inapppropriate it becomes for an outpatient service. There is a significant relationship between the increase in distance and the severity or flagrancy of the disorder which compels people to overcome this barrier. Outpatient services are more frequently unsuitable, and follow-up is more impractical. If anything, distance causes an even greater impairment of community services (consultation, in-service training, community planning, coordination)—the services essential to the maintenance of a public health orientation in the program and those more closely involved with social structure.

Financing

Stable and sufficient financing is basic to the proper development of a full service, and the initial budget is critical. If realistic provision is not made at the outset for the predictable complement of professional and clerical personnel at regionally competitive salaries and for the necessary equipment and supplies, then neither personnel nor facilities will be sufficient and an overburdened agency will be repeatedly turning to its backers, hat in hand, for one item or another—a process guaranteed to antagonize and discourage staff, board, and local government. By contrast, a complete initial budget facilitates recruitment to complement and the purchase of all necessary equipment (budgeted funds not expended may simply be returned to source or placed in a special fund for a future contingency). Then, in the second and third years, the funds previously necessary for equipment, say $4,000 (likewise, fee revenues), are available as a cushion to accommodate salary increments, with the result that the cost to the sponsors remains stable for at least three years while the center establishes and proves itself. At this point, the likely attitude, on returning to the sponsors and, if necessary, seeking a moderate adjustment of the budget, will be one of reasonable expectation and efficient management.

A positive relationship exists between community visibility, knowledge of services, public support, and local financial backing. Quite apart from the wider range of services received through a program stressing community services, such as consultation, community planning and promotion, in-service training of community professional groups, and social science research, the program by the very nature of its activities is highly visible and known to many key figures locally. The details of clinical services, by contrast, are never known. They are (as they should be) strictly confidential. Few persons learn the value of this service; the client is seldom outspoken, and those who are to provide financial backing have only a statistical report and a formal description of the services for consideration. This is a difference which may well be critical.

Services do not operate properly without sufficient fiscal support and reasonable assurance of continuity, while insufficient staff or facilities result in qualitative as well as quantitative program curtailment. Modern programming in the community mental health field is supported by some forward-looking legislation [8] that typically, on a matching-grant basis, leads to a partnership between state and community, with the dual advantage of central leadership and local involvement. Local identification and responsibility are encouraged, leading to a more flexible adjustment of service in keeping with local needs. Then, too, within budgetary limits expenditures are subject to determination by the local community, which may place a greater value on professional talent and service because it seeks them.

The cost of staffing may seem higher, for decentralization requires a greater number of costly, well-trained personnel since greater responsibility is delegated. Turnover is generally lower, however, and the effective productivity of smaller quality units is higher.

A larger proportion of the total cost is allocated to personnel (who do the work) rather than being tied up in equipment and major capital expenditures (buildings). In the Minnesota program, salaries typically account for 80 per cent of a mental health center's budget, while the total annual cost per capita, for the area served, at full-scale operation is only 90 to 95 cents. In terms of cost per hour, based on total expenditures and total professional hours in the fiscal year 1960–1961, the median hourly cost was $9.77, while the local cost was under $5 per hour. Considering the extent of service, it seems an excellent return.

Professional Participation

Community mental health programs are designed to provide a broad range of services at the local level. The open-ended, complex, and flexible nature of these programs, however, calls for fully trained personnel in all disciplines. There is no institutional control to fall back on, no available professional senior to turn to; "you are it": you stand or fall on the ability to assume responsibility, provide service, cooperate with others, and fit in with the community.

In effect, the diversity of local demands and problems underscores ability and accomplishment to a greater degree than professional background.[21] Also, particular abilities and talents do not necessarily follow professional stereotypes in hierarchical fashion or the definition of function by profession. The generalization frequently required on the part of the staff may be one factor accounting for the less strict division of roles and responsibilities among professions in this type of program. Professional growth and maximum achievement, however, are encouraged by delegation of responsibility. The opportunity inherent in a diversified program for the utilization of training and skills not only precipitates growth but also facilitates recruitment, provides greater job satisfaction, and encourages tenure. The administrative task is to create a climate in which each staff member is free enough and challenged enough constantly to precipitate himself into just manageable difficulty,[9] an expectancy of excellence which leads to its pursuit. Quite apart from the impact this may have on the pace, nature, and direction of program development, it creates a favorable professional climate, lending, in turn, desirable reinforcement to the service.

Even before it was so clearly documented by Albee,[1] the severe professional shortages in the mental health field were widely felt, if not known. In the face of the magnitude of this dilemma, it is incredible that greater measures have not been taken in both the recruitment and the training of personnel. The modest "indenture-stipend" programs, now fairly common, only scratch the surface. What attempt is made to heighten the potential interest of undergraduates, let alone those in high school? And few are the mental health services that have well-developed training programs in coordination with the universities for the main mental health professions. To project the continuation or development of a network of services without an active plan for and role in training is rather irresponsible. Are we too busy with the difficulties of personnel shortages to take measures to solve the problem?

A frequent stopgap is the "hand-over-hand" competition with neighboring mental health services for personnel. Even this expedient, which only shifts the shortage, fails because there is a failure to appreciate that the competition for such manpower is basically not with other comparable services but with industry and private practice.[4] Moreover, some services, despite the noise from wheel spinning, have not yet really answered the prime question: Do they really want well-qualified psychiatrists, psychologists, social workers, and others—and all that this implies?

Service and Salary

All too often, neither training, responsibilities, conditions of employment, nor salary bear a realistic relationship to each other. Following the more common pattern, professional standards are too low; responsibilities, too varied and far in excess of training; personnel, equipment and space, insufficient; and salaries, noncompetitive. There are many very serious ramifications to this situation. Two conditions seem most prevalent:

1. A salary unlikely to attract well-qualified personnel: to fill positions, professional standards are progressively lowered, but once inferior staff

has been recruited, the agency is deprived of the caliber of staff originally wanted, and, more serious, the least qualified are the least mobile. Intended responsibilities become inappropriate. Whoever heard of someone with a year or two of medical training (incomplete training) being recognized as a physician? The same principle holds true equally for psychologists, social workers, and medical specialists.

2. Seduction by fringe benefits: the basic position, remuneration, or both are uninviting. By recourse to various "arrangements," the wrapping for the package is made attractive. Once recruited, the man's talent and identification are divided, and his income is cumulative. And the basic task?—probably still unmet. This solution is an insidious one, bearing the seeds of self-destruction. It leads to professional drift from the agency and obscures identification. Service becomes less reliable, and the arrangements progressively more difficult to justify—certainly to the public. Both service and staff are prostituted; yet they eventually may be held accountable.

Professional Standards

Suppose we accept the notion of the "team" and the fact that various professions can make a serious contribution to mental health services. If so, all members of the team must be fully trained and sufficiently experienced for an atmosphere of cooperation and respect to prevail, indeed, be possible. The conviction that only fully trained persons can adequately bear full professional responsibility results in comparable competency among the professions, and artificial hierarchies tend to dissolve. Administrative responsibilities may then be determined on a "best-man" basis. Responsibility is thus directly related to talent, and an effective and efficient service can be expected.

Paradoxically, it might be added that though mental health personnel, with all too few exceptions, exhibit a general disinterest or dislike of broad administrative and fiscal matters, the number of able or qualified administrators falls substantially short of the number who believe that the role is properly theirs. Academic training in psychiatry, psychology, or social work is rarely germane to administration. Thus, it is difficult enough to secure an able administrator from the three professions, let alone any one of them.

When we deal with services, positions, and qualifications, we are faced with the trials of job classification or merit-system procedures. The aim is very clearly an orderly arrangement by duties and responsibilities of all positions,[4] but this fair and logical aim is all too often burdened with two major handicaps. In the first place, technology and the professions are in fairly rapid change, with the result that civil service structures lag behind professional developments, and there is often a rigidity, because of the mere size of the structure, that impairs adjustment to professional developments or makes it almost impossible to accommodate them. More serious is the strong conflict in value systems between the ways in which competence is assessed by the profession and by civil service.[14] This is most evident in the two differing views of a college degree, particularly a graduate degree. The common professional assumption that specific academic achievement per se qualifies an individual for a job is a presumption not always shared by civil service. In fact, professional requirements are often considered discriminatory, supposedly blocking unjustly the appointment of persons who, it is averred, can do the job though they have not met the usual professional requirements.

This procedure runs contrary to the notion that, with intimate knowledge and experience, a profession knows its resources and limits best. Rather, the classification officer becomes the ultimate judge. Regardless of the inaccuracy, this is hardly an approach designed to elicit the cooperation and interest of well-qualified (by the profession's standards) personnel.

In some professions, notably medicine, and in some services, such as Minnesota's Community Mental Health program,[15] this conflict has been solved by resort to legislation (or rule and regulation) of professional standards. Any amendments, as deemed necessary, may then be sought directly by the professions or the department concerned. In setting standards for public service in this way, it is likely that the minimum requirements will be high, and the maximum open. The only clear direction for change then is up, that is, toward improved standards and standards having professional recognition.

Summary

Comprehensive community mental health programs follow the pattern of public health philosophy, which places the need for community service paramount over individual considerations. Public support and professional participation are seen as the cornerstones of such a program, but both the social and the professional aspects are influenced by factors which we tend to overlook. In the community mental health field we have been all too prone to develop services without consideration for solving the vast community problems created by a wide range of disordered behavior. Proper integration and control of local services could have a preventive impact. This must become the ultimate goal, for without it there is no solution.

References

1. Albee, G. W.: *Mental Health Manpower Trends*, Basic Books, Inc., Publishers, New York, 1959.
2. Astin, A.: *Amer. J. Psychol.*, 16:75, 1961.
3. Buell, B., et al.: "Reorganizing to Prevent and Control Disordered Behavior," *Ment. Hyg.*, 42:155, 1958.

4. Donovan, S.: *Amer. J. Publ. Hlth.*, 51:591, 1961.
5. Dörken, H. O.: *Ment. Hyg.*, 44:442, 1960.
6. Glidewell, J.: *Relationship between Social Structure and Community Mental Health*, Regional Workshop on Leadership Training, St. Louis, 1957.
7. Greving, F.: *Basis and Plan for a More Effective Use of Community Resources for Mental Health*, Northeast State Governments' Conference on Mental Health, New Hampshire, 1957.
8. *Highlights of Recent Community Mental Health Legislation*, APA and NAMH Fact Sheet 8, 1959.
9. Hobbs, N.: *J. Clin. Psychol.*, 15:237, 1959.
10. Hodges, A., and H. O. Dörken: *Publ. Hlth. Rep.*, 76:239, 1961.
11. Jaco, G.: *The Social Epidemiology of Mental Disorders*, Russell Sage Foundation, New York, 1960.
12. Jahoda, Marie: *Current Concepts of Positive Mental Health*, Basic Books, Inc., Publishers, New York, 1958.
13. Lewis, A.: "Between Guess Work and Certainty in Psychiatry," *Lancet*, Jan. 1 and Feb. 1, 1958.
14. McCullough, M.: *J. Clin. Psychol.*, 15:244, 1959.
15. *Minnesota Community Mental Health Services*, Minnesota Department of Public Welfare, St. Paul, 1960.
16. Parsons, T.: "The Physician in a Changing Society, 1958: Some Problems of the Place of Medicine," *What's New*, Abbot, 1960, pp. 6-7.
17. "Planning of Facilities for Mental Health Services," *Surgeon General's Ad Hoc Committee Report*, Public Health Service Publication 808, Washington, D.C., 1961.
18. Rogers, C.: *J. Consult. Psychol.*, 21:95, 1957.
19. Sanford, F.: *Amer. Psychologist*, 13:80, 1958.
20. Slack, C., and R. Schwitzgebel: *Reducing Adolescent Crime in Your Community: A Handbook*, Educational Design of Alabama, Tuscaloosa, Ala., 1960.
21. Southard, C.: "A View of Local Community Mental Health Programs," in *Progress and Problems of Community Mental Health Services*, Milbank Memorial Fund, New York, 1958.
22. Woodward, L., et al.: *Amer. J. Orthopsychiat.*, 31:292, 1961.

11. Mental Hygiene in the U.S.S.R.

B. A. Lebedev

Introduction

Mental hygiene in the U.S.S.R. is founded on one of the basic principles of Soviet public health: prevention. Implying as it does a system of measures for the improvement of public health, prevention is at one and the same time an important aspect of internal government policy and the basis of Soviet medicine. It is the purpose of this chapter to review Soviet concepts of environmental prevention, general mental hygiene measures, and the services of neuropsychiatric dispensaries.

Environmental Conditions

Environmental factors, among which social factors are of vital importance, are regarded by Soviet medicine as of decisive significance, both in the origin of illness and in the maintenance of health. The government, therefore, devotes a very great deal of attention to the everyday living and working conditions of Soviet people. The Socialist national economy has completely abolished unemployment. It guarantees every member of society wide opportunities for choosing the occupation suited to his individual bent and abilities and gives him confidence in his future, which, of course, is an important prerequisite for mental stability and a favorable emotional background and provides him with a source of satisfaction. At the same time, intensive efforts are made to improve working conditions. Introduction of advanced production and elimination of occupational health hazards are among the first priorities where labor questions are concerned, whether in industry or in agriculture. The provision of good housing and amenities is facilitated by a large-scale

Previously presented in *Some Problems of Psychiatric Service, Organization, and Forensic Psychiatric Examination in the U.S.S.R.*, U.S.S.R. Ministry of Public Health, Moscow, 1962; adapted for this volume.

building industry and rapid construction methods. Big projects are under way for the improvement of urban sanitation and for the control of air and water pollution in towns and areas of industrial concentration. Large appropriations of funds are made by the government for these purposes.

In addition to improving the external environment, the closest attention is given to strengthening the population's mental and physical health and to fortifying the resistance of the organism to various pathogenic factors. Here, mention should be made of a series of important government measures to effect a steady rise in the standard of living, based on the rapid expansion of industrial production and of all branches of agriculture. The improvement of material well-being is ensured by the rise in real wages and salaries, accompanied by a reduction in the length of the working day.

The far-reaching measures taken to improve the cultural standards of the public are of great importance to mental health. The abolition of illiteracy, so characteristic of the old Russia, is an advance that has now long since been left behind. Universal secondary education and wide opportunities for university education have considerably raised the general cultural level. The recent introduction of polytechnic training, providing for a combination of intellectual and physical work, promotes the harmonious development of the personality. Physical culture has become extremely widespread.

Government concern for the different age groups is a characteristic feature of public health policy. The widely organized crèche, nursery school, and boarding school systems, with the active collaboration of the teaching and medical professions, ensure the development of a healthy attitude to life and a strong, stable personality. In addition, the adult population enjoys extensive insurance coverage. Among the advantages particularly worth mentioning are annual vacations, during which time a large proportion of those who need it have the right to sanatorium and rest home treatment, either free or at only 30 per cent of cost.

The increase in expectation of life and the consequent aging of the population have given rise in a number of countries to difficult and sometimes insoluble problems, particularly when there are in a family elderly persons with little means and no occupation. In the Soviet Union these problems have been rendered much less acute. Elderly people have fairly high pensions and take an active part in social life in a large variety of ways.

Advances in economic development and improvement in material well-being and cultural standards form the basis for the development of Soviet public health. At the same time, the public health system exerts an influence in all spheres of the national economy and of social and cultural development, making use of them in the interests of health. The national health services fulfill an advisory, organizational, and supervisory role.

General Mental Hygiene

In reviewing mental hygiene measures, a distinction should be made between general mental hygiene and special neuropsychiatric measures. In the first group come those measures designed to prevent conditions which in some degree contribute to undermining mental health. Among these should be mentioned the series of measures designed for the health and medical care of expectant mothers. They are given 112 days' leave on full pay, constant medical supervision in special gynecological clinics, and obstetrical care covering all deliveries in towns and most of those in rural districts. This approach creates the conditions for a normal pregnancy, prevents birth injuries, and, combined with the constant medical supervision of children, contributes to a reduction in child morbidity, particularly mental disorders. In this connection, the marked drop in the numbers of mental defectives should be mentioned.

The important work done by the public health authorities to control communicable diseases should also be noted. The incidence of children's infections has dropped sharply, while diseases that undermine or organically affect the nervous system, such as syphilis, malaria, typhus, and others, have almost completely disappeared. This has resulted in a marked decline in mental disturbances due to infection, while syphilis of the nervous system is very rarely encountered.

Constant supervision is exercised by the health authorities to ensure the elimination of occupational health hazards and the observance of labor and safety regulations in industry. The decisions of the authorities' representatives are binding on managements.

The consistent control exercised over potentially pathogenic environmental factors is also reflected in the incidence of those disorders in which there is considered to be an important substrate of hereditary pathologic factors. A typical example of this development has been the drop by more than 90 per cent in the number of manic-depressive psychoses.

Health education plays an important role in raising health standards and in disseminating medical knowledge among the public. At the health education centers and departments set up all over the country, popular lectures on medical subjects are given by members of the medical profession. These lectures deal with the rearing of children, the arrangement of a proper regimen for good hygiene, housing, problems of disease prevention, and the care of the sick. Popular scientific pamphlets are issued in large quantities. All this assists in spreading medical knowledge, helps to foster the right attitude toward health, and ensures that proper steps are taken when illness arises.

Free outpatient and inpatient care, fully accessible to the public, promotes the early treatment of those who fall ill. The danger of illness becoming progressive and creating complications is thereby reduced, particularly where the nervous system is concerned.

Should an illness take an unfavorable course and permanent disability result, the patient is examined by the medical assessment board, on the basis of whose findings he is given a pension. Where partial disability is involved, the board makes recommendations on the selection of suitable forms of employment. These recommendations are legally binding on managements, which are required to provide the disabled person (who at the same time receives a pension) with appropriate employment and conditions of work. Thus, even when a person becomes partially disabled, he is provided for materially. At the same time he is not discarded but can take part in useful work and thus does not become a burden on his family. This is an important factor in rehabilitation.

The foregoing is only a very general description of the system of state and medical measures which, in the long run, contribute to mental health. The scale on which these measures are implemented is a vast one, embracing the whole population of the Soviet Union. That does not, however, mean that all our problems have been solved. For example, the progressive introduction of polytechnic training into the schools raises problems in connection with the pupils' scholastic and productive work load which call for solution. Improvements in productive processes and their organization present special features that call for study. Measures need to be taken to ease the intensive concentration required by automation and the monotony and speedup introduced by the conveyor belt for persons who are slow by nature. Methods of health education also require further improvement to exclude any possibility of iatrogenic and other influences. Soviet physicians, teachers, psychologists, and other specialists are collaborating in a special endeavor to solve problems of this kind.

Neuropsychiatric Dispensaries

Let us now turn to special questions relating to the prevention of nervous and mental disorders. The prophylaxis of mental illness can, of course, only be practiced to full effect if we have knowledge of its etiology. Since, however, the causes of many mental disorders have up to now remained unknown, prevention can only be successfully directed against conditions known to promote the appearance of pathologic effects. Supported by the widely implemented social and general medical measures described above, work in this field comprises the following main branches:

1. Mental hygiene.
2. The detection of cases requiring observation and curative psychoprophylactic measures.
3. Prevention of acute mental illness or of relapse after illness.

These activities are carried out by the system of work adopted by the curative and preventive services, designed for prevention, active case finding, treatment, and so-called "dispensarization." Dispensarization (active case finding, followed by outpatient care) is practiced by all branches of Soviet medicine and is particularly developed in mental health.

The neuropsychiatric dispensary is a center for outpatient care which organizes preventive work in the mental health field. It has the closest contacts not only with mental hospitals and similar establishments but also with the curative and preventive health services as a whole and is thus in a position to carry out its tasks as described above. Inpatient care may be possible in the same building, perhaps with the same staff. It is the neuropsychiatric dispensary's ties with the rest of the curative and preventive health services that enable mental hygiene to be carried on successfully.

Mental hygiene, as a special branch of general hygiene, rests on the theory of "nervism," seeing the mind on the one hand as a product (the highest function) of the brain and, on the other, as the regulator of the organism's activity. The task of mental hygiene is to prevent the possible pathogenic influence of the mind on different aspects of the personality and vital activities of the individual. Hence, a review from the mental hygiene standpoint of educational and training problems, including intellectual and physical work and the influence of art, the radio, the cinema, and television on the proper all-around harmonious development of the human personality, is very much to the point. We have already touched on some educational problems. Here I should like to emphasize the importance of fostering a community spirit, which helps a person to rid himself of any pathogenic sense of loneliness, isolation, or helplessness, and also of excluding from literature and art criminal or flagrantly sexual elements that will undermine young people's morale. These problems are considered in consultation with psychiatrists. Mental hygiene plays a particularly important role in preventing the development of neurotic, psychopathic, and asthenic conditions.

Of equally vital importance for mental health is teamwork between the neuropsychiatric dispensary and other medical services for the early detection of cases requiring observation. Postinfectional asthenia, the not very marked impairment of higher nervous activity in cardiovascular diseases, and that in various chronic conditions of a different etiology attract the attention of the staff at neuropsychiatric dispensaries, which arrange for appropriate curative and preventive measures.

An independent task, taking up a large part of the dispensary's time, is the prevention of relapses and of the development of acute forms of mental disorder. To this end, combined therapeutic, preventive, social, and legal measures are taken.

To render care as accessible as possible to the population, the dispensary works on the sector principle, dividing the town or district (in big cities) into sectors served by a specially designated doctor and nurses. Cases of incipient or marked mental disorder are indexed at the dispensary. The program is a flexible one. Those under observation are divided into groups, depending on the need for more or less active supervision, care, and treatment. Provision is made for removal from the index after a stable cure has been effected. The dispensary's therapeutic and preventive work is done by doctors and nurses in close teamwork.

The nurse's tasks are very varied, and she plays an important role in dealing with patients coming to the dispensary. Besides being the doctor's direct assistant, she has a number of independent functions of great significance. This is particularly true of her investigative duties. The regular follow-up of patients on the dispensary index, done by the nurse at home or place of work, is far from being confined to recording the conditions. The main task of such a follow-up is the painstaking detection of unfavorable environmental factors and their active removal. The latter is of great importance from the standpoint of prevention and mental hygiene, since the removal of conditions adversely affecting the patient plays a decisive role in changing his pathologically impaired relationship with the outside world. The methods used by the nurse are many and various, ranging from advice and recommendations on mental hygiene to relatives and those living or working with the patient to the prescription of a change of conditions at the patient's workplace. Another important aspect of the dispensary nurse's task, which has developed greatly in recent years, lies in observing the course and results of supportive therapy. Changes in the patient's condition, noted by the nurse, very often lead the doctor to alter the patient's index status, admit him to a hospital, or remove him from the list as restored to a stable state of mental health. The nurse also gives vital assistance in decisions affecting social and legal rights, matters of guardianship, and so forth.

The availability of constant dispensary observation and treatment is of fundamental significance. Observation shows that premature hospitalization and the removal of the patient from his family and accustomed surroundings can have highly traumatic effects and, in a number of cases, lead to a worsening of the patient's condition. There are, however, further links in the mental health service that help to avoid severance from familiar ties: these are the neuropsychiatric day hospitals and sanatoriums.

Work therapy is carried on in special workshops attached to each dispensary. Its main purposes are to provide treatment by special "dosage" of work, to train patients in new work habits, to achieve the rehabilitation of the patient, and to restore his normal relationships with the outside world. The goal is to restore mental health, to return the patient to his family, and not to exploit his residual working capacity. The method used in work therapy is gradually to introduce more complicated working procedures for each patient and to arouse pride as well as material interest in the results of his work. With the medical specialist and inspector, the nurse plays an important part in the conduct of work therapy.

When a doctor finds, from analyzing the course of the disorder, that the therapy in the dispensary is inadequate to prevent the illness from becoming worse, or if at any stage of the illness the patient becomes a danger to himself or to those around him, the doctor will send the patient to a neuropsychiatric hospital. Here there are specialized departments suited to the patient's condition. (Special mention should be made of the sanatorium department for convalescence.) Every form of modern active chemotherapy, physiotherapy, and psychotherapy is practiced.

It is characteristic of neuropsychiatric hospitals in the U.S.S.R. that they are well staffed with physicians. As a rule in the departments for acute cases, no doctor has more than twenty to twenty-five inpatients to treat. Nevertheless, the role of the nurse in the ward is extremely important. The nurse is the doctor's foremost and active assistant in the ward in implementing all his therapeutic measures. Moreover, her role is not limited to this function. The doctor's working day lasts six hours. During the rest of the twenty-four hours, the nurse copes with the main work of the department, observes the patients, and carries out the doctor's orders. She therefore has the closest and most constant contact with the patients. This contact is most valuable, as it gives her the opportunity to exercise a very great therapeutic effect on the patients. At the end of her period of duty, she notes in a daybook her observations and conclusions regarding the patients' behavior, the changes that have taken place in their condition, and the psychotherapeutic work that has been done. Neuropsychiatrists attach much importance to these notes, because they provide a wealth of material for the correct diagnosis and choice of appropriate methods of treatment. The training, education, and guidance of junior medical staff also occupy an important place in the work of the ward nurse.

In the main, mental hygiene among children is organized on the same lines, although it has a number of special features. Without dwelling on these in detail, it should be stated that preventive and curative work among children receives a great deal of attention. The prevention of mental abnormalities in children is believed to be the most important factor in reducing the incidence of mental illness.

Summary

In the Soviet Union extremely great importance is attached to mental hygiene. The general public health and social measures introduced by the government create favorable conditions for the promotion of mental health. In circumstances in which impairment of mental health does occur, however, the patient receives free, medical psychiatric specialist care, which is organized in a series of steps ranging from "dispensarization" (active, preventive, and curative measures, together with social and legal aid) to hospitalization. At all stages in this program, the nurse plays an important role, as she is in constant contact with the patient, exercising care and supervision over him, defending his interests, and taking the most active part in his treatment.

12. Psychiatry and Culture in Japan

William Caudill and L. Takeo Doi

Introduction

It is the purpose of this chapter to discuss the proposition that the practice of psychiatry in Japan is interrelated with broader patterns of behavior found in the general culture. After sketching certain aspects of Japanese psychiatry, we shall consider some of the data on values, emotions, and family relations in the country.

Aspects of Psychiatry in Japan

After his arrival in Japan, Caudill chose three small contrasting private hospitals for study. One hospital was organically oriented in its treatment program, one specialized in Morita psychotherapy, and one specialized in psychoanalytically oriented psychotherapy. Some of the material collected during this research has already been published.[5,6,7]

While it might seem easy to offer a straightforward description of these three hospitals and their patients, things are not so simple for types of treatment or symptoms. For example, with respect to treatment, we have said that the three hospitals are "psychiatric" hospitals, but that is not what they are called. All three are called "internal medicine and neurology" hospitals, even though the great majority of the patients are neurotics or psychotics (particularly patients with schizophrenic reactions). Equally, all three of the hospitals have close connections with universities, but the connection in the case of the psychoanalytically oriented hospital is rather strained because the university does not formally recognize

Adapted, with permission, from an article previously published in Iago Galdston (ed.), *Man's Image in Medicine and Anthropology,* International Universities Press, Inc., New York, 1963, pp. 374–421. The investigations on which this chapter is based were aided, in part, by a grant from the Foundations' Fund for Research in Psychiatry.

psychoanalysis as a useful treatment method. A close connection with a university is more pervasive for hospitals in Japan than in the United States. There is, therefore, a definite need to know how these three hospitals fit into the organization of psychiatry in Japan and, beyond this, to know something about the broader question of the place of medical treatment in Japanese culture.[21,33,41,49]

As in the matter of treatment, there is also a need to know the cultural context within which the symptoms of patients occur in Japan. A person from another culture finds it hard to evaluate correctly what he sees and hears. For example, a twenty-six-year-old neurotic girl leaves the hospital for a weekend visit at home, and her father tells her that it is warmer in his room and that she should come and sleep beside him. She goes and does this. If a father were to make this suggestion in the United States, the anthropologist or psychiatrist would suspect him of having certain neurotic problems of his own. It is harder to say this in Japan, for there, one realizes, a child may sleep with his parents until he or she is four or five years old, and, in general, people wish to sleep together in one room more often than is true in the United States.[17]

A second example concerns a twenty-nine-year-old male patient, who was thrown into a temper tantrum because his mother would not come with him to buy a pair of trousers. Such behavior by a man in the United States would arouse suspicion about his problems, but, again, one needs to know that in Japan many men turn over their salary checks to their mothers or their wives, who, in turn, give them an allowance for their daily needs (carfare, lunch, and evening drinking), and hence such men do not have money readily available for additional purposes. More than this, one needs to know about the close ties to the mother which seem to persist in almost childhood form for a much longer time in Japan than in the United States.

We shall have more to say about the cultural context of treatment and symptoms, but first it is probably useful to indicate certain general characteristics of the practice of psychiatry in Japan, many of which have been discussed elsewhere.[4,9,23,25,28,37,47,48]

General Characteristics

Japanese psychiatry shares with Japanese medicine a general historical background inherited from Chinese medicine and the subsequent strong influence from European medicine after the Meiji Restoration. In particular, there was a heavy German emphasis in the training of psychiatrists. Since World War II, there has been an increasing influence from the United States on Japanese psychiatry. On the whole, the major focus of psychiatric theory and treatment in Japan is organic, and there is relatively little interest in psychotherapy as a systematic procedure in its own right. Despite this situation, there are some indications of a growing concern with psychodynamics; this topic, as well as that of Morita psychotherapy, will be touched upon later.

As of 1957, there were 90,579 doctors engaged in clinical work in Japan, of whom 1,470 were classified as psychiatrists or neurologists. It is interesting that these psychiatrists or neurologists were quite young (64 per cent were thirty-four years of age or younger), compared with all doctors (36 per cent of whom were thirty-four years of age or younger). Also, the psychiatrists and neurologists were almost all working within a hospital setting (97 per cent), compared with a figure for all doctors of fewer than half (40 per cent) so engaged. Making this comparison in another way, we note that 51 per cent of all doctors were in business for themselves (as owners of hospitals or clinics or simply in private practice), while only 12 per cent of the psychiatrists and neurologists were so engaged. The 49 per cent of the doctors who were employees were divided into 11 per cent attached to the clinical facilities of medical schools and 38 per cent attached to other types of facilities. By comparison, the 88 per cent of the psychiatrists and neurologists who were employees were divided into 33 per cent attached to the facilities of medical schools and 55 per cent to other facilities. In summary and in contrast to all doctors, psychiatrists and neurologists in Japan in 1957 were young and worked as employees in hospital facilities, which were frequently connected with medical schools. These data were obtained from the Japanese Ministry of Health and Welfare and are, as far as we know, unpublished. For similar but less detailed data, see the annual pamphlet published in English under the title *A Brief Report on Public Health Administration in Japan*, the most recent example of which is cited in the References.[35]

In 1958 there were 404 psychiatric hospitals in Japan, with a median capacity of 116 beds.[34] By 1960 the number of psychiatric hospitals had risen to 514, but the median capacity had remained approximately the same, at 107 beds.[35] Japanese psychiatric hospitals are thus small in comparison with the typically large psychiatric hospitals in the United States. Moreover, the great bulk of the Japanese hospitals are private, in contrast with the situation in the United States, where the majority of the psychiatric hospitals are public. For example, in 1960 there were in Japan 85,472 beds for psychiatric patients, and of these only 20 per cent were in national and prefectural public hospitals.

Payment for treatment for psychiatric illness differs considerably between Japan and the United States. In Japan, the patient usually comes into contact with the psychiatrist through the outpatient department of the hospital and is charged the going clinic fee, which is relatively small. Even this fee, whether for outpatient or inpatient services, is often largely covered by a government-sponsored health insurance program. In a survey of 10,000 patients (approximately one-fifth of the total) who were under treatment in psychiatric hospitals during the first six months of 1956, approximately 32 per cent were covered by health insurance, 59 per cent were receiving direct support from the government, and 9 per cent were paying full fees.[34]

The preponderance of men over women in psychiatric hospitals in Japan may be, in some part, a result of the health insurance program, which covers a person fully for a period up to several years of hospitalization if he is employed in an industry encompassed by the program, while members of the family of such an employed person are entitled only to a coverage of one-half of the cost of hospitalization. Since the vast majority of employed persons in Japan are men, it may be that this financial factor has a bearing on the greater number of males than females in Japanese psychiatric hospitals. On the other hand, Japanese hospital statistics showed such a sex distribution long before the health insurance program was put into effect. Whatever the causes, the 1956 survey of patients under treatment in psychiatric hospitals showed a ratio between men and women of 3 to 2. This ratio was also true within the approximately eight hundred cases, representing all admissions in 1958 to four hospitals (the three small private hospitals discussed in this chapter, plus one large public hospital chosen for comparative purposes), which were abstracted as part of the research reported here.

There was a further interesting preliminary result from the analysis of these eight hundred cases from four hospitals: in three of the hospitals (and, culturally speaking, these three were all fairly traditional), greater numbers of firstborn than last-born males were hospitalized. The fourth and psychoanalytically oriented hospital presents something of an anomaly, in that greater numbers of last-born than firstborn males were hospitalized. In all four hospitals, there seems to be a tendency for greater numbers of last-born than firstborn females to have been hospitalized. These preliminary figures are all computed in terms of patients whose sibling ranks, as of the time of admission, included at least two siblings of the same sex.

Similarities in the Three Hospitals

Despite their different philosophies of treatment, certain similarities were found in all three hospitals. The first of these concerns the matter of privacy. In the United States, patients often complain that they do not have sufficient privacy, but this complaint is less frequent in Japan. Possibly this fact is related to life in Japanese houses, where spatial privacy is difficult to achieve and perhaps not too highly valued.[17] The lack of a concept of spatial privacy is fairly apparent in the living arrangements in Japanese hospitals but is even more obvious at those times when the doctor is talking with the patient. There is a stream of interruptions—

telephone calls, office girls with messages, nurses with questions, and so on—to the point where it is difficult to see how doctor and patient can sustain a meaningful relationship during their conversation.

In spite of all this, we are impressed by the ease with which patients in Japan talk about their problems. We do not mean that patients talk easily about very deeply felt or very private matters, but they do talk freely about the contents of symptoms and past behavior in a rather open manner that American patients find difficult to achieve. This became apparent during a series of case conferences which took place over a period of six months at one of the hospitals. At these conferences, quite sick patients would be brought in and would talk with the examining doctor for an hour or even an hour and a half in the presence of six or seven other doctors. American patients are, of course, brought into case conferences but usually not for such long periods, and they seldom seem to feel as much at ease as did the patients in the Japanese hospital.

A patient would frequently say to the doctor: "*Watashi o omakase shite imasu*" (I am completely in your hands). In saying this, the patient is indicating that he wants to be cared for and is asking to take a passive and dependent position with reference to the doctor, and the doctor accepts and fosters the wish. When this sort of interaction happens, the doctor and patient begin to relate to each other in a way for which it is difficult to find a satisfactory English word.

At first in our discussions we called this a "colleague relation," because it seemed that doctor and patient were discussing the patient's illness as if it were a thing separate from the patient and they were working together in an attempt to defeat the "illness." Shortly, however, we became dissatisfied with this term. The relationship is an apparently intimate one, but it has a subtle quality of play acting on the part of both participants which prevents it from being characterized as truly personal. It is similar, and yet not so, to the relation between doctor and patient that existed in the United States when a family would have an "old family doctor." Somewhat later in our discussions, Doi suggested that the word *nareai* might characterize this relationship. *Nareai* can be translated as "collusion," but it does not necessarily have the fraudulent connotations that collusion has in English.

In Japanese, *nareai* connotes an exclusive relationship among the participants, in the sense that they enjoy an emotional, at times an almost familial, warmth together, while excluding others. And this *nareai* relationship can pass without censure in Japanese culture, although it can also be put to bad use. This sort of emotional undertone is not very usual in professional relations in the United States; when it does occur, particularly in a hospital, it is often described in English as the doctor's being "too much involved with the patient." A second word, which suggests a further aspect of this Japanese relationship between doctor and patient, is *tokekomu,* which might be translated as "to melt into," or "to fuse with." Whether a person is able to *tokekomu* with others is one measure of social ability in Japanese culture. Patients frequently complain that they are not able to *tokekomu,* yet even they give an appearance of melting into the relationship when they talk with the doctor about their symptoms.

The sort of relationship we have been describing not only exists between patient and doctor, or more generally among patients and staff, but also exists among and between the various staff groups themselves, the doctors, nurses, and office workers. This was perhaps most obvious in the fall and spring trips which the staff took together in several of the hospitals. The picture of a group of doctors, nurses, and office workers going off together in an excursion bus for a day's outing or a weekend at an inn is quite an ordinary one in Japan but is seldom to be seen as a part of life in hospitals in the United States.

In a general sense, we feel that the rather peculiarly Japanese type of close relations among staff and patients and among the staff themselves that we have been attempting to describe results in better communication about routine matters in Japanese than in American hospitals, where communication is more formalized. Our general impression is one of smoothness in the handling of administrative problems in Japanese hospitals. This is in contrast to the difficulties in such matters noted in the literature on hospitals in the United States.[2,3,45] This contrast, however, may be due to certain special qualities of American hospitals. For example, interpersonal relations and administrative routines in Italian hospitals, as described by Anne Parsons,[42,43] seem to be similar in many respects to those in Japanese hospitals, and the situation with regard to these matters in hospitals in the United States may turn out to be rather specifically American in comparison with hospitals in other cultures.

We do not feel that smoothness of communication on the surface and the existence of a personal quality in the relation between doctor and patient are all to the good in Japanese hospitals. These attributes may make for easy administrative operation, but they may also prevent effective psychotherapy from being carried out, at least as this involves the technical use of resistance and transference as tools in the process of therapy.

To help the patient attain insight into his problems and to go beyond support and advice, the doctor must be somewhat removed from his patient. Such a situation is difficult to achieve in the Japanese psychiatric hospital, where doctor and patient are in a somewhat "mutually dependent" relationship which has obligations attached to it that frequently extend well beyond the point of formal termination of treatment. This type of relationship is very ego-syntonic in Japanese culture, and indeed both the doctor and the patient would be at something of a loss to know how else to behave. At the same time, the conscious or unconscious encouragement of this relationship by either party may serve to intensify the state of mind signified by the phrase *jibun ga nai*, which means "not to have a personal sense of self." If the patient is playing his cultural role in relation to the doctor, he is not able freely to communicate about his "real self" (or perhaps not able to be aware of the possibility of such a self), and he may indeed feel hopeless if he senses that he cannot make use of such a relationship, even with his doctor, in the attempt to verbalize his deeper feelings. These problems in role relations were not created by the hospital but have their roots in the broader culture. In the Japanese family, for example, such "intimate but not personal" relations often exist between husband and wife. The wife may know really very little about her husband, and the husband very little about his wife, because they have so structured their relations that good communication between them as separate individuals is not possible.

These ideas are closely related to those which Doi has developed regarding the psychodynamics of Japanese neurotic patients.[9,10,11,12,13,14,15,16] In part, Doi's discussions begin with a critique of Morita's theory,[38] elaborated below, of *shinkeishitsu*, a diagnostic term which would include much of what is covered under the several Western headings of neurasthenia, anxiety reactions, and obsessive-compulsive reactions. According to Morita, the essential feature of *shinkeishitsu* is the way in which a symptom is formed by the patient when he focuses undue attention on a sensation, feeling, or idea and this very attention produces greater sensitivity about the matter in him. Morita called this process *toraware*, which means "a feeling of being caught or bound."

Doi contends that behind *toraware* lies another process, which became evident in his clinical work with Japanese patients. Doi characterizes this more basic process as the wish to *amaeru* (to depend and presume upon another's love, or to indulge in another's kindness). If a person is prevented from engaging in the process of *amaeru*, because of the repression of such wishes or their psychological isolation, and yet the desires to presume upon another's love persist, then distorted interpersonal relations will result. The feelings accompanying such distorted relations are displaced, often as hypochondriacal complaints and phobic or obsessive ideas, and the end result is the feeling of being bound or frustrated, *toraware*. In reverse order, this process is often enacted in the transference relationship in therapy.

In his publications Doi has discussed, at greater length, the implications of the usage of such Japanese words as *toraware* and *amaeru*. It is not that similar words or phrases cannot be found in other languages, but that these words carry unique emotional connotations in Japanese which are very difficult to translate. Perhaps, with this question, we are touching some of the basic emotional currents in Japanese society which give rise to the similarities we found in the three psychiatric hospitals under discussion despite the surface differences in their methods of treatment and administrative organization.

Special Points in the Three Hospitals

Although all were small and private, the three hospitals chosen by Caudill were quite different in their therapeutic approaches. We should now like to turn to a few of the many points that interested us in each of them.

The Organically Oriented Hospital

This hospital was exceptionally well staffed at all levels and was organized as a smoothly functioning unit. The main methods of treatment were tranquilizing drugs, electric shock, insulin coma, and continuous sleep. The last-named treatment was introduced into Japan in 1922,[27] after having been developed in Switzerland. It was in vogue in the United States during the twenties, but interest in it did not persist.[8] Continuous-sleep treatment is still popular in Japan, however, possibly for meaningful psychological reasons connected with the staff's orientation to the patient, as well as for those organic benefits it may produce. Essentially, in this treatment the patient is kept under heavy sedation (through the use of a combination of drugs) for a period of two weeks. During this time his bed is surrounded by black curtains, and he is in a semiconscious condition. As at other periods in his hospitalization but with increased attention during this time, he is cared for around the clock by a type of subprofessional nurse called a *tsukisoi*.

We are not able to judge what happens to the patient organically during continuous-sleep or insulin treatment, but, like Federn,[19] we are highly interested in intensive nursing care and in what we believe is possibly an important part of the treatment, the relationship between the *tsukisoi* and the patient. For Westerners, it is necessary to indicate a bit more fully who the *tsukisoi* is. The *tsukisoi* is a woman who acts as the personal attendant of a patient and takes care of him twenty-four hours a day. These women are paid by the patients' families and live most of their lives within the hospital; yet they are not formally a part of the hospital staff. This problem of an entire group of people who live within, and yet are not formally a part of, the hospital has many ramifications for the social structure of Japanese hospitals, but we can only mention it in passing here.[5]

In private psychiatric hospitals in Japan, the relation between the *tsukisoi* and the patients is of a one-to-one nature, each patient having his personal *tsukisoi*. The *tsukisoi* sleeps in the same room as the patient and serves as housekeeper and companion. Hospitals in Japan consider these women largely in terms of their domestic services, but a meaningful relationship, either positive or negative, may develop between *tsukisoi* and patient within the limits set by the relative status positions of the two roles. *Tsukisoi* frequently speak of their role as analogous in some ways to that of mother or elder sister. Since, in Japan, such pseudokinship relations are both structured and frequent, the emotional currents underlying them are probably less turbulent than would be the case among persons entering into such relations in the United States. The existence of these behavioral patterns in Japan, however, serves to indicate the high degree of gratification that is permitted dependency—or, perhaps better, inter-dependency—wishes in the culture.[39]

The Morita-therapy Hospital

This hospital was symbolized physically by its cleanly swept gardens, its bamboo grove, and the group life of its patients and staff. Dr. Morita's own influence has been great upon Japanese psychiatry, although only a small proportion of psychiatrists use his method in an unmodified form. Probably there are not more than six Japanese psychiatric hospitals which, at present, specialize in this type of psychotherapy. Following World War II, there was an increasing interest in Morita therapy in the West.[24,30,31] To a degree, Morita therapy shares some characteristics with Mitchell's [36] earlier "rest therapy." [18,40]

Neurotic patients are usually hospitalized for one or two months in Morita therapy; the "steps" in this treatment seem to be of particular interest to Westerners. In general, during the first week of treatment, the patient is put to bed in a room in which furnishings have been reduced to a minimum, and all conduct and activity (except eating and eliminating) are prohibited.

Following his period of semi-isolation, the patient begins to communicate directly with his doctor each day, often in informal meetings, and also to communicate indirectly through a diary, upon which the doctor comments, in writing. Also at this time he engages with other patients in simple manual tasks around the hospital, which brings him in touch with nature and physical reality: he is set to cleaning up the garden, washing the dishes, working with wood and other materials, and so forth. During this second stage he begins to listen, once a week, to lectures (*kōwa*) by the senior physician.

The third stage in treatment usually begins during the third or fourth week and includes the resumption of more taxing work, often in a job or other activities outside the hospital, and increased interpersonal relations. This stage is followed, finally, by the return of the patient to the community. He frequently, however, maintains contact with the hospital through visits with his doctor and through participation in a very active discharged patients' association, which publishes a journal and meets once a month at the hospital.

The emphasis in this treatment is to help the patient to recapture a feeling of unity with himself and his surroundings through his participation in hospital life. It is felt that a direct approach to the constructive forces within the patient is to be preferred to an analytic approach to the obstructive, pathologic conflicts in his personality. As Kondo [30] says: "First is the stress on the curative effects of nature; second is that of manual work; and third is the importance of the attitude called 'acceptance.'"

This attitude of "acceptance," by which is meant the sense of unity with oneself and one's surroundings, is usually expressed in Morita therapy by the phrase *aru ga mama*, which may be translated as "to take things as they are," or, more freely, "to meet reality as it is." This state of mind, which is the main goal of therapy, is often compared to *satori* (enlightenment) in Zen Buddhism, and some Morita therapists make use of Zen literature in their explanations, although Dr. Morita himself specifically disclaimed any special knowledge in this area. The related topic of the similarities and differences between Western types of psychotherapy and Eastern ways of understanding has received considerable attention in recent years.[1,20,46,51]

It was interesting to find that, paralleling to some extent the work that goes on in psychotherapy in the West, the doctor in the Morita-therapy hospital expected his patient to go through a series of ups and downs in his progress. If the patient did not do this, the doctor felt that there was little chance of recovery. For example, for a week or so after the period of semi-isolation the patient would often feel better, but as the responsibility of work increased, he would become worse and believe that he was not making progress. At this point there would begin a "struggle" between doctor and patient, which was worked out through the diary and through direct talks, until the patient came to feel that he was able to go forward and to reach a further understanding of the meaning of *aru ga mama*.

There would seem to be something in Japanese culture that makes it particularly difficult for people to express verbally their feelings about each other. Such difficulties in adulthood may be related to the early childhood situation, in which the child remains in close physical contact with the mother for a very long period and the mother teaches the child as much through physical manipulation as through the use of words. Be this as it may, adult Japanese find it easier to communicate in writing, and the use of diaries in Japanese psychiatry is not unrelated to the exuberant development in Japan of the *shi-shōsetsu*, or "I" novel. The *shi-shōsetsu* may be written in the third person, but its chief character is usually a plausible likeness of the author. The frequent use of this literary form has been criticized in Japan, but it is still very popular.[22]

Most of the neurotic patients who come for treatment at the hospitals specializing in Morita psychotherapy are young adults suffering from anxiety, obsessive-compulsive symptoms, and hypochondriasis. This type of patient is commonly found in any Japanese psychiatric hospital, but Dr.

Morita [38] and his followers have focused their theoretical ideas and psychotherapeutic procedures on a syndrome to which, as we have indicated earlier, they have given the name *shinkeishitsu* (nervosity, or nervous temperament). In line with this syndrome and with the conception by Japanese that their own interpersonal relations are particularly difficult, Morita therapy attempts to deal with a problem which might be translated as anthrophobia (*taijin kyōfushō*). Anthrophobia is manifested by feelings of inadequacy, fear of meeting people, and other signs of anxiety. These symptoms are certainly not unknown in American culture, but American society has not focused on them so specifically as to group them into a special category. Equally, many patients coming to Morita-therapy hospitals are diagnosed as suffering from blushing, or erythrophobia (*sekimen kyōfushō*). Again, blushing is a fairly universal phenomenon, but in America it does not loom very large in the complaints of patients.

The theory behind Morita psychotherapy includes the hypothesis that these patients are somewhat more "constitutionally nervous" than are more average persons. We say "more than average" because we feel it is to Dr. Morita's credit that he believed that, to a degree, all people share in these symptoms and problems, and the somewhat authoritarian attitude of the doctor in the Morita-therapy hospital is tempered by his sympathy for the patient as a fellow human being suffering from an essentially human condition.

It seems to us that the frequently successful outcome of Morita therapy is a result of the patient's having had a "corrective ego experience." In general, we feel that this type of treatment is well thought out. The goals of the treatment are defined, the kinds of patients who would benefit from such treatment are known, and the staff go about their work in a positive manner.

The Psychoanalytically Oriented Hospital

Of the approximately eighy patients who were under treatment at this hospital at the time of the research, only about fifteen were being treated by psychoanalytically oriented psychotherapy. Partly because of the small size of the staff, the remainder were predominantly receiving insulin treatment, supplemented by occasional psychotherapeutic sessions.

The psychoanalytically oriented work of this hospital was being carried out very sincerely, but it did not compare favorably with corresponding work in the United States. Some of the difficulties in conducting good psychoanalytically oriented work in the hospital can perhaps be attributed to the fact that there is little satisfactory training available in psychoanalysis in Japan. In 1959, there were approximately three hundred members of the Japan Psychoanalytical Association, but most of them had not received any training in psychoanalysis. The Japan Psychoanalytical Society, on the other hand, which is the component society of the

International Psychoanalytical Association, is much smaller; it had forty-one members, including associate members, in 1959.

It is necessary to raise the question as to why psychoanalysis has not had a greater development in Japan. The question is a valid one, considering the fact that, some thrity-five years ago, Dr. Marui of Tohoku University was very active in his attempts to bring psychoanalysis into Japanese psychiatry, as a result of his study in the United States at Johns Hopkins University, and that Dr. Kosawa, after studying under Marui, went to Vienna to receive training. It should also be added that Freud's writings in essentially their complete form have been available in two separate translations for many years in Japan.

The answer to the question of the slow development of psychoanalysis needs to be treated historically and also needs to be viewed in the light of the relative lack of formal advanced training for specialization in most fields of medicine in Japan. There is not, however, space to go into these matters here. To some extent, the history of psychoanalysis in Japan has been discussed elsewhere by Doi,[9,16] Kitami,[29] and Kaketa.[26] We feel, though, that any thorough answer to this question must concern itself with cultural patterns of interpersonal relations in Japan.

Indications for the Future

What are some of the trends toward the future in Japanese psychiatry? Certainly, interest in and development of organic therapies will continue. Equally, the ideas of Dr. Morita, if not his specific treatment, will continue to play a significant role in Japanese psychiatric thought. But what of the future of psychodynamic psychotherapy? It seems to us that there are some indications that changes taking place in the structure of Japanese society will provide an impetus for increasing use of such psychotherapy. One of the cases at the psychoanalytic hospital can be used to illustrate a point in this regard.

The patient was the first son of a farming family that lived at a considerable distance from Tokyo. In the traditional world, this first son would, in all likelihood, stay on the farm, whatever his personal desires. This young man, however, became psychologically sick and was treated at a hospital in a nearby city. He showed little improvement, and one of the doctors, who was a friend of the head of the psychoanalytic hospital, suggested to the patient that he go to Tokyo for treatment.

At the time we saw the patient, he had been in treatment for a year with a female therapist, toward whom he had developed a close positive transference. The therapist was impressed by the many surface changes that had taken place in the patient. His manner of dress, goals in life, and relations with other people had all shifted in the direction of urban middle-class behavior. He refused to return to the farm to assume his duties as first son, and his family seemed resigned to this decision. His plan was to obtain further education and then to find employment in a company. The therapist believed that, through this patient's identification with her, he had begun to internalize her values and way of life and had started to behave in a new manner.

What seemed to have occurred with this young man is similar to a process going on, to a degree, throughout Japan. There are many stresses on old values, and changes are taking place, particularly in such areas as education, business, and government. As these changes continue, there will be increasing numbers of people with personal problems who will look for help. Many of these people will be actively seeking a new way of life and, in a sociological sense, will be mobile from one group to another. Since they will wish to break with old patterns, they will be reluctant to discuss their problems with close family members. In such a situation, these people, as illustrated by the patient at the psychoanalytic hospital, might well benefit from working through some of their problems with a psychotherapist. And indeed, the wishes of these people for such help might increase the demand for psychotherapists in the society. Thus, the process of psychotherapy can become one road along which to travel toward a different life. In this broad sense, psychotherapy is itself an agent of social change.

Related Patterns in Japanese Culture

Sweeping changes, particularly of concern for youth but affecting the entire population, have been taking place in Japan since World War II. Both the continuities with the past and the changes in the present in the general culture are reflected in the symptoms of psychiatric patients and in the types of treatment that we have been describing. The scope of the changing culture of Japan has been discussed by Reischauer,[44] Dore,[17] Matsumoto,[32] and many others. What we can do here is to relate our psychiatric observations to some of the findings from several small studies in which we have been involved. Specifically, Caudill has gathered materials on value orientation, patterns of emotional expression, and child rearing, and we shall indicate a few of the main points from the data in these three areas of life.

From the study of value orientations, published more fully elsewhere,[7] we wish to indicate only that on those schedule items which measured relations among men, particularly in the sphere of family life, there was a strong emphasis on *collaterality*. Collaterality stresses the welfare of the group and consensus among its members as primary goals. As such, in terms of the theory behind the schedule, it is distinct from *lineality* or *individualism*, the former emphasizing superior and subordinate relationships and the latter focusing on the relative autonomy of persons. Surprisingly, in the Japanese data, the younger generation had a greater preference for collaterality as a value than did the older generation, although this value was strongly represented in both generations. This trend was particularly true of those items in the schedule referring to family and occupational life but was reversed in the sphere of political life, in which the young were more individualistic than the old.

Values can be linked to preferred channels of impulse gratification or restraint. Given the fondness of the Japanese for collaterality in family life, we wished to try to find out what sort of emotional patterns formed an underlying part of this value emphasis. To study this question, Caudill [6] chose to develop a series of pictures of everyday life events—concerning eating, drinking, sleeping, bathing, sex, sickness, and so on—in Japan and to use these as "visual questions" in an interview designed to elicit feelings about impulses and emotions in the situations covered by the pictures.[3] During 1959, seventy-two tape-recorded interviews were carried out in the three small psychiatric hospitals previously described. The sample was fairly equally divided among doctors, nurses, tsukisoi, and patients.

From this study, we shall mention here only two patterns of responses that emerged from an analysis of the material on three pictures. The first of these pictures, concerned with the treatment of a minor illness in the home, depicts a sick man being cared for by a woman. The main issue we are interested in here is whether or not the woman is seen as giving "sympathetic care" to the man. The second picture shows a young adult man and woman in a room, with bedding laid out in the background. The issue here is whether or not the young man and the woman are seen as indicating any "sexual interest" in each other. The third picture shows a young boy and girl playing together in a Japanese bathroom. The issue here is whether or not bathing is seen as "pleasurable" for the children in the picture and for the subject being interviewed (since in this case he was asked directly about the matter after he had given his thoughts concerning the picture).

In terms of the alternatives just presented for each picture, two main patterns emerged. The first and most frequent pattern is represented by thirty-two persons, who had a positive emotional response to one or the other, or both, of the situations of sickness and bathing and who treated the situation of the man and woman in the room in a rather emotionally warm but very nonsexual manner. On the other hand, the second and next most frequent pattern is represented by twenty-one persons who did not have a positive emotional response to the situations of sickness and bathing and who treated the situation of the man and the woman either by indicating, with distaste, the existence of sexual interest or by a flat response lacking emotional feeling. The first of these general patterns might be thought of as "an emphasis upon nonsexual satisfactions," to be found in a variety of situations, extending even to those situations in which sexual interest ordinarily would be expected. The second general pattern might be characterized as "a denial of pleasure and emotion" in an equally wide variety of situations, including specifically sexual ones.

We believe that these two general patterns of handling situations in which emotional impulses may easily be aroused are very common ones among the Japanese. Why should this be so? In brief, many everyday events in Japan, whether for children or for adults, offer greater opportunities than is true in the West for the gratification of simple physical pleasures in situations of close contact with other persons, as in bathing, sleeping arrangements, nursing care, child rearing, and so on.[5,17] If sexual feelings were allowed to intrude into these events, this intrusion would complicate matters and the simple pleasures to be derived from them would be reduced. Japanese value such simple physical pleasures very highly, and one way of assuring their continued existence is to ignore, exclude, or in some way isolate (as by joking) any sexual feelings from them. This mode of behavior results in the general emotional pattern which is called an emphasis upon nonsexual satisfactions. The "price" paid for adherence to such a pattern is the tendency to emphasize the nonsexual satisfactions to be gained from situations where an interest in directly sexual matters might well be appropriate.

What about the second general pattern of a denial of pleasure and emotion, which we feel is a strong minor theme? Again starting from the frequency of occurrence in Japanese life of events which offer the opportunity for the gratification of physical pleasures in situations of close contact with others, it seems likely that a significant number of persons (possibly for various combinations of genetic, social, and cultural reasons) have not been able to meet the emotional impact of such events by an emphasis upon nonsexual satisfactions. For these persons, sexual feelings do tend to intrude, insistently and uncomfortably, into such situations. Thus the "answer" is a general restriction of impulse gratification and a distaste for all too consciously recognized sexual matters. In the extreme, this may result in an overall denial of emotional feeling, whether positive or negative.

In summary, then, we feel that the dominant value orientation of collaterality, particularly prominent in the sphere of family life, is in line with the major emotional pattern of an emphasis on the nonsexual satisfactions to be derived from everyday events, represented here by sympathetic concern and care for those who are sick, pleasure in bathing in the company of others, and a rather peaceful and unexcited married life.

Given the presence of such values and emotional patterns in the lives of adult Japanese, it seems likely that these ways of behaving are first learned in childhood, in the home. The intense, almost symbiotic, tie between mother and child in Japan is repeatedly emphasized in the literature (see, for example, Vogel and Vogel [50]). The experiences of the Japanese and the American child are very different in matters of feeding, bathing, carrying, and sleeping, these differences all being in the direction of greater bodily contact and sensory gratification in Japan. For example, an unpublished study of sleeping arrangements among urban and rural sample groups, carried out under the direction of Professor Muramatsu at Nagoya University, showed that, in both samples, the eldest child slept with the mother until approximately the age of three, the middle child until the age of four, and the last child (as well as the only child) until the age of five or more. Essentially the same results are reported by Ezra Vogel, in an as yet unpublished study carried out in seven urban and rural communities. Vogel also found that the parent and child bathed together until the child was approximately seven years of age on the average and that the average age for the completion of weaning from the breast was two years.

We do not attach any particular significance to any one of these child-rearing practices, taken singly; rather, taken together, they indicate that the Japanese child grows up in an atmosphere of interdependency and collateral relations, so that one of the real psychological tasks for the young person is to achieve some separation of his identity from what he is in relation to others—at first in the family, later in school, and still later in his occupation and marriage. In general, we believe that the patterning of childhood experience and of adult value orientations and emotions that we have sketched helps to explain the structure and quality of the relation between doctor and patient and contributes to an understanding of other aspects of behavior in Japanese psychiatric hospitals. It would seem, not unreasonably, that the currents of life in the broader culture also run strongly in the technical setting of the hospital.

Summary

In this chapter we have tried to describe some aspects of the organization of Japanese psychiatric hospitals and the care of patients. We have indicated how Japanese psychiatry differs from that of the West but equally how it fits well with broader aspects of Japanese culture. We have also directed some attention to the patterning of value orientations, emotions, and childhood experiences in Japan. In a real sense, one of our goals has been to try to facilitate closer communication and thereby, in some small measure, to increase the understanding, by people in diverse cultures, of each other.

References

1. Becker, Ernest: "Psychotherapeutic Observations on the Zen Discipline: One Point of View," *Psychologia*, 3:100–112, Kyoto, 1960.
2. Bellknap, Ivan: *Human Problems of a State Mental Hospital*, McGraw-Hill Book Company, New York, 1956.
3. Caudill, William: *The Psychiatric Hospital as a Small Society*, Harvard University Press, Cambridge, Mass., 1958.

4. ———: "Observations on the Cultural Context of Japanese Psychiatry," in Marvin K. Opler (ed.), *Culture and Mental Health*, The Macmillan Company, New York, 1959.

5. ———: "Around the Clock Patient Care in Japanese Psychiatric Hospitals: The Role of the Tsukisoi," *Amer. Sociol. Rev.*, 26:204–214, 1961.

6. ———: "Patterns of Emotion in Modern Japan," in R. J. Smith and R. K. Beardsley (eds.), *Japanese Culture: Its Development and Characteristics*, Aldine, Chicago, 1962.

7. ——— and Harry A. Scarr: "Japanese Value Orientations and Culture Change," *Ethnology*, 1:53–91, 1962.

8. Diethelm, Oscar: *Treatment in Psychiatry*, 2d ed., Charles C Thomas, Publisher, Springfield, Ill., 1950.

9. Doi, L. Takeo: "Some Aspects of Japanese Psychiatry," *Amer. J. Psychiat.*, 3:691–695, 1955.

10. ———: "Japanese Language as an Expression of Japanese Psychology," *West. Speech*, 20:90–96, 1956.

11. ———: *Seishinbunseki* (Psychoanalysis), Kyoritsushuppan, Tokyo, 1956.

12. ———: "Shinkeishitsu no seishinbyōri (Psychopathology of Shinkeishitsu)," *Seishin-shinkeigaku Zasshi* (*J. Psychiat. Neurol.*), also entitled *Psychiatria et Neurologia Japonica*, 60:733–744, 1958.

13. ———: "'Jibun' to 'amae' no seishinbyōri (Psychopathology of 'Jibun' and 'Amae')," *Seishin-shinkeigaku Zasshi* (*J. Psychiat. Neurol.*), 62:149–162, 1960.

14. ———: "Naruchishizumu no riron to jiko no hyōshō (Theory of Narcissism and the Psychic Representation of Self)," *Seishinbunseki Kenkyū* (*Jap. J. Psychoanal.*), 7:7–9, 1960.

15. ———: *Seishinryōhō to seishinbunseki* (Psychotherapy and Psychoanalysis), Kaneko Shobō, Tokyo, 1961.

16. ———: "'Sumanai' to 'ikenai' ('Sumanai' and 'Ikenai')," *Seishinbunseki Kenkyū* (*Jap. J. Psychoanal.*), 8:4–7, 1961.

17. Dore, R. P.: *City Life in Japan*, Routledge & Kegan Paul, Ltd., London, 1958.

18. Earnest, Ernest: *S. Weir Mitchell: Novelist and Physician*, University of Pennsylvania Press, Philadelphia, 1950.

19. Federn, Paul: *Ego Psychology and the Psychoses*, Basic Books, Inc., Publishers, New York, 1952.

20. Fromm, Erich, D. T. Suzuki, and Richard De Martino: *Zen Buddhism and Psychoanalysis*, Harper & Row, Publishers, Incorporated, New York, 1960.

21. Fujikawa, Yu: *Nihon igakushi* (History of Japanese Medicine), Tokyo, Shinrisha, 1952.

22. Hibbett, Howard S.: "The Portrait of the Artist in Japanese Fiction," *Far East. Quart.* (now *J. Asian Stud.*), 14:347–354, 1955.

23. Ishikawa, Kiyoshi: "Nihon no seishinigaku shi (History of Psychiatry in Japan)," in Akira Kasamatsu (ed.), *Reinshō seishingaku* (Clinical Psychiatry), Chūgaiigakusha, Tokyo, 1959, pp. 769–771.

24. Jacobson, Avrohm, and Albert N. Berenberg: "Japanese Psychiatry and Psychotherapy," *Amer. J. Psychiat.*, 109:321–329, 1952.

25. Japanese Psychiatric Hospital Association (ed.): *Nihon no seishin byōin* (Japanese Mental Hospitals), Shikisha, Tokyo, 1958.

26. Kaketa, Katsumi: "Psychoanalysis in Japan," *Psychologia*, 1:247–252, Kyoto, 1958.

27. Kasamatsu, Akira (ed.): *Reinshō seishingaku* (Clinical Psychiatry), Chūgaiigakusha, Toyko, 1959.

28. Kato, Masaaki: "Report on Psychotherapy in Japan," *Int. J. Soc. Psychiat.*, 5:56–60, 1959.

29. Kitami, Yoshio: "Senzen ni okeru nihon no seishinbunsekigaku hattatsushi (De-

velopment of Psychoanalysis in Japan before the War)," *Seishinbunseki Kenkyū* (*Jap. J. Psychoanal.*), 3:2–6, 1956.

30. Kondo, Akihisa: "Morita Therapy: A Japanese Therapy for Neurosis," *Amer. J. Psychoanal.*, 13:31–37, 1953.

31. Kora, Takehisa, and Koji Sato: "Morita Therapy: A Psychotherapy in the Way of Zen," *Psychologia*, 1:219–225, Kyoto, 1958.

32. Matsumoto, Yoshiharu Scott: "Contemporary Japan: The Individual and the Group," *Trans. Amer. Philos. Soc.*, vol. 50, no. 1, Philadelphia, January, 1960.

33. Mestler, Gordon E.: "A Galaxy of Old Japanese Medical Books with Miscellaneous Notes on Early Medicine in Japan (Parts I–V)," *Bull. Med. Library Ass.*, 42:287–327, 468–500, 1954; 44:125–159, 327–347, 1956; 45:164–219, 1957.

34. Ministry of Health and Welfare: *A Brief Report on Public Health Administration in Japan*, Japanese Government Printing Bureau, Tokyo, 1959.

35. ———: *A Brief Report on Public Health Administration in Japan*, Japanese Government Printing Bureau, Tokyo, 1961.

36. Mitchell, S. Weir: *Fat and Blood*, J. B. Lippincott Company, Philadelphia, 1877.

37. Moloney, James Clark: *Understanding the Japanese Mind*, Philosophical Library, Inc., New York, 1954.

38. Morita, Shōma: *Shinkeishitsu no hontai to ryōhō* (Essence and Treatment of Shinkeishitsu), Hakuyōsha, Tokyo, 1928; new ed. with commentary by Hiroshi Kawai, Hakuyōsha, Tokyo, 1960.

39. Nakamura, Hajime: *The Ways of Thinking of Eastern Peoples*, compiled by the Japanese National Commission for UNESCO, Japanese Government Printing Bureau, Tokyo, 1960.

40. Nomura, Akitsune: "Morita ryōhō no enkaku to saikin no dōkō (Origin of Morita Therapy and Its Modern Trends)," *Seishin Eisei (Ment. Hyg.)*, 57:1–3, 1958.

41. Odaka, Kunio, and Tatsuzo Suzuki: "Ishi no shakaiteki chii to iryō seido ni taisuru iken (Report on the Social Position of Medical Doctors and the System of Medical Treatment)," *Nihon Ijishimpo (Jap. Med. J.)*, September–October, 1957, pp. 1744–1747.

42. Parsons, Anne: "Some Comparative Observations on Ward Social Structure: Southern Italy, England and the United States," *L'Ospedale Psichiatrico*, Naples, April–June, 1959.

43. ———: "A Schizophrenic Episode in a Neapolitan Slum," *Psychiatry*, 24:109–121, 1961.

44. Reischauer, Edwin O.: *Wanted: An Asian Policy*, Alfred A. Knopf, Inc., New York, 1955.

45. Stanton, Alfred H., and Morris S. Schwartz: *The Mental Hospital*, Basic Books, Inc., Publishers, New York, 1954.

46. Stunkard, Albert: "Some Interpersonal Aspects of an Oriental Religion," *Psychiatry*, 14:419–431, 1951.

47. Tsushima, Tadashi: "Notes on Trends and Problems of Psychotherapy in Japan," *Psychologia*, 1:231–236, Kyoto, 1958.

48. Uchimura, Yushi: "Nihon seishinigaku no kako to shōrai (Past and Future of Japanese Psychiatry)," *Seishin-shinkeigaku Zasshi (J. Psychiat. Neurol.)*, also entitled *Psychiatria et Neurologia Japonica*, 55:705–716, 1954.

49. Veith, Ilza: "Medicine in Japan," *Ciba Symposia*, 11:1190–1220, 1950.

50. Vogel, Ezra R., and Suzanne H. Vogel: "Family Security, Personal Immaturity, and Emotional Health in a Japanese Sample," *Marriage and Family Living*, 23:161–166, 1961.

51. Watts, Alan W.: *Psychotherapy East and West*, Pantheon Books, a Division of Random House, Inc., New York, 1961.

13. Patterns of Psychiatric Care in Developing African Countries: The Nigerian Village Program

T. Adeoye Lambo

Introduction

The pilot experiment in community psychiatry which was started in Aro, Abeokuta, Western Nigeria, in 1954 has become a model for developing African countries. A modified version is used in Ghana, and various adaptations are contemplated in East African countries. The author recently advised the government of the Eastern Region of Nigeria to start a similar scheme after it had called him for consultation. The original experiment took the form of a "village system" which permitted full treatment of the mentally ill by utilizing inherent dynamic resources of the social environment as the principal therapeutic technique.

It is important, before describing this scheme, to mention preliminary work which preceded the experiment. To find the most practical way of treating the mentally ill in Africa, a special study was made of the traditional social institutions among various African peoples. We soon discovered that many African countries were, and still are, in a state of rapid change—social, economic, and cultural. It became obvious that, because of the essential nature of the societies and their dynamic characteristics, an independent diagnosis of our position followed by a formulation of patterns of care in tune with our social structure would be the most realistic procedure. By the very nature of their economic and manpower position, developing countries in Africa cannot afford, at a time like this, the building and administration of huge institutions. Necessity would therefore force us not only to compromise but also to explore all possible

Especially prepared for this volume; also published in the *International Mental Health Research Newsletter*, vol. 6, no. 1, 1964.

avenues for the most effective, economical, and socially acceptable ways of treating the mentally ill in Africa.

Day Hospital

In October, 1954, two projects were started at Aro, a rural suburb of the ancient town of Abeokuta, sixty miles from Lagos, the federal capital. The first phase was the adoption of the day hospital scheme. This and other projects dealing with community psychiatry were undertaken in full recognition that the African patient must ideally be treated within his social environment. The scheme of treatment within the framework of the community was based on the use of four large traditional villages. On these four villages we grafted our therapeutic unit, which could accommodate from 200 to 300 patients. The normal village population consisted of Yoruba tribesmen and their extended families, the majority of whom were peasant farmers, fishermen, and local craftsmen. The four villages surround a central institution, Aro Hospital, a most modern 200-bed mental hospital with all facilities for treatment and research.

It was part of the regulations leading to admission that patients should be accompanied by at least one member of the family—mother, sister, brother, or aunt—who should be able to cook for them, wash their clothes, take them to the hospital for treatment in the morning, and collect them in the afternoon. This was easily accomplished, and the relatives of the sick people came forward readily. This approach was adopted because of our appreciation of the important fact, gained during our preliminary study of the African community, that there were still in many places a strong sense of social security in a closely knit society, well-organized and well-defined kin groups with definite traditional roles, and culturally prescribed mutual obligations.

The first phase lasted two years. Patients and their families, as well as the ordinary villagers, were regularly invited to attend church services, films, traditional plays, dances, and social functions in the hospital itself. One of the most important lessons learned during the first phase of the experiment was that this form of treatment provided the best and the most effective way of dealing with family attitudes to the patients from the beginning of treatment. Personal experience and insight gained by members of the family accompanying their sick relatives to, and fully participating in, therapy proved to have a great deal of influence on the rehabilitation of the patient, since this unique experience considerably influenced social attitudes within the family and within the community. It also made it easier for the relatives, who were in constant contact with the patients, to adjust themselves smoothly to the sick person and his future emotional needs. In view of this design, we regard village admission and therapy of the patient (in the company of his relatives) only as a point in the therapeutic continuum.

Village Care

The second phase of our experiment takes the form of comprehensive village care services by gradually extending the first phase. By this we mean that all treatment facilities are now provided. In addition, we have now taken full responsibility for the health administration, management, planning, and public health of these villages, in full collaboration with the village elders, who serve on the health planning council. Regular monthly meetings are held between the staff of the Department of Psychiatry of the University of Ibadan (which has now assumed full responsibility for teaching, research, and clinical work in these villages) and the village chiefs and their councils.

Clinics have been built in two of the villages, where all forms of modern therapy are provided; the doctors and nurses also use these clinics as their administrative centers. Each clinic is equipped with a small laboratory, sufficient to carry out routine investigations. A mobile clinic is used to travel to other distant villages in the area in which epidemiologic research has been going on for some time.

Loans are made available to the people in the four villages to enable them to expand or build homes to accommodate the influx of new patients from distant villages and towns. Care is taken that the ratio of normal villagers to patient population is constantly maintained at six villagers to four patients. To this end, small villages in the immediate vicinity of our mental health clinics have been encouraged to take patients into their homes. There have been no difficulties, since the rewards accorded to the original villages participating in this unique scheme are obvious. Among other things, we have paid for the installation of pipes which bring scientifically purified water from the waterworks of Abeokuta, a few miles away; pit latrines; and a mosquito-eradication squad. Men and women from the villages are employed in the clinics and the hospital (as gardeners, porters, cooks, etc.), and they are in turn the landlords of the patients. Thus efforts are made to raise the public health standards and subsistence economy of the village population, without interfering in a significant measure with the social structure and traditional atmosphere of village society.

Clinical facilities available at the clinics consist of electroplexy, modified insulin therapy (modified because of the resulting cachexic states of most African patients), abreactive techniques, group psychotherapies of the most diversified nature, and drug medication. Emphasis is laid on using every conceivable sociopsychological concept and method.

One of the unusual features of our pattern of care of the mentally ill in Nigeria is our unorthodox collaboration with the traditional healers (so-called "witch doctors"). We have discovered through our long practice in Africa that it is essential to the understanding of man and his social environment to work in close collaboration with other disciplines and even to establish some form of interprofessional relationship on a fairly continuing basis with those who, by Western standards, are not strictly regarded as "professional." For example, my Sudanese colleague Dr. Tijani El Mahi and I have for a number of years made use of the services of African "witch doctors," especially selected for epidemiologic work and other aspects of social psychiatry (e.g., community attitudes surveys), a procedure which is indefensible by Western standards. Through their participation, we have enriched our scientific knowledge of the psychopathology and psychodynamics of the major psychiatric disorders occurring in these exotic societies. We have also been able to accumulate a mass of data on the natural history and prevalence of many psychiatric disorders in terms of cultural and social variables (variables which are ill defined and remain resistant to Western forms of categorization). Without the help of traditional healers we would not have known how and where to look and what obstacles were to be skirted in searching for such simple disorders as obsessional neurosis in the indigenous population. Most of these traditional healers who are employed by us and are participating in this scheme have considerable experience in the management of African patients. They supervise and direct the social and group activities of our patients in the villages under our guidance.

During the first phase of this community psychiatry, the patients who were boarded out in the villages were especially chosen, or handpicked, as it were, but now no selection of patients is made. We admit, amongst others, catatonics and other schizophrenics with symptoms. Even patients who have exhibited aggressive and antisocial tendencies in their homes and have to be heavily restrained mechanically have become quite manageable under the village conditions.

The second phase emphasizes the fact that a patient can be admitted into the village, treated within the village community, and discharged from the village without having entered any form of formal institution, such as a hospital.

Therapeutic Rationale

Before going on to a brief description of the third and final phase of our experiment, let me summarize, and perhaps for the first time highlight, the therapeutic rationale, including the major therapeutic techniques, and lastly dilate on the advantages and limitations of this approach.

The present approach is based fundamentally upon our discovery that certain changes with an obvious therapeutic tinge were opportunely present in the indigenous culture and that certain factors in the traditional environment, for example, of the village, act as a powerful buffer against social pressure and conflicts and, consequently, promote good mental health. Confession, dancing, rituals, suggestions inherent in traditional cults, flexibility, and tolerance of the environment, to mention a few, could be mobilized and utilized as powerful psychotherapeutic armament, especially in psychoneurosis. Anxiety, which is the most common and crippling psychiatric disorder in Africa, also forms the central core of other neurotic reactions in the African.

In any group situation (normal or therapeutic) in Africa, transference is the vital problem. We have found that, where recovery is probable, the success of all the other measures depends upon an adequate effective transfer. Even when the prognosis is unfavorable, a positive transfer of affect under the emphatic conditions of the village and within the broad social context of warm, sympathetic, and tolerant therapeutic relationships may be used to prevent patients from deteriorating (secondary prevention). By permitting the ego of the patient to gain sufficient strength to function without overwhelming anxiety, through reality testing without any fear of being further traumatized, the village community disinhibits and desensitizes the sensitive ego. Multiple-therapy techniques are used through the participation of two or more therapists (the traditional healers and one psychiatrist) in the treatment of one patient. The permissiveness of the group in the traditional village facilitates the use of learning situations which bring about desirable effects in certain patients. It is also due to the atmosphere of the group that frequently latent behavior becomes manifest in some patients and this is dealt with without fuss.

Constant evaluation of the effects of therapy goes on, and this forms a major part of our operational research. As a result, a comparison of the patient before and after therapy in terms of his described or observed behavior and feelings in his relationships with others is always fully explored and recorded. Such a comparison is based on reports from the patients and their families, frequently supplemented by reports from the village heads, friends, and workmates on the farm, especially in terms of modification or alteration in social roles.

Advantages and Limitations

After nine years of continuous experiment in this pattern of community psychiatry in Nigeria, a pattern which would seem acceptable to African populations and which has proved the most economical and practical way of providing therapy for a large group of people in need of help, what then are the advantages and limitations? The advantages are threefold—social, medical (therapeutic), and economic.

1. Social advantages
    a. This pattern of psychiatry makes psychiatric care an integral part of the community and therefore a part of the culture to which it is highly sensitive.

b. It promotes a measurable degree of relaxation in community attitudes.

c. It creates a positive and more natural environment for measuring the degree of social competence or impairment in patients, in contrast to the very often artificially structured social environment of the institution (hospital).

d. It makes it easier for the psychiatric personnel to communicate freely with one another and with the community.

e. It lessens the risk of social stigma and promotes better social adaptation and integration of the patients.

2. Medical (including therapeutic and research) advantages

a. This pattern provides an optimal therapeutic environment for the treatment of certain psychiatric disorders, such as character disorders, sociopathy, alcoholism, and neurosis, especially nonrational, malignant forms of anxiety. By the utilization of environmental factors it creates optimal advantage for treatment and rehabilitation to go on almost at the same time. It is our finding, through follow-up studies, that this kind of psychiatry promotes quick recovery, lessens the risk of social and other disabilities, and reduces the problem of rehabilitation or aftercare.

b. This pattern promotes a spirit of collaboration with behavioral scientists (anthropologists, sociologists, social psychologists), providing an opportunity for an interdisciplinary approach and allowing major variables to be measured multidimensionally.

c. It allows for built-in research. Community psychiatry of this type offers a "laboratory" in which certain variables can be observed to operate without contamination. It affords full opportunity for empirical research in the general area of group dynamics and group and individual psychotherapy.

d. It gives an excellent chance for deploying meager human and material resources in the most effective and strategic manner.

e. It creates a diversity of therapeutic maneuvers and forms an excellent avenue for the teaching of psychiatry and mental health.

3. Economic advantages

The cost (in material and personnel) of this type of psychiatry is low, both for the medical authorities running the scheme as well as for the patient and his relatives.

4. Limitations

Some international visitors to this Nigerian experiment have constantly put forward the argument, among others, that a scheme of this kind could operate only in a nonindustrial agrarian community, such as those of Africa and Asia, where the threshold of community tolerance is high, and that with the advent of social change difficulties may ensue.

Future Plans

An expansion program of our scheme is expected to enable us to provide service for about a thousand patients and to undertake the training of mental health workers, the teaching of community psychiatry, and research training for undergraduate medical students and physicians. To this end, the building of hostels for medical students and flats for doctors and nurses on the periphery of the villages is being planned. It is also envisaged that the present village clinics will be expanded to provide a limited number of inpatient beds, essentially for treating acutely ill patients with physical complications, such as we often encounter in African countries.

In conclusion, I should like to emphasize that this is a modest experiment which has proved useful to our community and in which the community has a great deal of confidence. There is no doubt that the greater the confidence which members of the community have in the *nature* and *form* of the treatment they can obtain and in the *people* who will treat them, the more spontaneous is their willingness to come forward for treatment and to encourage others to do the same. In the same way, the greater the responsibility that is given to the community in the care and management of its mentally ill, the better and more sympathetic their response and the greater their understanding.

Our community psychiatric practice and research in Nigeria obviously raise many questions and unfortunately provide few answers. Nevertheless, they have contributed significantly to our understanding of many of the problems of mental ill-health in the emerging nations of Africa.

References

1. Lambo, T. A.: "A Form of Social Psychiatry in Africa," *World Mental Health*, vol. 13, no. 4, November, 1961.
2. ————: "Neuropsychiatric Observations in the Western Region of Nigeria," *Brit. Med. J.*, 2:1385, 1956.
3. Leighton, A., T. A. Lambo, et al.: *Psychiatric Disorders among the Yoruba*, Cornell University Press, Ithaca, N.Y., 1963.

14. Community Services in Israel: An Integrative Overview

Louis Miller

Introduction

It is the purpose of this chapter to integrate some of the major observations of the contributors to Part Three, comment on pertinent experience in Israel, and consider emerging trends in the continuing development of broad-based community health centers. Particular emphasis is placed on the growing awareness of community social factors and their relationship to the prevention of mental ill-health.

Community Trends in Psychiatric Care

Psychiatric care in the community has historical origins in community services unrelated to hospitals. The community services which have influenced present-day community psychiatry are those providing care for handicapped and disturbed groups, especially of children and youth. There is no doubt that special classes and schools for disturbed or retarded children, youth clubs, probation services and remand homes, clubs for alcoholics and the aged, sheltered workshops, and the like prove to have been forerunners of psychiatric care in the community. A special place must be accorded to the child guidance movement as a pioneer of team and social techniques of psychiatric care in the community and to psychoanalytic practice. As Kathleen Jones points out in her chapter in this section, the development of outpatient departments constituted the first definite step toward the bringing of psychiatric care into the community. After World War II, the day hospital offered a pattern of community care which was to become decisive for the future.

The development of psychiatric care in the community has been considerably stimulated by the changes which have occurred in hospital psychiatry. An appreciation of the changes which have taken place in

Especially prepared for this volume.

154

mental hospitals and of the problems encountered there is thus essential for an understanding of community psychiatry.

All springs from the profound change in the relationship between the psychiatrist and his patient. This change, which has been far-reaching, is still in the process of development; it is not yet fully understood nor even easily described. The psychiatrist now tends to allow himself to develop a deeper and even emotional relationship with his patient. Such a relationship has all the dangers of any relationship, magnified by the disturbed personality of the patient and other factors. It demands from the therapist constant self-searching. Isolation from the patient is less demanding and less painful for the psychiatrist but tends to isolate the patient as well.

In this section, William Caudill and L. Takeo Doi describe the nature of the close patient-staff relations in Japanese mental hospitals and contrast them with such relations in hospitals in the United States. (The situation in the United States hospitals probably resembles that in most Western hospitals.) The relations in these hospitals are, as the authors suggest, an extension or reflection of the general Japanese social and cultural pattern.

The staffs of the hospitals of the West which are bringing about changed relations with patients are to some degree at variance with their own culture, which resists involvement with the patient and thus tends to resist community relations with the patient and his care in the community. The Japanese, as an example of non-Western culture, would presumably have less of a problem in establishing footholds for psychiatry in the community. T. Adeoye Lambo's account of the natural extension of psychiatric care from a hospital environment into the adjacent community underscores the possibility of using a positive cultural factor for community work. Cultural resources and advantages for community psychiatry, as described in Nigeria and Japan, will no doubt be retained and extended there as far as possible. Westernization may tend to negate this community resource. The rejection of the mentally disturbed and the handicapped and the destruction (generally) of community institutions and patterns of life are all too obviously concomitants of developments in Western society. They carry in their wake a decreasing tolerance of those at a disadvantage and militate against direct community participation in solving the problems of such persons.

In Israel, processes of rapid sociocultural change (westernization processes) have been much in evidence among ethnic groups which have immigrated from Middle Eastern and North African countries. In these societies the family unit was frequently large and extended, receiving absolutely no service beyond that which it could provide itself, either individually or mutually on a kinship-group basis. In Israel, especially in the cities, the clan structure has almost disappeared, and the family unit, after half a generation of change and a sudden rise in living standards, has become much reduced in size. This new family pattern allows for very little tolerance and care for the handicapped at home; the demand for hospital care is intensified, and the family tends to reject its role in the community care of patients. Where the clan structure has been retained in the newly established, homogeneous cooperative villages, however, it seems apparent that the family is still capable of playing a decisive role in the care and rehabilitation of the patient.

Social change and rising standards of living, as exemplified in the case of Israel, will, it appears, create unavoidable difficulties for community psychiatry—difficulties with which community mental health workers in the Western countries will be able to deal only partially and after great effort. Under such conditions, little change in community attitudes can be expected before far-reaching changes have been effected in hospital care itself. It is well, therefore, that psychiatry in the West has taken another look at human relationships in the hospital before proceeding into the community.

The conscious attempt to change the content of the patient-therapist relationship in Western psychiatric hospitals has sometimes been accompanied by intellectualized overtones, usually expressed as concepts of value or of philosophy. The mental patient is said to be like "any other patient," and mental illness like "any other illness." The recent improvements in hospital care are said to be based on increasing "respect for the patient." Hospital care, it is suggested, should be not only protective but "humanitarian." These expressions may represent a real change in the attitude to the patient, but they may also be merely intellectualizations, occurring without a really basic change in the therapist-patient relationship.

While the changed relationship to the patient has been most noteworthy during the last few decades, it has, as Kathleen Jones stresses, a much longer history, one replete with periods of progress in mental health care, followed by setbacks. It is still too early to maintain that the revolution in psychiatric hospital care will not lose some of the progress it has made, but it is evident that, unless the change in attitude to the hospital finds its counterpart in the attitude of society to society's deviants, much of the struggle will have been isolated and perhaps in vain. It is essentially for this reason that the hospital psychiatrist has begun to exert an influence for community care.

Changing Attitudes and Structures

The change in the patient-therapist relationship in the hospital leads, in many cases, to further changes in human relationships in psychiatry. Foremost among these is the different relationship of the patient to himself. A great deal of the stasis encountered in cases of severe mental disturbance may have been due to the patient's acceptance of his bizarre or deviant role. A changing view of himself predicates the possibility of his changing his relationship to the society from which he has withdrawn and returning to it. A further dynamic possibility following a changed patient-therapist relationship is a change in the community's view of the patient in the hospital or of the patient who has returned to the community. This, in turn, draws in its wake changing attitudes to the mental hospital and the psychiatrist himself. A most important development in such a cycle of change is the reorganization of relationships among the hospital staff and of the therapist's view of himself or his group.

However intricate and devious the human dynamic involved in the changing relationship of the community to the psychiatric hospital and patient, it is greatly influenced by the relationship of the psychiatrist to his patient. It is therefore of little avail for the psychiatrist to demand tolerance from the community while he is unable to deepen his own relationship to the patient. How really complex the situation is may be realized from the fact that the psychiatrist is himself a representative product of the community which he is trying to influence.

The structural changes which have occurred and are still occurring in mental hospitals should be seen against these human dynamics. Structural changes lacking this content may tend to be sterile or confusing to the therapist, patient, and community alike.

Among these structural changes, representing the new trend, are the location of the hospital in proximity to the community, the improvement of communication channels between them, the reduction in size of the hospital, and its adaptation to the needs of the patient. In its internal organization, the hospital has attempted to model itself more closely on the life patterns of the community, with smaller wards and intimate social amenities providing freedom of access and movement. Other professional and technical innovations, such as the interdisciplinary team, intensive training of the staff, and the introduction of reeducational facilities and outpatient care, all represent the idea of a more profound relationship to the patient and his needs and allow for its implementation. As with matters of technique, organization, and conceptualization, however, structural adaptations and facilities are not in themselves enough to alter the content of psychiatric care. The quality of care remains wholly dependent on the quality of human relationships.

A very important and early manifestation of structural change appeared in the psychiatric ward in the general hospital. There, in one stroke, the psychiatrist could attain all the physical changes required for the housing of his new concept of patient care. The general hospital was able, at a relatively low initial cost, to deal with the problems of the isolation of the hospital and to limit its size. On the whole, this advantageous position was highly suitable for improved patient-therapist relations. As

Herbert Dörken holds for other types of community facilities, general hospital psychiatry opened a new field of practice with patients not formerly reached; it undoubtedly produced positive effects, if sometimes in varying degree.

The most remarkable influence was on the general medical profession. In many cases, practitioners and hospital staffs found themselves in a new and tolerable relationship to the psychiatric patient. This advance, however, did not effect an equal change in the community attitude to emotional disorder. A defect of psychiatry in general hospitals lies in the tendency of all concerned to isolate themselves from the mainstream of psychiatry and the major problems of psychiatric care. On the other hand, among the greatest contributions of the general hospital to psychiatry have been the positive effect on the psychiatric practioner there and his new self-image.

The progress made at the general hospital has been followed by that of the mental hospital, which, in many instances, has been able to absorb functions developed by general hospital psychiatry (for example, early care), thus freeing the latter for further progress, such as comprehensive and integrated practice with other departments in ambulatory and inpatient work.

The paths developed in general hospital psychiatry led to the readier acceptance of other adaptations of psychiatric hospital care, moving ever closer to the community, bridging outpatient and inpatient care. Such adaptations were the halfway house, the hostel, the sheltered workshop, the therapeutic club, and the day hospital. The appearance of these "bridge" institutions, in turn, has given further impetus to the evolution of the psychiatric hospital as a small, open, and short-stay unit.

A factor of paramount importance in the swing in emphasis from prolonged hospital care to continuing care in the community was the increasing willingness of other services and agencies to participate in patient care. General medicine, public health, social welfare, and educational services now play an increasing role in patient care and rehabilitation. Adequate psychiatric services tend to be organized on the basis of an increasing shift toward community services.

Community Facilities

Whatever cultural and local influences may be in evidence, it seems that the general approach to psychiatric services oulined here is being increasingly accepted. Psychiatric services are planned on a regional basis, with a range of interlocking facilities adapted as far as possible to categories of patient needs and allowing for flexibility in meeting local requirements.

It seems that the hospital and care services, which form the cornerstones of such a regional structure, will usually include the following types of institutions:

1. A small psychiatric hospital of approximately three hundred beds for twenty-four-hour care in the more densely populated areas. Such a hospital will have an active outpatient department for frankly disturbed patients, who may also be treated at a day hospital or admitted to the hospital itself.

2. The psychiatric service in the general hospital. This service will have a small number of inpatient beds, but its chief contributions will be its well-developed outpatient department and inpatient consultative service. A special feature may be the ambulant and day care service for children and perhaps for geriatric cases.

3. The community care center. It is this particular service which is the least defined at the present time. Perhaps it should remain so, in view of the differences—at times, even in a single community—of social structure, cultural needs, and attitudes.

The community care centers which have been suggested or initiated range from the social club to the day hospital unattached to a traditional hospital. To a large extent, the character of the community centers will depend directly on the type and extent of the activity at the general and psychiatric hospitals. Thus, the community center may be simply an unattached psychiatric outpatient clinic, a hostel or halfway house, a day hospital or a day-night hospital, or a combination of any of them. These facilities may also be attached, of course, to an active psychiatric hospital located in the city.

Another type of institution generally found is the longer-stay hospital, covering needs of a fairly large number of patients that are not met by the three above-mentioned categories. Patients will still require full hospital facilities for longer periods, for reasons related to neglect or failure of early care, and especially for those mental conditions which are involved with organic disease or deterioration. This hard core of patients is still the despair of the profession and of society.

In Israel, such patients have been admitted to small "therapeutic communities" or "work villages," catering for about four hundred patients. Work villages are run with a great deal of patient participation. They offer a full community life, based on work and social activity, while not neglecting elementary individual needs. The day-to-day community life and activities of the villages are used for the activation and resocialization of the patient, who becomes, in time, involved in the community life of the town near which the village is situated.

The work villages, while retaining their essentially rehabilitative character, are currently being remodeled as readmission and retreatment centers. These developments indicate that, on the basis of his changing relationship with the patient, the psychiatrist has developed new techniques and new organizational forms of care which are adapted to the patient's needs and which allow for a mobilization of personal and community resources previously lost to both the patient and the therapist.

Community psychiatry has thus far been discussed from two points of view: the development of community influences within the hospital population and the effect of society upon the hospital. Its primary concern, however, is with the forces at play on mental health and on the patient in the family and community. These functions are the focus of the community center.

Trends in the Development of Community Centers

The extension of psychiatric care into the community introduced new service elements of quite remarkable strength. It may therefore be helpful to attempt some general assessment of the *need for mental health services in the community* of today.

From the point of view of curative psychiatry, the need for early case finding, diagnosis, and treatment of the patient in the community, as well as his full rehabilitation, has been stressed. The emphasis in implementing this approach has, to date, been placed largely on adults. There has been little progress in extending this approach to children, whose care remains an important need, as yet hardly considered. One reason for the delay is that, as the disturbance in the child develops, it manifests itself as untoward behavior or as a difficult family situation. These states neither lend themselves to traditional psychiatric diagnosis nor respond to classical methods of psychiatric therapy. The psychiatrist was therefore at a loss and tended to enter the picture during adolescence, when the individual and traditional psychiatric picture began to crystallize. A great opportunity for early care was lost. The child guidance movement arose as a gallant attempt to meet this need in the community—a need unmet and sometimes unfelt by the psychiatrist.

Perhaps the needs most neglected, however, were in those spheres of possible influence by the psychiatrist which are included in the concepts "preventive psychiatry," "community mental health," and "mental hygiene." These concepts are built upon the hypothesis that the family situation and community life in some degree determine the mental state of the individual and that they may be modified sufficiently by guidance to enable him to develop or function with less stress or suffering. The hypothesis has been greatly strengthened by the modern experience of the rapid changes which societies and cultures have undergone and the obvious changes and disturbances which occur in the individual personality, especially among children and the aged in such circumstances.

While the psychiatrist will accept intrusion into the problem family, where the mental health of the child or the rehabilitation of an adult patient is seriously at stake, as a legitimate preventive activity, he will often reject as alien or irrelevant the broader fields of mental health work in which an attempt is made to mitigate untoward social and community influences. This denial probably occurs for two main reasons: first, it is not always clear that a real connection exists between the general social situation and mental reaction or deviation; and, second, if such a relation is perceived, it seems hardly possible that a service structure could be erected to deal with the social problem. Both objections have at least a certain validity.

The hypothesis of the relation of social malaise to the incidence and type of personal disturbance does not have any more conclusive proof to its credit as yet than any other hypothesis of the cause of mental ill-health. There is, however, mounting evidence that dislocation in the family and social failure may be at the root of many conditions which are accepted in the psychiatrist's nomenclature. This is especially true of problems of character, of behavior and learning, and of addiction. In any event, the direct relation of case finding, treatment, and rehabilitation to the family and community is hardly questioned today.

For the psychiatrist who accepts a definite relationship between social influences and mental health and the outcome of treatment or the nature of mental disturbances, a second problem automatically arises: what can be done about it?

As the lack of early psychiatric care for children gave rise to the child guidance movement (even though rather limited in extent), so the lack of psychiatric intervention in the field of deleterious social forces has given rise to a community organization movement which has spread among nations across the face of the globe.

Community organization work, like child guidance, is based upon an interdisciplinary team. In the case of community organization, the team is composed of service and agency members (medical, welfare, educational, agricultural, etc.) and provides for a whole village or neighborhood in stress rather than for a particular family.

Psychiatry as a discipline was late in utilizing the child guidance movement. It will not neglect the obvious value of the community organization movement as a comprehensive mental health instrument.

Cooperation between the psychiatric profession and such movements for social and mental health makes possible at least some form of preventive approach to massive social disturbances which reveal themselves in the forms of delinquency, alcoholism, and other phenomena and which arise from unsuccessful social change, especially in cities. It may possibly even provide an approach to the social malaise of the affluent Western city.

With this view of the mental health needs of the community, the *functions of the community center* may be summarized as follows:

1. In the case of adults, early case finding, diagnosis, and treatment in the community; continuing care, at times, after hospital action; and support and rehabilitation.

2. In the case of children and their families, early elicitation and mitigation of difficulties of devlopment, of learning and behavioral problems, and of parent-child and family stress and conflict.

In both of these instances, a great deal of the case finding and care may be performed indirectly, through the guidance of other agents in the community, such as the physician, nurse, social worker, teacher, and probation officer. Case consultation with, and counseling of, these agents prepare and mobilize them under supervision for certain early psychiatric and mental functions.

3. Community mental health work. This function, as has been intimated, should not be based only on the individual case or family or on the agency worker in touch with them. It is also served by the influence of a community organization apparatus in the neighborhood which mobilizes service agencies and community groups in an attempt to promote a healthy community life.

Emphasis should be placed on the fostering of a mental health team at school, composed of the teacher, the social worker, the public health nurse, and, if available, the school psychologist. The business of this team is to understand and modify the dynamics of the child's personality and of the situation at his home in order to influence his social behavior and learning process.

Of special importance is the impact of the mental health center on the public health and family nurses and doctors who are favorably placed for influencing the parent-child relationship in the families of the community.

With these functions in mind, the *forms of the community center* may now be considered.

In practice, the recent tendency in planning community centers has been to place the emphasis on curative work, especially with adults. The psychiatric hospital and the general hospital ward have thus been at times considered or taken as the base for the community center. Such an approach tends to emphasize the treatment of the developed psychiatric case. Because of the often justifiable priority of the clinical case, early work with children will suffer, and preventive mental health work in the community may lie completely in abeyance.

The indirect approach to community mental health, which operates, for example, with the team of public health workers or the school or community services, requires special training, techniques, and experience on the part of the mental health center group. The clinical demands which predominate at a community hospital center rarely permit the development of such community preventive mental health skills.

The establishment of the mental health center on the foundation of a day hospital has similar disadvantages, for even the day hospital will tend to extend its functions only in the direction of specialized community care, such as outpatient facilities, sheltered workshops, patients' clubs, domiciliary services, and emergency services. It may be preferable, therefore, to move the functions of full-day care and the more intensive outpatient activities to the general or specialized hospital.

It would seem more suitable, as B. A. Lebedev stresses, to construct the community center around a clinical service which is predominantly for outpatients. The center would then serve as the place for early diagnosis and initial ambulant treatment for adults and children, with the possibility of a family approach through a single team working with all age groups. Since, by definition, all degrees of disturbance cannot be catered for at such an outpatient center, many will be referred, for shorter or longer periods, to day care, full hospital care, or a retreatment and rehabilitation unit working in the same area and in relation to the center.

The "sectorization experience" of Philippe Paumelle and Serge Lebovici describes a community center in the Thirteenth Arrondissement of Paris, linked to a short-stay psychiatric hospital which serves the "sector" from a distance. The sector is composed of 165,000 people and divided into three subsectors. A minimum of two teams, one for adults and one for children, serves each subsector population of 55,000 inhabitants. Teams are intended to fulfill functions of care and prevention. The therapeutic and care functions of the team extend to day or night care, emergency and domiciliary calls, and sheltered occupations, in addition to consultive and counseling service and mental health activity. The subsector teams strive for intimate involvement with community life and, at the same time, for a complete clinic service, providing continuous care in the community as far as possible. The center teams resemble earlier phases of community care, insofar as they are separate for children and adults.

In Israel, experience has shown that for a population of 150,000 two centers are required, based upon a single integrated team for both adults and children and backed by one active psychiatric hospital in addition to a retreatment and rehabilitation village, each of 300 to 400 beds.

While continuity of patient care at the center is most important, much of it will depend on the processes at work in the patient and his family. Routine return to care at the center, after hospitalization, should not override the needs of the patient or family nor the therapeutic relationships established with them at the hospital. Limited day, club, emergency, or similar facilities may be established at the center itself, but it may be inadvisable to place too great a stress on comprehensiveness, especially if the hospitals are geographically and professionally well related to the community and to the centers. Too great an emphasis on the clinical service may lead, as has been remarked, to an impairment of other functions.

The schools and nursery schools serve as points of departure for the work of the community center, as do the general health centers or practitioners, the social welfare agencies, the labor exchange, and so forth. It is often from these services that the clients of the outpatient departments of the center are drawn. The mutual responsibility of service agency and mental health center for the patient may without difficulty be used in initiating the personnel of the general services as adjuncts in early case finding and in the rehabilitation of the patient or his family. It is on the basis of experience with the individual case that the agency workers grow in time toward the general employment of mental health principles in their own areas. Of special importance is early case finding by public health nurses among children of preschool age and by teachers in the earliest grades at school.

A unified mental health family and community center team, which deals with both adults and children, does tend to lose some of its specialized clinical functions, especially in the fields of complex organic problems and investigations. It does not, however, lose anything of its therapeutic and community health functions. On the contrary, it is in these fields that its chief advantages, development, and potentials lie. The prevailing tendency is for the team leader to be a psychiatrist who is fully qualified in both adult and child psychiatry.

At a community mental health center working with cases in all age groups, the creation of an interdisciplinary team capable of such a broad range of action may pose a problem. In Israel, this difficulty has been met by the development of a demonstration project, with a special training program and improved liaison with the specialist services. The experimental center, organized four years ago in a small city (Petah Tikva; population, 70,000), showed that it is possible to establish an effective team, capable of handling a client of any age within his family setting and, at the same time, of finding its way into all services and most forms of community life.

The comprehensive mental health team not only has undeniable advantages in its unified care of the family; it also provides a solid base from which an influence can be brought to bear on the agency workers. A continuing influence, arising from a single mental health focus, exerted upon the general services, fosters greatly improved patient care and valuable mental health work with the general clientele of the community services. The mental health team becomes really rooted in the community. This is a great advantage for psychiatry in the local area, an advantage which possibly offsets the loss, if any, in continuity of care resulting from the displacement of some community clinical functions back to the area hospitals.

In the city, individuals' lives in the family, school, place of work, friendship group, and entertainment activities are often widely separated from a geographical point of view. In the light of the fragmented social organization of a large city, the concept of a single integrated center serving a defined community adequately and influencing its day-to-day life may not be tenable. It may be more advisable to allow for the development of separate and specialized adult and child teams, serving, as in the case described by Paumelle and Lebovici, a particular segment of the city. Such centers may provide highly specialized curative care, in a fairly continuous way, to individuals who may have no particular community connection but who live in the part of the city served by the teams. These teams will tend to focus on the individual patient and his family, but the preventive work in families (and certainly with groups in the community) will be greatly limited. In any case, with two separate teams involved simultaneously, there is a constant danger of uncoordinated work with patients' families.

In small cities, in towns, and, indeed, wherever the sociological structure creates a geographical and social entity with sufficient cohesion as a community or a series of neighborhoods, it seems that a single community center should be the focal point.

Experience in Israel and England has shown that merely arranging common housing for the adult and the child guidance teams attains neither integrated professional care for the family nor the desired patterns of family and community preventive work.

As has been stressed, an important, if evasive, function of the community center is its search for a broader impact on the community. Neighborhood organization programs attempt to influence and promote community life. These programs are not a function of the center but of a department of local authority. They do, however, provide the center with a potent agency for community mental health. The community organization movement has developed particularly in the United States, whence it takes much of its impetus, and in Latin America, Africa, the Middle East, and some Asian lands. Among the European countries, Britain has also emphasized this approach to communities in stress, particularly in its larger cities and new towns. Israel, in settling its new immigrant populations in both old and new towns, has relied heavily on this type of group social work.

With the help of the community services, the community organizer attempts, by working directly with local groups, to activate them to deal with their own material and social problems. Such activation leads to social cohesion, personal identification with the community, and the growth of the community member. The movement also aims at producing leadership from the community itself and militates against apathy, resentment, and antisocial behavior. It may have a very special impact on the social and mental health of families by its influence on the relationships between the younger and older generations.

In addition to creating a services team for cooperation in the solution of family problems, the community organizer encourages the services to consult with the community itself or its leaders and to employ groups from the community in the solution of their problems.

The community organizer is a mental health worker of prime potential. He provides the mental health center with a ready instrument for mental health work of the broadest range, from early case finding and group rehabilitation, for example, to problems of deviant youth. Experiments in Israel have shown that since the organizer is usually responsible only for one neighborhood (often an underprivileged or new-immigrant area), it is advisable to employ a specially trained community organizer as a member of the mental health center team. His task is to coordinate the work of several neighborhood organizers for community mental health projects and to act as a liaison between the mental health center and neighborhood service teams. Compared with this approach to preventive action in city neighborhoods, especially of the underprivileged type, any approach that restricts itself to individual and family counseling has severe limitations.

The attainment of the goals of community mental health, in the broadest sense of the term, becomes a possibility through the liaison of the mental health center with the teams in community organization, at school, and in the health and welfare services.

Summary

While psychiatric care in the community takes some of its origin from traditional mental health work in the community, hospital psychiatry has recently become a new force for its promotion. Changes in hospital psychiatry and its developing community approach are, in essence, the result of a new relationship between the psychiatrist and his patient. This new relationship, in turn, has given rise in the therapist to a need to foster a change in the community's attitude toward the patient. The community-individual relationship is seen as a most important factor in psychiatric illness and health.

The modeling of a range of interlocking care institutions according to patient need is described with some reference to the community influences at work and those influences which society brings to bear on the hospital. The possible place of the community center in the range of services is discussed. It is concluded that some community clinical services, such as day care, may be located at hospitals related to the center, in order to free the center for its preventive, early diagnostic, treatment, and rehabilitation tasks.

The curative outpatient core of the center is emphasized, and the ambulant case seen as the point of departure for family mental health work, especially through the agency of the community services. The need for psychiatric action early in the development of personal disturbance is stressed, especially for the relatively neglected younger age groups.

The need for modifying family relationships deleterious to the child or adult patient has been accepted. The effect of adverse general social conditions as a factor in mental ill-health has not been as readily accepted and, in any case, is a problem which challenges the available psychiatric and mental health techniques.

As the child guidance movement arose in an attempt to modify family relationships for the benefit of the child, so the community organization movement gathers momentum for an attack on deleterious social influences on social and mental health. The center should incorporate functions of child guidance and utilize community organization activity for preventive mental health work.

part four

Children and Schools

15. Promoting Mental Health in the School

Samuel R. Laycock

Introduction

In Cornwall, England, there is an old tradition that the way to tell whether or not a person is mentally ill is to put him in a room where an open tap is running and tell them to mop up. If he turns off the tap before starting to mop up, he is considered sane; if he lets it continue to run and still tries to mop up, he is considered unbalanced.

Schools could well pay greater attention to this homely example. Only too often teachers spend much of their time in "mopping up" various types of classroom problems, rather than "turning off the tap" through constructive efforts to promote the mental health of their pupils.

To build mental health in pupils, teachers, supervisors, principals, and other administrators need actively to seek answers to three questions: *Why* should the school concern itself with mental health? *What* are the characteristics of a mentally healthy pupil? *How* can a school provide the kind of conditions for living and learning which will promote the mental health of its pupils?

Occasionally educators say that mental health is no concern of the school—that its job is solely intellectual development. Even on this basis, however, the school has no choice but to promote emotional stability and maturity in its pupils. There is a great deal of evidence that emotional factors hinder learning, that they frequently lie at the basis of under-achievement, and that they are prominent in school dropouts.[5] Aside from a limited group of children, such as perfectionist youngsters, there is evidence that the emotionally upset, the insecure, or the inadequate child cannot learn effectively. Consequently, even the teacher who sees education only as getting children through examinations must interest

Previously published by *Canada's Mental Health*, Supplement 40, March–April, 1964, as adapted from *Pulse*, March, 1963; adapted for this volume.

himself in his pupils' emotional health. But, as we know, most teachers are genuinely concerned with helping their pupils achieve maximum self-realization and become mature citizens able to make a contribution to their fellowmen. It is the purpose of this chapter to consider in further detail the promotion of mental health in the school.

What Is Good Mental Health?

Since a definition of mental health involves a value judgment, there can be no consensus as to what mental health means. Nevertheless, there is reasonable agreement about some of the characteristics of a mentally healthy person in our society:

1. A child's attitude to himself (his self-concept) is thought to be of prime importance. The mentally healthy child feels reasonably comfortable about himself and reasonably secure and adequate. He neither underestimates nor overestimates his ability. He accepts his shortcomings. He has self-respect, self-confidence, and self-reliance. He strives to realize his potential and his talents.

2. The mentally healthy child learns to have a reasonably effective relationship with his peers, his teachers, his parents, and other adults. He is able to be interested in others and to love them. He has satisfying friendships. He can feel a part of the group without being completely dominated by it. He learns to do things for others.

3. To become a mentally healthy adult, a child must learn to face reality in reasonable fashion and to cope with a fair degree of anxiety and stress. He must learn to think for himself, to make his own decisions, and to do something about his problems as they arise. He must learn to balance his life so that he can handle his emotions, his instincts, and his conscience without undue conflict; he needs to be able to set realistic goals.

These are not "pie-in-the-sky" objectives. Each of them is influenced for good or ill by what goes on in school every day. How a child feels about himself, how he reacts to others, and how he tackles life's problems are all affected by the interrelationships of teachers, pupils, and administrators; by the teacher's mental health, methods of teaching, and discipline; and by administrative policies and the provisions that are made for individual differences. If the school is to teach effectively, it must view its practices and policies in the light of how these affect the mental health of its pupils.

Teachers and Teaching

There is certainly evidence to suggest that the teacher's mental health is very important in fostering the mental health of pupils. Consequently, administrators must seek ways of fostering and improving the mental health of teachers. I believe that, to do this, superintendents, principals, supervisors, and special counselors will need to concern themselves with three things: (1) providing working conditions which will preserve and enhance the teacher's mental health, (2) encouraging and promoting his professional and general intellectual growth, and (3) finding ways of increasing his self-understanding.[4]

Teachers must be provided with both the physical and the psychological conditions of work that will satisfy their emotional needs for achievement, recognition, and a sense of worth. A class of reasonable size, a reasonable teaching load, an uncrowded classroom, adequate teaching equipment, freedom from too many nonteaching duties, job security, and an adequate salary are all important factors in meeting teachers' mental health needs.

The psychological conditions of work are sometimes the most important. The climate of the school—the tone set by the school board, the superintendent, and the principal—as well as the teacher's relationships with his fellow teachers, counselors, supervisors, parents, and the public, profoundly affects the teacher's mental health and, in due course, that of his pupils. Poor staff relationships, friction between teachers and school board, and undue criticism by parents and the public can do great harm to the quality of teaching and learning in the classroom. The correction of such conditions is often more important than specific attempts to improve teaching methods.

Some mental hygienists, such as Maslow,[6] think of mental health in terms of growth and self-realization. To be mentally healthy, the teacher needs to continue to grow through participation in various forms of in-service education. To find lasting satisfaction for his needs for achievement, recognition, and sense of self-worth, he needs to grow in knowledge about child and adolescent development, newer teaching methods and trends in education, and ideas in the general field of education. With the present explosion of knowledge, no one can afford to quit learning. Any teacher who does so is likely to find his job dull and boring. In addition, he is likely to feel insecure and inadequate as the tide of progress surges past him. Every help must be given by school boards, administrators, and teacher federations to help teachers to continue to grow. Both industry and the armed forces have learned that high dividends of improved efficiency accrue through providing salary and expenses for their employees while taking further training. School boards have been slow in following their example.

From Socrates to modern psychotherapists there has been an emphasis on self-understanding as a means of enabling the individual to handle more effectively his personal problems and improve his relationships. How to develop this best poses a difficult question. Too direct an attack on a teacher's weak spots only leaves him feeling more insecure and inadequate. The process of developing self-understanding must be gradual and basically more subtle than the use of the "trouble-with-you-is" technique. It probably can best be approached by giving teachers, through in-service education, the opportunity of replacing the traditional surface approach to pupil behavior with the causal approach (discussed below). From there, using group discussion and other techniques, the teacher can be helped to understand why teachers in general react to pupils in the way they do and, later, why they personally react as they do to their pupils and colleagues. Seminars such as these can often best be conducted under the auspices of teacher organizations.

Discipline

Nowhere should the stress on pupil growth in mental health be greater than in the field of discipline. Discipline is not the equivalent of punishment. Rather, it is a form of learning which leads to self-control and self-direction. Like other forms of classroom learning, discipline should enhance a child's concept of himself, improve his relationships with teacher and classmates, and enable him to direct his own behavior more effectively and to deal with his personal problems of living. Teachers should examine their methods of discipline in the light of what these do to the emotional growth of the pupil.

The argument that traditional methods work is not good enough. What often happens is that the teacher chases the pupil's undesirable symptom out of the classroom, only to find an equally undesirable expression of it elsewhere. It is also true that teachers, like doctors, must often treat symptoms temporarily, while trying to find the underlying causes of the child's antisocial behavior.

Teachers must be helped to grow in their ability to use the causal rather than the surface approach to behavior. An effective way of doing this (which yields double dividends in both pupil and teacher insight) is that advocated by Ojemann.[7] This method systematically encourages pupils in the elementary grades to interpret human behavior in thinking rather than nonthinking terms. Teachers take summer courses in which they study the causal approach to pupil behavior. They also participate in rewriting the topics in the social studies, English, and science curricula, so that pupils have a chance to discuss the reasons underlying the human behavior of those they have been reading about. Gradually pupils learn to apply these principles to school problems, and eventually to personal problems. It is a dull teacher who does not have some of this understanding rub off on himself!

Another method of developing the causal approach to problems of learning and behavior can be achieved through case conferences on specific problems in which the teacher is accepted as a partner by psychiatrists, psychologists, social workers, and counselors, rather than just being told what to do. Such conferences help the teacher to develop an understanding approach to classroom problems, as well as constructive methods of dealing with them.

Teaching Methods

The methods used in teaching can be basic in meeting or frustrating the emotional needs of pupils. Formalized methods may get pupils through their examinations and can provide a measure of security by telling them what to do, but they are also apt to frustrate the pupils' need for independence and the sense of achievement that comes only through active participation in the learning process. In addition, the pupils are denied that sense of personal worth which comes from mastering a problem. More flexible methods are likely to meet the pupils' mental health needs, since they tend to foster growth by stressing creativeness, investigation, experimentation, and active problem solving.

Getzels and Jackson [1] have shown that creative individuals approach problems quite differently from those who are chiefly concerned with getting the right answer. Torrance [9] has shown that creativity can be killed at critical periods in the child's school career. He has also shown that some schools foster creativity more extensively than others. In creative teaching, a class lesson is a shared experience, in which teacher and pupils together think through problems or conduct investigations and experiments and in which pupil contributions are welcomed and independent study and thinking encouraged.

Administrators and supervisors need to realize that building positive mental health is an integral part of quality teaching. Departments of education and administrators should give teachers enough freedom to teach creatively. Because creative teaching is much more difficult than formalized teaching, teachers should be given a great deal of help through in-service education, so that they may teach in ways that foster self-actualization and creativity in their pupils.

Probably the most serious way in which schools damage the mental health of pupils consists of denying them a sense of achievement and recognition in their classwork. This is almost certain to result when pupils of the same chronological age are grouped in one class and taught a uniform curriculum. If a pupil's self-image is as important as mental hygienists believe, then this image is enhanced by success and recognition and damaged by continued failure to achieve. There is abundant evidence that nothing succeeds like success—and nothing stultifies like persistent failure! Since children have basic needs for achievement and recognition, it follows that the school should provide them with work at which, with effort, they can succeed. In many, many classrooms this must be true of only a minority of pupils, possibly the high average or those in the lower range of superior ability. The gifted, the very superior, the low average, and the below average frequently have little opportunity to taste achievement in a class where there is a uniform curriculum for children of widely varying abilities. Various types of grouping may help somewhat but do not solve the problem. They may even have adverse effects on the mental health of those pupils who are placed in groups of low prestige value.

One hopeful aspect of the present explosion of knowledge is that it may strike a blow at the conception of education as being chiefly the acquisition of specific knowledge and skills which every child should acquire and which will last a lifetime. Today, facts and skills become rapidly outdated. As a result, education may be forced to shift its emphasis to the mental health concept of pupil growth, whereby each child develops skills in problem solving, critical thinking, investigation, experimentation, and creativeness, all in accordance with his own pattern and rate of growth.

In learning to read and compute, a student's mental health may be fostered through individualized reading instruction and programmed learning. These have the twin virtues of providing continued experiences of success and recognition and of allowing children to proceed at their own pace. Educators must continue to seek ways of organizing each child's school experiences so that he be stretched to achieve his best and receive appropriate recognition for his effort. This will probably involve a differentiated rather than a uniform curriculum and a different learning pace for each child. At present, in many classrooms, emotional and growth satisfaction are denied when, at the beginning of the new school year, both the teachers and the pupils, for the most part, know who is going to receive A, B, C, D, and F standings in the year's work.

Administration and Promotion Policies

In a democracy, departments of education, superintendents, and principals seldom make administrative decisions solely on the basis of logic and practicability. They nearly always consider the reactions of those to be affected: teachers, pupils, parents, and the public. Thus, attitudes and feelings influence administrative policies. Nearly all school policies involve the emotions of teachers, pupils, and parents in one way or another. Think, for example, of administrative decisions dealing with promotions, examinations, homework, and school regulations. These are loaded with emotional content. Clearly, administrative policies are influenced by feelings and attitudes, just as feelings and attitudes are influenced by administrative policies.

There is little in education that can be so damaging to the self-concept and to relationships with pupils as most types of *report cards*. In our society, where success in moving up the socioeconomic scale is a major criterion of an individual's worth, children who do not receive high marks (on a uniform curriculum for their age group) are apt to receive severe blows to their self-esteem from their middle-class parents and teachers. What is assumed to be underachievement is regarded as a cardinal sin. Yet, if pep talks, scoldings, exhortations, pressure, punishments, or bribes could solve the problem of low marks, it would have been solved long ago, As someone has said: " 'Pull yourself together' is seldom said to anyone who can." Even if intelligence tests were a fair measure of achievement (which they often are not), there still remain a host of factors involved in school failures. Karnes,[3] Getzels and Jackson,[1] and Lichter[5] have supplied much evidence that emotional, character, and personality factors, as well as home conditions, cultural standards, and environmental situations, are important aspects in school achievement. Riessman[8] has made a strong case for the culturally deprived child. The Great Cities Program for School Improvement in the United States is a serious attempt to attack the problem. There is growing evidence not only that the culturally deprived group contains a reservoir of untapped talent but also that intelligent attempts to meet the educational needs of this group can be successful. The latter will be the case if the emotional and situational needs of these children, as well as their own particular approach to learning, are considered.

From many points of view, I believe the only ultimate answer for most types of report cards is to replace them with intelligently conducted teacher-parent conferences. Since this is presently impossible, because parents seem wedded to report cards (complete with percentages), the only practical alternative would seem to be to try to reduce the harm done to children's self-concepts and to their relationships with parents and teachers. Adequate teacher-parent conferences should be used to supplement report cards. Here, teacher and parent can search together as to how they can cooperate to help the child achieve his potentialities at his own rate of learning.

It should also be noted that there is nothing evil about *examinations* per se. It is the undue emphasis placed on competitive examinations by parents and teachers that may cause damage. Actually, children continually seek to test themselves in athletics, games, and many other ways. As far as schoolwork goes, there should be more, not fewer, examinations in which pupils test their progress and growth.

One of the possible values of programmed learning is that it continually tests the student on specific items in which he can reasonably hope to succeed and for success in which he receives some form of immediate recognition. In any case, examinations should move away from too great an emphasis on fact getting toward testing pupils' ability in fact using. Examinations should test the ability to solve problems in new settings, to do logical and critical thinking, to ask questions, to foresee consequences, and to produce new ideas.

The burden presently placed on teachers by too heavy a teaching and extracurricular load and by a lengthened school day sometimes tends to the too exclusive use of objective tests based on ability to recall or recognize factual information. An examination, to be a good one, must test abilities that are most worth developing and should lead to a sense of achievement and recognition in pupils, as well as an eagerness to continue learning. If examinations test abilities that are not worth developing, if they frustrate the child's need for achievement and recognition and mar his relationships with parents and teachers, then they had better not be administered.

The rigidity of the *grade structure* in many schools also creates problems of policy for promotion and nonpromotion. Goodlad and Anderson [2] have cited research evidence that nonpromotion does not significantly raise achievement. With regard to pupil attitudes, there is much evidence that nonpromotion often results in emotional depression and discouragement, in the pupil's distrust of his own ability, and ultimately in his expectation of further failure. In the area of personal-social adjustment, Goodlad compared a group of nonpromoted with promoted children and found that the nonpromoted children, at a high level of statistical significance, showed up poorly on self-ratings, peer ratings, and teacher ratings. This research concluded that the hypothesis that there are no differences between promoted and nonpromoted children in social and personal adjustment must be emphatically rejected.

Under our present grade system, the battle between those favoring nonpromotion and those favoring promotion is likely to continue. From a mental health point of view, administrators and counselors would do well to be guided by four principles:

1. Placing any child in a group for instruction requires a careful balancing of all the available data: mental age, chronological age, probable learning rate, school achievement, work habits, physical health, and level of physical development, as well as the degree of emotional and social development.

2. The decision for placement must be made in terms of a considered judgment of what is best for the child concerned, including the probable effects on his self-concept and his relationships with peers and others.

3. When nonpromotion is decided upon, it should be viewed not as a punishment but as the best means of meeting the child's needs.

4. There must be wise counseling, over a period, of both the child and his parents, so that as little damage as possible be done to his self-concept and his sense of security with his parents, teachers, and peers.

School Regulations

Ideally the purpose of homework is to develop in pupils the sense of achievement and self-esteem which comes from competence in independent study. Homework should not be "busy" work or be assigned merely to help parents keep the child off the streets. Rather, it should be meaningful to the pupil and stress investigation and discovery. Where, in the higher grades, it is considered a necessary extension of classroom endeavor, pupils should share in the planning of their work, both that done in the classroom and that done at home. There should be greater discussion of homework in home and school and parent-teacher associations, so that parents may be able to cooperate more effectively with the school in making it a satisfying growth experience for the pupil. Only too often does homework damage study habits and develop frustrations and dissatisfactions in pupils.

In a variety of ways school regulations affect the mental health of pupils. They may foster or frustrate a pupil's developing sense of independence and his sense of belonging, as well as his sense of achievement and personal worth. Pupils' growth will be promoted if, from earliest years, they have a share in forming classroom rules and in planning school regulations. On the other hand, pupils can be greatly frustrated when they feel that school regulations are unfair or unnecessary. One example of this is a rigid regulation that a pupil must attain a certain standard on examinations to play on a school team or participate in other extraclass activities. This can work a hardship on the mediocre pupil who may even be "overachieving," since it denies him alternative achievement and recognition he might attain through such activities.

The principle to be applied by principals and counselors is that each child's program (including both class and extraclass activities) should provide for his best all-around growth. Some children need help in balancing their program with fewer extraclass activities; some need a greater number. In any case, the feelings of pupils toward school regulations are likely to affect both the morale of the school and their own effectiveness in classroom learning.

Conclusions

Readers may have reacted to our views in two ways: (1) that mental health teaching is merely good teaching; and (2) that, with the present emphasis on quantity rather than quality education, the point of view expressed is "pie in the sky."

Teaching which meets the emotional needs of the child is merely teaching at its best. Teaching which best promotes the highest potential of a particular pupil is likely to be that which gives him a feeling of independence, achievement, recognition, and a sense of worth. This does not mean being "soft." Pupils can be led to test their limits in learning if the material means something to them, if it can be mastered by good effort and brings them the satisfactions of success and recognition. Education is not a "filling-station" job but one of great artistry and skill. Teachers should not be technicians. They must be educational statesmen with long-range views of what education can mean to the growth and maturity of students and how they can help to bring this about.

Although current reaction to world tension and global change seems to make people think of education in terms of quantity (a longer school day, a longer school year, a greater number of years at school, and greater emphasis on factual knowledge, reading, and computational skills), the present explosion of knowledge will eventually force an emphasis on quality. There is an ever-increasing need for people who have the ability to investigate, discuss, experiment, invent, solve new problems, and be creative in a variety of ways.

The new type of education, which the closing years of this century will demand, will cost money. If teachers are to teach in accordance with the principles I have advocated, changes will certainly be needed. Although new equipment may be involved, the chief need is for the better utilization of teachers to do a creative job in promoting pupil growth. This will probably involve giving teachers more time for preparing material, more time for critical evaluation of pupils' work, and more time for both individual and group discussion with pupils and parents. It will involve, too, an increasing awareness of administrators and teachers that teaching, to be effective, must take full account of the emotional needs of the pupil.

References

1. Getzels, J. W., and P. W. Jackson: *Creativity and Intelligence,* John Wiley & Sons, Inc., New York, 1962.
2. Goodlad, J. I., and R. H. Anderson: *The Non-graded Elementary School,* Harcourt, Brace & World, Inc., New York, 1959.
3. Karnes, M. B., et al.: *Factors Associated with Underchievement and Overachievement of Intellectually Gifted Children,* Champaign Community Unit Schools, no. 4, Champaign, Ill., 1961.
4. Laycock, S. R.: *Mental Hygiene in the School,* Copp Clark, Toronto, 1960.
5. Lichter, S., et al.: *The Drop-outs,* The Macmillan Company, New York, 1962.
6. Maslow, A. H.: *Motivation and Personality,* Harper & Row, Publishers, Incorporated, New York, 1954.
7. Ojemann, Ralph H.: *Developing a Program for Education in Human Behavior,* The Department of Publications, State University of Iowa, Iowa City, Iowa, 1959.
8. Riessman, Frank: *The Culturally Deprived Child,* Harper & Row, Publishers, Incorporated, New York, 1962.
9. Torrance, E. Paul: *Guiding Creative Talent,* Prentice-Hall, Inc., Englewood Cliffs, N.J., 1962.

16. School Refusal:
A Comprehensive View of School Phobia

Jack H. Kahn and Jean P. Nursten

Introduction

"School phobia" has been the subject of a large number of papers in recent years, and the topic has aroused a great deal of interest in the psychiatric and educational fields. The purpose of early papers was of necessity to show that the condition existed and differed from voluntary absence from school. That purpose has been amply achieved, as can be seen from the literature summarized below. It is our aim to discuss the meaning of the symptom in relation to the community and to personality development. Clinically the cases can be grouped into three categories. These are the psychoneurotic states, character disorders, and the psychoses of childhood, and each is considered along with treatment needs.

The Literature

In the United States nearly thirty years ago, Broadwin[5] noticed an atypical group with psychoneurotic elements when studying truancy, and a similar observation was made a few years later in England by Partridge.[44] The term "school phobia" did not appear in the literature until 1941.[29] The first planned studies, which compared the differences between truants and children who were refusing to go to school for irrational reasons, were made by Warren[55] and Hersov.[25] Both writers confirmed, to a large extent, that truants were showing indications of conduct disorders which would often include delinquent trends, whilst those who failed to attend schools for irrational reasons were showing one aspect of a neurosis which often involved the whole family.

Compulsory school attendance provides a framework within which the

Adapted from a paper previously published in the *American Journal of Orthopsychiatry*, 32:707–718, 1962.

major part of the child's behavioral life is enclosed. It therefore provides an area where symptoms of different types of disturbance may be expressed.[22,34] Failure to attend school may imply truancy, which is taken to be absence from school on rational grounds, consistent with the known character of the child in his setting. The truant is often rebelling against adverse home circumstances. Lack of satisfaction, whether at home or at school, is probably the most important condition contributing to truancy.[51] Failure to attend may also be due to withdrawal of the child from school because of the parents' own needs or to the inability of child and parents jointly to accept normal social obligations. These can be considered to be social problems. Truants can be socially maladjusted [10] but can be helped by social measures.

The school-phobic child remains at home despite threats, bribes, and punishments from parents and others drawn into the problem. Many cases conform to a definite pattern. There is fear of school and of leaving mother. Somatic symptoms usually accompany the acute anxiety: the typical picture is of the child vomiting or having abdominal pain at breakfast time. Although the distress, sometimes amounting to panic, is consistent, the term "school phobia" is too specific. The descriptions of clinical categories by various writers differ and include a wide range of underlying psychopathology. Suttenfield [48] and Hitchcock [26] considered it to be a specific phobia and thought that anxiety had become detached from a certain situation in early life and displaced onto the school situation as a neurotic fear. According to some writers, the reason for the anxiety was due to faulty family dynamics, especially between the mother and the child. [8,39,50,52,57,58] This point has been taken further, and consideration given to the parent-child relationship in a time of social change.[31] Other papers [17,19,29,40] show that the condition can be taken as a form of separation anxiety, and another group [3,23,25,42,55] accepts the condition as a phenomenon manifested by different psychopathological types. Amongst the latter it has been observed that cases of school refusal can occur in neurotic and borderline psychotic cases and even in children who, whilst actually present at school, absent themselves from the learning process.

School refusal has been referred to in papers on other topics: for instance, Bransby [4] takes it to be a factor in a survey of absences among 10,000 children; Burns [6] mentions the problem in a paper on preschizophrenic symptoms; Campbell,[7] in an article on manic-depressive illness in children; Kagan,[30] in a study of twins; Harrington and Hassan [24] consider a case in a study of depression in girls during latency; McWhinnie [38] discusses the problem in a classification of psychotic disorders in childhood; and Warren [56] in a follow-up study of adolescents who had had phobic symptoms. Influential factors in the outcome of treatment of school phobia in thirty children have also been examined.[27]

The paper of Johnson and her co-workers [29] in 1941 contained the germ of many subsequent studies. It had long been recognized that there was a type of emotional disturbance, associated with great anxiety, that led to serious absence from school. The children who fled from school usually went straight home to mother and subsequently refused to leave home. Their fears could not be verbalized, and their behavior was incomprehensible to parents and teachers alike. Eventually the mothers would be humiliated by criticism from neighbors and relatives. The children would not show themselves until others were home from school and out in the street.

There were all degrees of this disturbance. The mother was thought to be inconsistent, demanding an independent child, yet at the same time asserting absolute authority over the child. The teacher, a more consistent disciplinarian, became the phobic object. Johnson added to this in 1957.[28] She then stated that her ideas, formulated in 1941, could now be accepted as a scientific principle. It was felt that given (1) a poorly resolved dependency situation between the mother and child and (2) coincidence of precipitating factors causing acute anxiety in the child with a threat to the mother's security (e.g., economic or marital), school refusal would become overt. The child's anxiety and need for dependence maintained an attachment which the mother could not afford to forego. This principle has been shown to apply particularly in adolescence.[9,31,42] When dependency in the child has been unduly prolonged, the urges that arise during adolescence from within lead to conflict with the external pressures that already exist. The stability of the personality becomes precarious, and any change in the balance of the forces in this conflict leads to a state of panic and to regression to earlier levels of childhood.

Incidence

It is not yet possible to obtain reliable figures on a national scale, but in some child guidance clinics school phobia accounts for 2 to 8 per cent of the total referrals.[40,42] Boston, Massachusetts, an industrial and university city of some 800,000 people, has twenty-five severe cases a year treated by a special child guidance team.[43] Numbers seem to be increasing. It may be that, as attention becomes focused on the problem and as child guidance treatment is accepted, cases become channeled through clinics instead of through the courts. It may also be that ideas of the pathologic are changing, that as mental illness becomes milder, aspects of social behavior may appear more clinical and become acceptable as a medical problem.

Community Attitudes

Professional concern about the problem is mounting. The National Association for Mental Health held the Fifteenth Inter-clinic Child Guidance Conference on the topic "Truancy or School Phobia?"[41] in

1959, and the British Medical Journal devoted space to a main leader [16] and correspondence concerning the problem [37] in 1960. Similarly, teachers and education welfare officers are acutely aware of the difficulty, and the British Psychological Society's Mental Health Subcommittee is undertaking a research project based on clinical records.[2] This widespread concern may have arisen because of the irremediable aspects of some cases, which are amongst the most severe psychiatric disorders in young people.

There may be other reasons for the concern. Individual cases may represent a challenge to professional skills. The worker demands from himself a success where the parent failed and in doing so may repeat the processes in which the parents are involved. He may attempt a severity which is equally unsuccessful, or he may find himself protecting the family from the demands of reality by being too permissive. In these cases, the resemblance of the doctor-patient relationship to the parent-child relationship is particularly important, and the doctor comes to feel responsible for the child's continuing symptoms in the face of his own efforts. A psychiatrist often feels responsible for a patient's life if he is aware that the patient is suicidal. The child who refuses to go to school is being self-destructive. Contacts outside the family are avoided, the career is jeopardized, and the future is cut off in a way that could be described as social suicide. Sometimes awareness of these problems cannot be tolerated, and the patient has to be moved some distance—the suicidal patient to a mental hospital, the school-phobic child to a boarding school. Treatment can never be effective until the therapist is able to tolerate the anxiety that becomes reflected within himself.

The anxiety and frustration which this topic causes in different groups of professional workers have a social in addition to a personal cause, for as a society we include in our aims that there shall be equal opportunities for all. We are upset by those who "contract out" and apparently refuse to take what is being offered them. They are becoming a new sort of deviate. A cartoonist depicted a contemporary attitude when he drew a child standing in a doorway, reluctant to go out to play, with the mother saying: "But it's *fun* to have snowballs thrown at you." Fun is valuable. A personal disinclination for something so generally approved could not be understood or tolerated. When education has only comparatively recently been instituted for all in this country, and, more recently still, the right to secondary education, it is hard to accept that it need not be taken by some children. There are open wards, open prisons, and open schools, but it becomes a calamity if anyone actually walks out.

The symptom of school refusal needs to be taken as a communication of distress—an appeal that goes beyond the private communication within the family, as in the case of such disorders as enuresis or night terrors. Recent theories of suicidal attempts (as distinct from successful suicide) stress the appeal for help within the act.[49] School refusal resembles suicidal attempts in making the distress public. In both there is the self-destructive element alongside the wish to injure those to whom the individuals are closely tied. There are features in common with the suicidal attempts of later adolescence, and there is a similarity in the way that individuals of high intelligence interrupt their academic careers and are destructive in their family relationships. When a child refuses to go to school, it seems as though an attack is being made on society, and the whole machinery of school enforcement stands helpless in the face of such a child in a panic state.

It seems to be the panic in the child, as well as the despair and loneliness that are part of it, that is the signal for help; it is this that needs to be recognized, or we remain bound even by the term "school phobia" into thinking that the return to school spells the cure. The conflict itself must be treated, since Dixon and his co-workers have suggested that phobias, which are part of a pattern of anxiety, are best not treated by deconditioning.[15]

Psychopathology and Treatment

School can be rejected by children with psychoneurotic, character, or psychotic disorders. There is often some overlap between these three classes. The categories are not exclusive and vary in degree and kind, but each will be considered separately.

The *psychoneurotic states* can themselves be of different types. The state can be one of anxiety, or it can be phobic, obsessional, hysterical, or depressive, and of all degrees of intensity. The children who show such symptoms are more likely to be in a young age group and are mostly preadolescent girls.[53] This group often has the basic personality still intact, and, apart from the school phobia, children in this category exercise their social and intellectual functions quite well.[8] The school refusal is a symptom of conflict in the parent-child relationship. Three main triangular patterns occur. These are clearly described by Hersov [25] as families in which there is (1) an overindulgent mother and a passive father dominated by a willful, stubborn, and demanding child; (2) a severe, controlling mother and a passive father with a timid, fearful child, who is likely to become rebellious during adolescence; or (3) a firm father and an overindulgent mother bound to a dominating, willful child who can, however, be friendly away from home. In addition, many authors have noticed that the mothers of these children are often highly involved with the maternal grandmothers.[23,42,45] One study has paid particular attention to the fathers.[45]

The overindulgent mother finds it essential for her own equilibrium to keep the child dependent on her. The child is presented with the alternative ". . . whether to be active and independent and pay the price of feeling alone and unprotected, or to 'belong' and be protected and pay the price of losing his independence. Present-day education, for social reasons, increases the intensity of this conflict. This is the psychological basis of many social and cultural problems." [21]

The following dream, which was offered by a boy in a treatment situation, may illustrate this point. The boy was on a sports field, lying helplessly on the ground, giggling and unable to get up, as his mother was tickling him. Other boys were playing at the other end of the field. Whilst teasing her son, the mother was asking why he did not join in with the other boys. School with its reality pressures can be a rude awakening for such children. In some cases, adolescence provides an additional pressure with its burst of sexual, physical, and intellectual development. These increasing drives can be a threat to the child, because they are in opposition to his continued need for dependence, and they can be unwelcome also to the mother. As Helene Deutsch [13] states: "The stronger the neurotic disposition, the greater the mother's intolerance of her child's struggle for emancipation, and the greater her tendency to react with unhappiness and anxiety to his progressive separation from her."

When the family dynamics are faulty, the family as a unit needs treatment. The aim is to adjust relationships by casework and psychotherapeutic techniques. Early treatment seems to give better results. A change of school alone is insufficient, and even a voluntary return to school, without treatment, makes a relapse more likely. The child's readiness to return must be considered in relation to the mother's ability to let go. Prognosis seems favorable if the child does not find it essential to have constant emotional and material gratification. Secondary gains of this type are an important element, and such satisfactions can undermine treatment.[33] The degree to which the child was dominating the family does not jeopardize treatment; the greatest hazard lies in the mother's inconsistency.[52] This inconsistency can sometimes be observed by her quavering voice and trembling gestures that accompany empty verbal assurances. It is as though the child were being told by nonverbal communication that what has to be faced is even more terrifying than he had dared to think. The child's symptoms actually become comprehensible as the response to contradictory verbal and behavioral cues.[17,18]

Character disorders are "limitations or pathological forms of treating the external world, internal drives and demands of the superego, or disturbances of the ways in which these various tasks combine." [21] The children who refuse school and who come into this category may be handicapped not so much by what went wrong but by those things that failed to go right. We are not dealing here with the type of illness that comes to a normal personality, in which treatment returns the individual to his previous normal state. It can be taken that a person begins with certain inherited potentialities but requires essential experiences to help him respond by continual adjustment to the demands imposed upon him, both through internal and external processes. We are then concerned with the growth of personality and its adaptation to reality. If there has not been consistency and love in the way in which a child is presented with gratification and frustration from those around him in his earliest years, his successful development of ego strengths will have been impaired. He will not have the foundation necessary for a character that can bring into harmony the tasks presented by the external world and internal demands, which is the function of "the constant, organized, and integrating part of the personality which is the ego." [21] Children who have not been given the opportunity, or who have not had the capacity, for incorporating standards into their personality find that school drains their limited resources. School, with its structured organization of routine, timetables, and syllabi, is a definite reality and is hard to accept whilst *they* are as yet unorganized. Even the type of journey to school may affect the child's perception of his mother's accessibility, a variable linking maternal separation with maternal deprivation.[36]

Lack of adjustment is not so much a process of disintegration but is due to the children's *un*integrated state. School refusal comes not so much as a crisis but as an almost inevitable culmination. Coolidge and his co-workers,[9] in a study of school phobia in adolescence, found that prolonged dependency had impaired ego strengths and led to severe character disorder. In a clinical consideration of psychopathic personalities,[14] it has been found that some poorly organized personalities reveal depressive features, which can include homesickness.

In these cases, a framework of discipline has been lacking and therefore must be supplied. It needs dispensing in graduated doses if it is going to be retained and assimilated. There are some cases in which school placement, combined with psychiatric treatment, can be successful in giving standards which are acceptable because they come from individuals with whom the child is able to identify without fear.

Psychotic conditions are present in some of the cases seen, and failure to attend school may be only one manifestation of a serious disorder. Some authors mention certain children, who might comprise a separate group, who are severely disturbed and inclined to show paranoid, depressive, or schizoid features, and it is felt that school phobia can be associated with psychotic symptoms.[1,8,9,31,42,54] School is not the cause of this condition, but it can increase the strain, and the resulting absence is the first symptom to be revealed in the process.

There is a continuum between the psychosis of childhood, that of adolescence, and that of adult life. The unintegrated personality of the child who never became an organized individual with his own identity has features in common with the disintegrated personality of the adult schizophrenic. There are degrees of lack of integration which fade into the normal.

Laing, in *The Divided Self*,[35] lucidly describes the transition from sanity to madness, the change from being schizoid to being schizophrenic, as being the attempt to deal with the anxiety and dangers arising from the uncertainty of the sense of a personal identity. He portrays the schizoid in words that could be used equally well for this type of school-phobic child, who may previously have been unnoticeable and conforming. If there is a sense of personal identity and the corollary, other people's reality, Laing considers such a person to be "ontologically secure," and the hazards presented by the world can be met from a centrally firm core. The feeling of being real and alive in his own right may never have been given to a baby. At first he is physically and emotionally so closely related to his mother that he is not aware of a separate identity. As Winnicott describes it,[59] the baby gradually learns that there is someone outside himself, someone who comes and goes—the mother, with a life of her own. He later begins to develop a sense of his own identity. The mother lets him be himself, and a feeling of worth and autonomy grows. Such a process may not develop along normal lines, however, and the child may remain "precariously differentiated from the rest of the world, so that his identity and autonomy are always in question." [35]

This uncertainty makes relationships dangerous, and ontologically insecure children can feel threatened by the alien reality of school. These children exist only in their mother's orbit and, by returning home from school, are actually trying to preserve an identity. It is only in her orbit or surrounded by the familiar things in the home that they know what to be: home is the child's reality, even if it could be differently described as the place where the parents' fantasies are acted out. The terror and panic the child shows when he is coerced into going to school may not mean to him what it means to the school-attendance officer. Laing quotes the case of a patient who broke off an argument in an analytic group by saying to one of the protagonists that he could not go on. He continued: "At best you win an argument. At worst you lose an argument. *I am arguing in order to preserve my existence* [italics supplied]." School is broken off in the same way as this argument. Such children have a need to be at home, and it is often when the security of the home is threatened that the crisis occurs. Investigation of precipitating factors has shown that if the mother is ill or threatening to leave, or even if the whole family moves to another district, the child's balance can be upset. Reality is jeopardized. If the mother were to go away or die, it would be a matter of panic, not grief. The child would lose such identity as he had.

Treatment of children with borderline or established psychoses must be quite independent of school attendance. Here, school attendance is the mark of normality by which one could deny the existence of the mental illness which is suspected or feared. There is the belief that if only the child would *act* normal, he would *be* normal. Attempts are therefore made by parents, school authorities, and those in medical charge to force the child back to school. The attempts fail. These are the patients who are likely to find their way to inpatient child psychiatric units. The prognosis is a serious one, even with the best treatment available, and Warren [56] supplies figures in a follow-up of phobic cases that give naught for our comfort. Out of sixteen young adults originally admitted to an inpatient unit between the ages of twelve and sixteen years, six were quite well and ten still showed symptoms six years later. The outlook is poor for school-phobic cases when they have other phobic symptoms in addition. Rodriguez and his co-workers,[46] however, supply more encouraging figures.

Here we must emphasize the need for additional inpatient units and further opportunities to study the psychopathology and the therapeutic requirements of these children. It is also suggested that what is called for here seems to be not drugs or other physical methods but the acceptance of regression to infantile levels, followed by the chance to incorporate into the personality, for the first time, the factors that have been missing. These children have had no consistent models to build into themselves. They have not known what to be. The therapist has to provide a consistency in his framework of treatment that gives the patient a foundation from which to grow.[32] Recent papers by Sperling [47] and Davidson [11] on the treatment of school phobia add to our understanding.

The study and treatment of this group of patients would indicate that their condition has an importance that goes far beyond the question of failure in school attendance. It is the general question of breakdown in a social situation, a breakdown that occurs in a comparable form in later stages of development. Three examples can be quoted:

(1) Psychiatric breakdown in university students. Davy [12] notes that 50 per cent of schizophrenic undergraduates, or those suspected of schizophrenia, have had earlier attacks or symptoms.

(2) Desertion from the army. In a study of war neuroses [20] there is discussion of the compulsion to return home: "In cases in which the general symptomatology assumes a psychotic form, it is not uncommon for the compulsion in question to manifest itself either in a fugue or in a consciously executed flight such as to constitute, from a disciplinary point of view, either absence without leave or desertion, or else, where the individual's sense of duty is sufficiently strong, in an attempt at suicide."

(3) Absconding from approved schools. This is a frequent occurrence and usually has not even the features of a successful prison escape. The youths almost invariably proceed straight home—a home which has been rejecting to them—and they are picked up there. The absconding leads to loss of privileges and deferment of their eventual discharge home, but rational features are not the operative ones.

Summary

1. Failure to maintain school attendance may be due to factors with a rational explanation. These include (*a*) truancy without the knowledge of the family, (*b*) deliberate withholding of the child from school by the parents, and (*c*) apathy on the part of both parent and child. The causes in all these cases should be considered as social, and social measures applied through the school welfare department should be looked to for the remedy.

2. There are other cases in which the causes are not rational and social measures can provide no cure. The group with irrational causes has been described in many papers using the term "school phobia." The present authors are using the term "school refusal" as one which does not indicate too specific a pathology.

3. The cases of school refusal can be grouped under three headings. These are (*a*) psychoneurotic, including phobic, conditions; (*b*) character disorders; and (*c*) psychotic conditions.

4. Treatment should be directed to the underlying psychiatric disturbance and not to the symptom of school refusal.

5. Many of the cases represent severe personality breakdown or failure of personality integration. There is a continuum in these cases, beginning with early childhood psychosis, followed by a breakdown in adolescence, student life, and military service.

6. The lengthening of the period of compulsory education to the age of sixteen years may lead to an increase in the recorded number of school-attendance breakdowns. If this occurs, it may constitute a shift in incidence from clinical, industrial, or delinquent phenomena to those shown in school life. One should, however, consider the part that the school regime itself plays as a contributory factor.

7. The study and treatment of these cases should provide information as to essential emotional needs in the development of the normal personality.

8. There is need for additional facilities for psychiatric investigation and treatment of school-age children and for joint research into the sociological and educational factors.

Postscript

The contents of this chapter have been expanded, and the need for a multidisciplinary approach to treatment stressed, in *Unwillingly to School* by Jack H. Kahn and Jean P. Nursten, Pergamon Press, Oxford, 1964.

References

1. Agras, S.: "The Relationship of School Phobia to Childhood Depression," *Amer. J. Psychiat.*, 116:533, 1959.

2. *Annual Report of the British Psychological Society, 1958–1959*, London Tavistock House, 1959.
3. Bonnard, A.: "School Phobia," an address presented before the Association of Child Psychology and Psychiatry, 1959.
4. Bransby, E. R.: "A Study of Absence from School," *Med. Officer*, 86:223, 237, 1951.
5. Broadwin, I.: "A Contribution to the Study of Truancy," *Amer. J. Orthopsychiat.*, 2:253, 1932.
6. Burns, C.: "Preschizophrenic Symptoms in Preadolescents," *Nerv. Child*, 10:120, 1952.
7. Campbell, J.: "Manic Depressive Disease in Children," *J.A.M.A.*, 158:154, 1953.
8. Coolidge, J. C., P. B. Hahn, and A. L. Peck: "School Phobia: Neurotic Crisis or Way of Life," *Amer. J. Orthopsychiat.*, 27:296, 1957.
9. Coolidge, J. C., M. L. Willer, E. Tessman, and S. Waldfogel: "School Phobia in Adolescence," *Amer. J. Orthopsychiat.*, 30:599, 1960.
10. Croft, I. J., and T. G. Grygier: "Social Relationships of Truants and Juvenile Delinquents," *Hum. Relat.*, 9:439, 1956.
11. Davidson, S.: "School Phobia as a Manifestation of Family Disturbance," *J. Child Psychol. Psychiat.*, 1:270, 1961.
12. Davy, B. W.: "The Sources and Prevention of Mental Ill-health in University Students," *Proc. Roy. Soc. Med.*, 53(9):26, 1960.
13. Deutsch, H.: *The Psychology of Women*, Grune & Stratton, New York, 1945, vol. 2, p. 267.
14. Diethelm, O.: "A Clinical Consideration of Psychopathic Personalities," *J. Ment. Sci.* (now *Brit. J. Psychiat.*), 106:906, 1960.
15. Dixon, J. J., C. de Monchaux, and J. Sandler: "Patterns of Anxiety: The Phobias," *Brit. J. Med. Psychol.*, 30:34, 1957.
16. Editorial on school phobia, *Brit. Med. J.*, 2:848, 1960.
17. Eisenberg, L.: "School Phobia: A Study in the Communication of Anxieties," *Amer. J. Psychiat.*, 114(8):712, 1958.
18. ———: "School Phobia: Its Genesis and Clinical Management," *Ped. Clin. N. Amer.*, 5:645, 1958.
19. Estes, H. R., C. H. Haylett, and A. M. Johnson: "Separation Anxiety," *Amer. J. Psychother.*, 10:682, 1956.
20. Fairbairn, W. R. D.: *Psychoanalytic Studies of the Personality*, Tavistock Publications, London, 1952.
21. Fenichel, O.: *The Psychoanalytic Theory of Neurosis*, W. W. Norton & Company, Inc., New York, 1945.
22. Glaser, K.: "Problems in School Attendance: School Phobia and Related Conditions," *Pediatrics*, 55:758, 1959.
23. Goldberg, T. B.: "Factors in the Development of School Phobia," *Smith Coll. Stud. Soc. Wk.*, 23:227, 1953.
24. Harrington, M., and J. Hassan: "Depression in Girls During Latency," *Brit. J. Med. Psychol.*, 31:43, 1958.
25. Hersov, L. A.: "Persistent Non-attendance at School," *J. Child Psychol. Psychiat.*, 1:130, 137, 1960.
26. Hitchcock, A.: "Symbolic and Actual Flight from School," *Smith Coll. Stud. Soc. Wk.*, 27:1, 1956.
27. Jacobsen, V.: "Influential Factors in the Outcome of Treatment of School Phobia," *Smith Coll. Stud. Soc. Wk.*, 27:1, 1956.
28. Johnson, A. M.: "Discussion on School Phobia," *Amer. J. Orthopsychiat.*, 27:296, 1957.

29. ———, E. I. Falstein, S. A. Szurek, and M. Svendsen: "School Phobia," *Amer. J. Orthopsychiat.*, 11:702, 1941.
30. Kagan, J.: "The Psychological Study of School Phobia in One of a Pair of Identical Twins," *J. Proj. Tech. Pers. Assess.*, 20:78, 1956.
31. Kahn, J. H.: "School Refusal: Some Clinical and Cultural Aspects," *Med. Officer*, 100:337, 1958.
32. ———: "Some Observations on the Therapeutic Process in Child Psychotherapy, *Ment. Hyg.*, 44:560, 1960.
33. Klein, E.: "The Reluctance to Go to School," *The Psychoanalytic Study of the Child*, International Universities Press, Inc., New York, 1945, vol. I, p. 263.
34. ———: "The Psychoanalytic Aspects of School Problems," *The Psychoanalytic Study of the Child*, International Universities Press, Inc., New York, 1949, vol. III/IV, p. 369.
35. Laing, R. D.: *The Divided Self*, Tavistock Publications, London, 1960, pp. 38, 43.
36. Lee, T.: "On the Relation between the School Journey and Social and Emotional Adjustment in Rural Infant Children," *Brit. J. Educ. Psychol.*, 27:101, 1957.
37. Letters to the editor, *Brit. Med. J.*, 2:1015, 1960.
38. McWhinnie, J. B.: "The Classification of Psychotic Disorders in Childhood," *Brit. Psychol. Soc. Bull.*, 41:40, 1960.
39. Model, A., and E. Shepheard: "The Child Who Refuses to Go to School," *Med. Officer*, 100:39, 1958.
40. Morgan, G. A. V.: "Children Who Refuse to Go to School," *Med. Officer*, 102:221, 1959.
41. National Association for Mental Health, "Truancy or School Phobia?" *Proceedings of the Fifteenth Inter-clinic Child Guidance Conference*, 1959.
42. Nursten, J. P.: "The Background to Children with School Phobia," *Med. Officer*, 100:340, 1958.
43. Parad, H. J. (ed.): *Ego Psychology and Dynamic Casework*, Family Service Association of America, New York, 1958.
44. Partridge, J. M.: "Truancy," *J. Ment. Sci.* (now *Brit. J. Psychiat.*), 85:45, 1939.
45. Perry, J.: "Fathers of Delinquent and School Phobic Children," *Smith Coll. Stud. Soc. Wk.*, 26:69, 1956.
46. Rodriguez, A., M. Rodriguez, and L. Eisenberg: "The Outcome of School Phobia," *Amer. J. Psychiat.*, 116:540, 1959.
47. Sperling, M.: Analytic First Aid in School Phobias," *Psychoanal. Quart.*, 30:504, 1961.
48. Suttenfield, V.: "School Phobia: A Study of Five Cases," *Amer. J. Orthopsychiat.*, 24:368, 1954.
49. Szasz, T.: "The Communication of Distress between Child and Parent," *Brit. J. Med. Psychol.*, 32:161, 1959.
50. Talbot, M.: "Panic in School Phobia," *Amer. J. Orthopsychiat.*, 27:286, 1957.
51. Tyerman, M. J.: "A Research into Truancy," *Brit. J. Educ. Psychol.*, 28:217, 1958.
52. Van Houten, J.: "Mother-Child Relationship in Twelve Cases of School Phobia," *Smith Coll. Stud. Soc. Wk.*, 18:161, 1948.
53. Waldfogel, S., J. C. Coolidge, and P. B. Hahn: "Development, Meaning and Management of School Phobia," *Amer. J. Orthopsychiat.*, 27:754, 1957.
54. Waldfogel, S., P. B. Hahn, and G. Gardner: "A Study of School Phobia in Children," *J. Nerv. Ment. Dis.*, 120:399, 1954.
55. Warren, W.: "Acute Neurotic Breakdown in Children with Refusal to Go to School," *Arch. Dis. Childh.*, 23:266, 1948.
56. ———: "Some Relationships Between the Psychiatry of Children and Adults," *J. Ment. Sci.* (now *Brit. J. Psychiat.*), 106:816, 1960.

57. Watson, B.: "School Phobia: An Examination of Family Relationships," *Smith Coll. Stud. Soc. Wk.*, 30:98, 1959.
58. Wilson, M.: "Grandmother, Mother and Daughter in Cases of School Phobia," *Smith Coll. Stud. Soc. Wk.*, 25:56, 1955.
59. Winnicott, D.: *The Child and the Outside World,* Tavistock Publications, London, 1957.

17. A Community Mental Health Program for Children: A Case Study

Lewis B. Klebanoff and Arthur J. Bindman

Introduction

This case example attempts to describe the difficulties involved in organizing and developing a community mental health program for children and the problems encountered in working with school personnel and the community at large. It traces the philosophical and legal backgrounds, the development of the center, community organization, attitudes toward the center, mental health consultation, and community relations. It is expected that a discussion of real, rather than theoretical, problems will assist others in their planning of community mental health services.

Background of the Program

In recent years, there has been a major increase in the number of community mental health programs in the United States.[10] Some programs have been total-purpose in their emphasis, including both children and adults, as well as developing closer relationships with state hospitals and their aftercare programs.[11,12] Others have emphasized the preventive and promotional aspects of mental health and focused their attention upon children and their families.[3,9,15] Massachusetts has had a long history of traveling school clinics and child guidance clinics under the auspices of the division of mental hygiene.[17] In 1952, however, it shifted its program to a more public health–oriented basis and began to develop a community mental health program for children in partnership with local mental health associations.[3,9,15] Previous articles have described the method of community organization,[9] the techniques of the mental health consultant in his role of prevention and case finding,[1,7,8] and some of the administra-

Adapted from a paper previously published in the *American Journal of Orthopsychiatry*, 32:119–132, 1962.

tive problems in developing such a large-scale program and relating it to other programs for the retarded and the psychotic.[2,3,4,5]

At the same time, as changes have occurred in programming for community mental health services, there have been many new developments in school mental health and school mental retardation programs.[13,14] Many school systems have added such personnel as child psychiatrists, school psychologists, and school social workers to their staffs. In some states there has been legislation for special-class education for the emotionally disturbed.[6] In many states there are laws regulating special-class education for the mentally retarded, as well as the certification and standardization of school psychologists and school social workers. A number of papers have described these new developments and the general problems which may ensue from the interaction of school-based programs and separate community-based programs.[3,4,16]

This case example will explore some difficulties in organizing and developing a community mental health program for children, problems encountered more often in life than in the professional literature. For obvious purposes of confidentiality, there has been considerable disguising of those aspects which would make people or places readily identifiable, but without violation of the essential processes and principles involved.

In 1953, the Massachusetts Department of Mental Health, Division of Mental Hygiene, hired a clinical psychologist and a psychiatric social worker as the nucleus of a community mental health center for children. This center was to provide the usual clinical services, as well as consultation services to community agencies. In addition, it was hoped it would foster greater coordination in the use of the services of a general hospital and a state hospital in the area. The mental health center, which served six communities, was first housed in a building of the general hospital, and the two staff members were nominally responsible to the head of the hospital's pediatric section.

The program grew out of various desires: (1) The commissioner of mental health wished to see such a program developed in these communities, since they were close to training facilities for professional personnel, and he believed it might serve as a pilot project for other developments of the same type. (2) The director of the Massachusetts Division of Mental Hygiene was committed to the development of many community mental health centers for children, and this seemed to be a good setting. He thought the program could utilize the already developed state hospital services, as well as what he believed to be good community resources to support this center and its activities.

On the other hand, two major issues made this center unique among those sponsored by the Massachusetts Department of Mental Health: (1) No community group or organization asked for the establishment of such a center in any of the communities to be served, whereas other areas had more or less well-organized groups demanding a center and usually were willing to share with the commonwealth the expense of such an enterprise. (2) This was the first center to be housed at its inception in a hospital.

The major problem appeared to be how to begin rendering worthwhile services to the six communities in such a way as to arouse in them an awareness of their mental health needs; show them how some of these needs could be met by a skilled professional team; and organize these separate communities, which had rarely, if ever, joined together in anything, into a mental health association which would share with the state mental health agency the direction and financing of services.

Development of the Center

History

The project began in two rooms in the general hospital, which was located in the largest city of the six communities. This building also housed some seriously physically ill children, and at times the air was filled with cries and even screams from some of the patients. Periodically a bleeding accident case was brought into the waiting room of the nearby accident ward. The first families to use the services of the center shuddered at these occurrences but continued to come, to the surprise of the two staff members. Whether these families may have frightened others in the community by recounting these distressing details would be difficult to assess. It is probable that some persons were so frightened.

It may be wondered why the first families to use the center continued to do so, in spite of the often upsetting milieu in which it was housed. The explanation would seem to be that the children's symptoms were so severe, and the parents were so gravely upset by them, that their motivation for help was sufficiently high for them to endure the incidental environmental unpleasantness.

During its first five years, the center had a considerable turnover in personnel, as well as a considerable change in its location. In 1954, it moved to the basement of the nurses' residence in the hospital. The following year, it moved to a new building on the grounds of a mental hospital in an adjacent community, where it remained for three years. Because of the continued lack of community support and the hospital's need for space, the mental health center was finally forced to move back to the general hospital, to a newly redecorated wing of the medical-surgical building. This appeared to be a regressive step and was a great blow to staff morale, as well as to friends in the community who had hoped the center would be established in separate community quarters supplied by the area mental health association, which had started to grow. It was not until 1958 that new space for the center was obtained in a building rented by the association. This change, coupled with sudden and increased support from the residents of one of the wealthier communities, resulted in the mental health center's finally "escaping" from hospital settings after five years of effort.

During all these relocations, personnel continued to change, and the center staff slowly continued to grow. In 1955, a complete team had been allocated by the state: a psychiatrist-director, a mental health consultant, a social worker, and a psychologist. By 1958, the staff consisted of a psychiatrist-director, three part-time psychiatrists, a mental health consultant, two part-time psychologists, and two social workers.

Community Organization

The key problem of community organization in this case is related to one important fact: namely, the community did not ask for this center. This circumstance is in direct opposition to the philosophical framework described above, in which the Massachusetts Department of Mental Health said that it would work closely with communities in developing a mental health association to support a center if they wished to have one. In this case, the department introduced the beginnings of a center into the community and then asked the community to provide the support. The community organization section of the Massachusetts Division of Mental Hygiene had a most difficult task to carry out, since it was asked to "work backward." It had to develop an association to support a center that was already functioning. It had been previously noted that, in places where a program was supplied by the state, there was often a high degree of apathy on the part of community participants, because they needed to expend little or no energy to keep the program going. This seemed to be true in the present study, and the results of the attempted community organization are of interest in gaining a better understanding of how the mental health center was used by the community.

Although a major philosophical tenet of the department's community program was that the mental health association should have broad representative membership, including members of various professional, social, cultural, religious, political, and labor groups, the first attempt to get a community group organized consisted in approaching an energetic, self-made businessman in the largest city, who, in turn, was to form the nucleus for such an association. This man accepted the leadership role and got in touch with various community leaders in the other five towns as well as in his city. He seemed to be moving rapidly toward financial support for the center. Even after he had guaranteed to supply office space in one of his own buildings free of charge, however, the other towns were slow in accepting his offer, and he soon lost his original interest and dropped to one side.

This development was followed by the "election" of a very self-interested man from one of the towns as temporary chairman of the community group. He was a highly controversial figure in his town, and it was soon noted that any support of projects in which he was interested was sure to create a large group in opposition. He was greatly disliked by the school personnel because he had, as a member of the school committee, voted against pay raises. Things did not move very fast because of his presence as chairman, and, in 1956, he was shunted to one side. Toward the end of the year, after contact had been made with additional medical people in the communities, as well as with other community leaders from the largest city, the group was incorporated as a mental health association for the purpose of supporting the center. By that time three years had passed, but it still appeared that a great deal of work would be necessary before this association would fully support the community mental health services.

The president of the mental health association had no contact with the project before he was asked to head it. After his election, he took on many other community responsibilities, apparently mostly to further his political ambitions. He was an effective worker but only when someone prodded him. The board had thirty members, five from each town, but very few of them attended any meetings, let alone two consecutive ones. In 1957, despite all these handicaps, the board was able to persuade the city councils of two communities, and to obtain the unanimous consent of the town meetings of several of the others, to appropriate $2,000 each in order to participate in the mental health program. In one town there were false rumors and a great deal of local controversy about the possibility that seriously disturbed persons would be housed at the center. Finally, after much discussion and many meetings, support was forthcoming in 1958, and the center attained a more secure footing.

Attitudes toward the Center

One of the basic attitudes encountered in the development of this mental health center was attributable to its being housed first near the accident ward of a general hospital and later in a state hospital. Although the division of mental hygiene stressed the fact that this was a program for normal children under temporary stress, or emotionally disturbed children, and not seriously disturbed or "crazy" children, the fact that it was associated with a mental hospital with adult patients often had greater effect than explanations concerning the actual type of case load. The state hospital had been part of the community for a long time and was well known to the citizens of the other towns. This attitude seemed to be particularly strong in those who lived in the wealthiest town, even though these persons were probably the most sophisticated and best educated. Even after the association was officially formed, participants from this community seemed to "drag their feet" the most, as if they feared to get involved with the state hospital. The basic attitude on the surface was that they were uncertain whether the community really needed such a service for their children and they did not know whether they as citizens could speak for their community. On the other hand, persons from the largest city, which had the state hospital within its borders, seemed to accept this setting somewhat better; but they also showed unconscious fears concerning a possible hidden relationship between the community mental health program and the hospital services for deeply disturbed people.

Other attitudes and community values also seemed to play a part in the development of support for the program. For example, the individuals in the association from the wealthy town felt somewhat superior to the participants from the other areas. They even conjectured that perhaps they ought to have their own mental health program as part of the town health services, since they had "different needs." There were various degrees of feeling about the state's role in the program. Some felt that the state would be "telling us what to do"; others wondered how much control they could have over the center's personnel, who were paid by the state; still others felt that the state should continue giving this service and that there was no need for their support.

These feelings seemed to be communicated to the center's staff, and there was a high rate of turnover. Some of those who left remarked that they lacked a "feeling of belonging" in relation to the local community. They were also upset by the fact that the center might be closed if support was not forthcoming, and this reduced their feelings of long-term stability and security. Conversely, this turnover was often viewed by some community spokesmen as indicative of poor services on the part of the state, and they felt that the program could not be very important and challenging if professional personnel left so frequently.

We have thus seen the development of a program philosophy, its historical roots, and an attempt to implement it in a particular geographical area. The fact that the mental health center was set up contrary to all the philosophical tenets of the program and the detailed vicissitudes of its growth and development have been discussed. Despite great difficulties, there was slow but steady progress; and the center did continue to grow in size and service and in acceptance by the communities, although here was a continuous need to interpret the program to the communities at every opportunity.

Relationships with School Personnel

Parallel developments of several new mental health services took place within the school systems while the center was in its embryonic stages. As to actual professional practice, what did this center do that the usual child guidance clinic did and what did it do that was different, particularly in relation to the schools? Because of its organization as a mental health center, was it more or less effective in various aspects of its functioning? Is a community mental health center less effective in its classical clinical role than it is in the new mental health consultation function? Would a consultation service be more effective were it not linked with the clinic service? How did the various caretaking agencies of the communities view these "intruders"? These are some of the questions to which this chapter can provide some tentative answers.

The Teachers and the Center

Perhaps because they are the most visible and the most customary, it would be well to begin with a discussion of the clinical services. As might have been expected, initially several of the most disturbed children in the community were referred to this new facility. Through some fortuitous circumstance, the most difficult cases were not those chronic cases that had been sent from agency to agency in and out of the community but were cases of children whose symptoms were becoming acute at that particular time and were drawing much attention in the schools. The parents were, for the most part, overwhelmed by their child's difficulties but very eager for help. The fact that they were received with understanding and patience and had an opportunity to talk seemed to outweigh some of the frightening surroundings.

Of the first cases referred to the center for clinical service, several were in treatment for three years or longer. During this time and with the permission of the parents, the center was in close and continuing contact with the schools. This proved to be an excellent entrée to the schools and also one of the first clues to the kind of relationship the schools valued. Over and over again, school personnel recounted that they had detected other children in previous years and referred them to well-known psychiatric centers. They had waited eagerly for reports and help in dealing with these children in the classroom. If ever they received a report, and this was rare, they felt that it was not helpful to them in their everyday responsibilities with the child. They never received personal visits from agency staffs and generally felt excluded. Many school personnel harbored considerable resentment which they freely expressed to the workers of the center. They felt that they were expected to be professional enough to spot these cases but that they were not considered professional enough to be entrusted with any information, although they were responsible for the child thirty hours a week.

This was an excellent warning to the staff of the center concerning the potential danger spot for poor public relations, as well as a clue to the best way to establish good relations with teachers. Despite anxiety on the part of the center staff that teachers would not be able to handle the kind of material that is often elicited in clinical work, it was found for the most part that this fear was groundless. What developed was that the teachers were not particularly interested in case material and details, although that is what they seemed to be asking for, but that they were much more deeply concerned with an opportunity to talk about the child and to receive assurance that they were not to blame for the child's difficulties in school. They also needed encouragement that they were doing a good job. Minimal case details were necessary to achieve this end, but the establishment of relationships with the teachers was most important. Very often these disturbed children trigger old, partially resolved conflicts in the teacher, and often it was reassurance that she could handle her own conflicts that became the important issue.

Another great value in seeing teachers of children who were in treatment or in diagnosis at the center was that it provided entrée to the schools and an opportunity to explain some of the other services of the center. Entering a new social system to meet a need that is felt and meeting this need in a way that raises the self-esteem of the consultee provide a wonderfully receptive audience for other ideas.

Thus, contact with one major social system, the public schools of the large city, was established. As for the other towns, where less extensive service was received from the center, the lack of intial referrals might be postulated as an explanation. It is quite probable that the warm welcome that the center personnel received from the city schools and the distant evasiveness of the other communities decided where the greatest efforts of the staff would be made. There were several other explanations, some of which have been mentioned in the discussion of community organization. The major considerations will be briefly noted here again.

The residents of the wealthy town considered themselves somewhat above the others and felt that they should avail themselves of only the highly reputed agencies and private services in Boston, even though this required some traveling. This feeling might well be traced to a guidance counselor who held rather violent views on having an "upstart center" come to his community. He even advised several families already in treatment at the center to discontinue their treatment. Efforts were made for a long time to win him over, but it finally became evident that the only way to establish service in this community was by making contact with other forces and other interests which might be able to gain acceptance and entrée for the center, with or without his approval. It was only when the center had mustered greater force than he possessed that he reluctantly went along with the project. Let it be noted that, even at this point, he was invited to participate in many aspects of the program and was rendered the respect due to his position and seniority. Although there was a play of forces, it was not the intention or technique of the center to embarrass people who had opposed its program.

In another town, the closest contact was made with a very astute director of guidance. He knew the community well, had been there for many years, and had valued the traveling school clinics, if only because they removed a large burden of responsibility from him and allowed him to exert most of his endeavors in the secondary school field. He was friendly and willing but cautious. He made overtures to the superintendent of schools to allow the center to expand into their school system; but the superintendent was rather fearful of his school committee, and until the town meeting gave approval to this project, he kept the center staff at arm's length. By accepting the slow pace which this school system chose to follow and by keeping continuing contact with the guidance department, the center was able to take advantage of the first opportunity that was given it. The town had to examine some children for possible special-class placement and had the evaluations done by psychometrists with Binet certificates but with no training as psychologists. The center was requested to provide supervision for these people, and it quickly responded. The mental health consultant, who was a psychologist, met with the psychometrists and carefully reviewed every case. The three psychometric examiners, who traveled throughout the school system, were pleased with this help. Word apparently traveled with them that the mental health personnel were not strange or frightening individuals and were indeed able to be quite helpful in a nonthreatening way. Thus, principals, teachers, and others began to make referrals and tentative overtures to the center.

The School Psychologists and the Center

In 1954, new laws and regulations were enacted at the state level for the certification of school psychologists and for reimbursement to school systems for school psychologists and special education services. These laws were enacted with minimal advice and counsel from the psychological community, and only minimal standards were promulgated. One town was loaned the half-time services of a psychologist who had for many years been employed by the department of mental health. This individual had a good deal of experience, if not much contemporary formal training. A "pilot project" was set up to see how a school psychologist could develop his role in relation to the mental health center, with the usual violence that is done to such research terms when they are used for service programs. There was no structure to this project, and the individual who was to act as school psychologist was just turned loose in the schools. Possibly because he did not feel that he really belonged anywhere, he tended in some ways to upset the program of the mental health center. For example, he would tell parents to call the mental health center and insist that they had rights as taxpayers to have their child examined. This was contrary to the policy of the center, which hoped to help the teachers and other professionals in the community to handle as many of the problems in their professional work as they could. The school psychologist knew this but persisted in this sort of referral. Needless to say, relations between him and the center personnel were rather strained.

The director of guidance in the wealthy town was also the certified school psychologist. Although he was strongly opposed to the mental health center, he was a rather astute person who was quite skilled in his own way. He was overly concerned with maintaining the alleged intellectual superiority of the children of his community vis-à-vis the other communities. The biggest problem he seemed to have in professional practice was not that he was unperceptive or unskilled but that he tended to be quite outspoken and told patients exactly what he found and thought. Although on the surface relationships were more or less polite, the center was not able to establish any effective working relationship with him.

When the time came for another town to choose a school psychologist, it chose a former special-class teacher who had been taking additional course work over the years. The superintendent of schools later confided to the director of the center and to the mental health consultant that this individual was as fit to be a school psychologist as he, the superintendent, was to go down to the local hospital and perform surgery. He made it quite clear that this individual's greatest skill lay in having the right friends on the school committee, and the superintendent was helpless to do anything but hire whomever he was given. Thus, in several of the communities, what might have been a splendid adjunct and enrichment of services became instead a problem in each of them.

The School Adjustment Counselor and the Center

The originally proposed standards for employment of school adjustment counselors were for persons who would detect potential juvenile delinquents. As finally approved by the state legislature, the job description covered nearly every professional role and job imaginable, although the essential orientation was supposed to be that of a school social worker or of a guidance type of position. These people were to be paid by the public schools, with $4,500 of their salary reimbursed by the commonwealth. Because of these funds from the commonwealth, many school systems added several thousand dollars to the total salary. Even at the $4,500 figure, this meant that the state legislature was paying these sometimes poorly trained people more for working a school year and a shorter day than they were paying their own social workers in the state agencies, who had much higher qualifications and had to work the full year. The implications of this kind of legislation for morale are obvious. Thus, new jobs were created, and new personnel were thrust alone and unattached into school systems.

Of the communities under discussion here, only two availed themselves of the privileges of this legislation at the time it was passed. The city hired a social worker with minimal psychiatric experience, and the town with the poorly trained school psychologist hired a former teacher who had had a few courses in guidance but no experience. She did, however, have a powerful friend on the school committee. One of the first observable results of these appointments was that in many ways the school doors were a little more tightly shut to the mental health center. In trying to understand this, it became apparent that these new personnel felt that all the consulting functions that had been performed by the mental health center were now their responsibility and that the mental health center people should only enter the schools with their permission. Despite many problems and difficulties, a working arrangement was developed with the city school adjustment counselor. In the town, the school adjustment counselor and the school psychologist felt very much threatened by the mental health center personnel. They were quite aware of the limitations of their training, and they did not intend to have anyone come into the school system who could point this out to them or to others. They would at various lengthy intervals agree to meet with the mental health center personnel but never in the schools. They never allowed the mental health center staff members to come to see them but always insisted on coming to the center.

One of the problems was that these appointees frequently yielded to the teacher's immediate demands that somebody see the child. Although ultimately this was proved to be not necessarily the best approach, it did meet the initial demands. From the mental health center's point of view, this approach frequently interfered with an effective problem solution. One interesting sidelight of this development was that the new school psychologist and the school adjustment counselor, in addition to shutting out the mental health center, went to the school committee and managed to get themselves detached from the director of guidance, who, as previously described, was a person of considerable skill and experience. They were now completely without supervision, and no one knew what they were doing. In this situation, the director of guidance became more friendly with the consultant from the mental health center, to whom he told his travails; and this was in some little way contributory to the eventual support of the center by this community. It now became clear to the director of guidance, and through him to the superintendent, that if they wanted professional services of high quality for the children in their care, they were much more likely to get them from the personnel of the mental health center than from people who, as they rather bitterly observed, were "merely friends of school committee members."

The Center and the School System

While all these developments in special school services were in progress, another interesting development was taking place in the large city schools. This was the gradual replacement of women principals by young men.

Not only were women not appointed to new openings that became available, but the men chosen frequently had absolutely no elementary school experience. Young secondary school male teachers were being selected as principals of elementary schools. This greatly disturbed the morale of many of the women teachers; and some of the better ones, seeing all hope of promotion disappearing, resigned from the system.

The director of elementary education, who was an excellent person with quite a high level of professional training, served also as an officer of the board of the mental health center. The pressures put upon him were considerable, and he confided some of his difficulties to the mental health consultant, with whom he had a very good working relationship. One incident that he related had to do with the power of the school committee in making personnel selections. A young man, a senior at a school of education, who came in for an interview with the director, sneered at him, according to his report, and said that it really made no difference what happened in this interview, since it was merely a formality. He said: "I am going to be appointed to work in any school that I choose, and there is not a thing that you can do about it." This kind of situation can lead to rapid deterioration of professional quality in a system.

While much more detailed documentation of the stresses and difficulties of the social system could be made, they are really not necessary for the purposes of this chapter. The important thing is that here was a ready-made trap for the mental health center personnel. It was so easy to identify with the "good" professional people and with high professional goals and aspirations. Many of the mental health center staff did, in fact, identify with these people and these goals. Temptation was also strong to mention the "terrible things that seemed to be happening in the school" to other people in the community who might be in a position to influence the direction of these changes. It was necessary for the mental health center staff to examine their feelings and ideas and to realize that, although they might be witnessing the deterioration of what was on the way to being a first-class school system, there was little they could do about it by way of outside interference. The role of the mental health center staff was to supply consultation, support, and an opportunity to examine and consider their own positions to those members of the school system who sought this kind of help. To have done anything else would not have been helpful to the school system and would have very seriously compromised the position of the mental health center and its ability to render any kind of useful service in this community. It was necessary to maintain a position outside the social system.

One of the great strengths of the center was that its personnel were not part of the school social system and were not caught up in its conflicts, rivalries, jealousies, and tugs-of-war. School psychologists, school adjustment counselors, teachers, principals, and administrators were all part of the social system and were all involved with its jealousies, rivalries, and concerns about pay, working conditions, etc. Insofar as the school personnel were caught up in these problems, they were less effective in their particular professional roles. Because of the stress of these problems within the social system, it was often quite evident that many of the people who wanted to talk and discuss things with the mental health center people felt that they could not be sure whom they could trust. The mental health center operated on the principle that, by virtue of its being an outside agency that maintained its distance and minded its own business on administrative problems of the school system, it would, in the long run, become clear to everyone in that system that the mental health center people could keep a confidence and had no ax to grind. Often that did happen, and it was rather striking that many school personnel would confide to outsiders things that they would not tell their colleagues within the school system, for fear that it would be used against them. Similar mechanisms and experiences occurred in the school systems of all the communities.

An interesting reflection of this point of view is the fact that the juvenile court that served this area would not make any of their records available to school personnel. They would not tell school personnel when a child was before the juvenile court; and, with the rare exception of the attendance officers who were present at the time of bringing charges, they would not allow school personnel into the juvenile sessions, although they welcomed the mental health center personnel. It was a strong feeling of the court officials that school people might use the court facts against the children in question but that mental health center personnel were neutral and unbiased.

Mental Health Consultation

The consultation functions of the mental health center were of two main varieties. One was direct consultation about cases referred to the center for diagnosis and treatment. These cases were handled in the standard fashion, with the exception that, with parental permission, there was greater fact gathering and feedback in working with the schools than is usually the case.

Another type of consultation was used quite regularly in every case referred. An attempt was made to see the teacher before the child was referred to the center. The goal here was, if possible, to help the teacher deal with the problem in the classroom and not refer it to the mental health center. In the beginning this kind of consultation was very difficult, because it was the hard-core cases of the community that drew the initial attention. This type of consultation was flexible. It was not limited to helping the teacher deal more effectively with problems but often entailed suggesting other community resources, including, at times, the mental health center.

An offshoot of this kind of consultation was a special technique called "crisis consultation." [7,8] This technique is used when the consultant feels that what the teacher is recounting is not so much the difficulty of the child but the teacher's unconscious reaction to something in the child. In these instances, the child's behavior triggers unconscious reactions in the teacher, and she tends to stereotype the child as some figure or blend of figures from her past. The goal of the consultant is to "dispel the stereotype" by tangential means in a rather elaborate technique which is discussed in detail by Bindman [1] and Caplan.[7,8] It is important to note, however, that at no time does the consultant directly confront the teacher with the fact that it is her feelings that are the main problem and not so much the child's behavior.

Community Relations

The center staff participated in the well-child conferences of the visiting nurses' association and in juvenile-court conferences. They met with clergymen, physicians, and social agencies, as well as with school personnel. Consultation of various kinds and educational programs and talks, as well as regular group sessions for teachers, were offered. Although first located in one of the community outposts, the center generally tried to make itself a part of the community. Its task was made easier when it moved to private quarters. Personnel have tried to participate in community activities and to become known in the community as ordinary people who have special training and skills. Two of the greatest assets in such a program are time and community support. Time is necessary in order to settle down to learn the techniques, to become known in the community, to become accepted, and to become recognized as helpful. Community support means not only the provision of additional funds to help defray the expenses of the center but also the interest of the community citizens in looking at their own mental health problems and in organizing effectively for a solution of these problems. Community support opens doors to these newcomers moving into its social systems. It gives the community people a feeling that they have a stake in this project and that the state government has not simply imposed something upon them. When work and participation are required on the part of the community, people tend to place a higher value on what they receive, on much the same basis that the imposition of fees in a clinic implies that people value what they pay for.

During the years that the center was growing and new personnel were being added to the school systems, some of the school personnel began to attend center staff conferences and attach themselves more closely to the center. They were obviously trying to meet what was a serious flaw in the legislation: namely, people were turned loose, with no professional colleagues or supervision available, to do very complex professional jobs. The laws could have been much improved had they assigned these people to particular mental health centers and then had them work specifically in one public school system. In this way there would be supervision, there would be stimulating exchanges of ideas, there would be a home professional base for the school psychologist and adjustment counselors, and there would be better service to schoolchildren.

This generally brings matters up to date. The center staff has increased considerably, with many part-time people as well as a larger full-time staff. A greater number of members of the staff are working with the various schools and community agencies. Community support has grown and is continuing to grow, and the scope and the number of services are also expanding.

With respect to the nature of the state-local partnership, it is felt that neither complete state operation of the centers nor complete local autonomy will provide the most effective program. Rather, the state agency should provide from its central office a skilled staff who can make regular visits to the centers, facilitate communication, bring fresh viewpoints on the way in which other centers are dealing with various situations, clarify departmental policies and regulations, stimulate new programs and research, and help the center director and his staff to evaluate the quantity and quality of their work.

It would seem that this approach of state and local partnership, with a number of improvements based, in part, on the knowledge learned in developing this particular center, has applications for any community striving to develop a community mental health program for children.

Summary

Problems encountered in organizing and developing an actual community mental health consultation center are described. Reactions of community agencies and school personnel are noted, with numerous suggestions for avoiding pitfalls and fostering effective relationships.

References

1. Bindman, A. J.: "Mental Health Consultation: Theory and Practice," *J. Consult. Psychol.*, 23:473–482, 1959.
2. ——— (ed.): *New Developments in Community Mental Health*, Massachusetts Department of Mental Health, Boston, 1960.
3. ——— and L. B. Klebanoff: "Administrative Problems in Establishing a Community Mental Health Program," *Amer. J. Orthopsychiat.*, 30:696–711, 1960.
4. ——— and ———: "New Programming for the Mentally Retarded School Child in Massachusetts," *Amer. J. Ment. Defic.*, 64:875–880, 1960.

5. —— and ——: "A Nursery Center Program for Pre-school Mentally Retarded Children," *Amer. J. Ment. Defic.*, 64:561–573, 1960.

6. Bower, E. M.: "The Emotionally Handicapped Child and the School," *Except. Children*, 26:6–11, 1959.

7. Caplan, G.: "Mental Health Consultation in Schools," *The Elements of a Community Mental Health Program*, Milbank Memorial Fund, New York, 1956.

8. ——: *Concepts of Mental Health and Consultation*, U.S. Children's Bureau, Washington, D.C., 1959.

9. Hallock, A. C. K., and W. T. Vaughan: "Community Organization: A Dynamic Component of Community Mental Health Practice," *Amer. J. Orthopsychiat.*, 26:691–706, 1956.

10. *Highlights of Recent Community Mental Health Legislation*, American Psychiatric Association, Washington, D.C., 1959.

11. Hume, Portia B.: *The Short-Doyle Act for Community Mental Health Services*, California Department of Mental Hygiene, Sacramento, Calif., 1958.

12. Hunt, R. C., and H. M. Forstenzer: "The New York State Community Mental Health Services Act: Its Birth and Early Development," *Amer. J. Psychiat.*, 113: 680–685, 1957.

13. Kirk, S. A.: *Public School Provisions for Severely Retarded Children*, New York State Interdepartmental Resources Board, Albany, N.Y., 1957.

14. Krugman, M. (ed.): *Orthopsychiatry and the School*, American Orthopsychiatric Association, New York, 1958.

15. Vaughan, W. T.: "Mental Health for School Children," *Children*, 2:203–207, 1955.

16. ——: "Certain Real Problems in the Development of Community Programs for the Medical Care, Education and Training of the Mentally Retarded," *Amer. J. Publ. Hlth.*, 47:706–712, 1957.

17. Yerbury, E. C., and Nancy Newell: "The Development of the State Child Guidance Clinics in Massachusetts," *New England J. Med.*, 233:148–153, 1948.

18. Clinical Observations on Kibbutz Children

Shmuel Nagler

Introduction

In recent years anthropologists, behavioral scientists, and clinical psychologists have shown increasing interest in the "collective education" of the kibbutzim in Israel. This interest has found expression in a growing number of publications concerning the kibbutz collective and its educational system.[3,4,5,6,7,16,17,18] Since detailed descriptions regarding the economic, administrative, and ideological foundations of this society have already been presented, the focus of this chapter will be primarily on clinical observations.

"Kibbutzim" are communal settlements constructed on the basis of socialist principles of collective ownership of the means of production and collective ways of producing, marketing, and consuming, excluding paid labor. Using less abstract concepts and adopting the point of view of the conscious expectations of the people who get together to form a collective of their own free will, one might formulate the basis of kibbutz life as follows: The kibbutz expects every individual to contribute according to his capabilities and is under obligation to cover all his needs. Among these needs, which include food, housing, clothing, care for the sick and aged, cultural requirements, entertainment, etc., the education of children always takes first place. Besides the routine financial and administrative arrangements, constant studies and investigations are made in the educational sphere.

Every child is given schooling and education until he or she joins the army, i.e., for twelve school grades, normally to the age of eighteen.

Adapted from a paper previously published in the *Israel Annals of Psychiatry and Related Disciplines*, 1:201–216, 1963.

Classes are relatively small (up to twenty children), and the principles of Gestalt and field theory are used in teaching. Rather than being taught according to separate subjects, the learning material is arranged by themes. Instead of the usual "lecturer" system, a child-centered, democratic, group atmosphere prevails, with much discussion and individual work. Instead of marks and grades, achievements are evaluated individually in discussions between educator and student or in groups. Educators and teachers are usually very much devoted to their work, and the latter are especially trained, in special teachers' training colleges within the framework of the kibbutz movement, to develop a particular awareness of mental health problems. Intensive "in-service training" is provided by means of numerous panels, seminars for teachers and educators during the school year, and sabbatical leave. A team of "guidance teachers" supervises all daily educational activities. The diagnostic and therapeutic service of the Oranim Child Guidance Clinic is at the disposal of children with special problems. Parents and educators, including guidance teachers and special educators who provide individual help, make use of the counseling and guidance service of the clinic.

None of these educational facilities are original creations of the kibbutz movement but only a more consistent way of putting into practice the philosophy of "progressive education" and of the "child guidance movement," which had been struggling against the traditional school system since the beginning of the century. What is original and characteristic of kibbutz education is that from earliest infancy the functions of child care (with the exception of feeding during the first months of life) and socialization are in the hands of child care personnel (*metapelet*) in children's houses. Children have a second center in their lives besides their parents' rooms, beginning right after birth and continuing to the time of graduation from school.[11] Here they sleep, take their meals, are cared for when sick, play, and study. They spend only two hours daily, apart from Sabbaths and holidays, in their parents' rooms.

Thus we find a highly developed Western culture in the kibbutz, with the existence of two emotional centers in the children's lives all through infancy, childhood, and adolescence, functioning side by side as socializing agents. This situation is not caused by environmental emergency requirements but represents an emotionally fully accepted "pattern of culture."

The keen interest of behavioral scientists in the kibbutz culture is not surprising. Anthropologists and behavioral scientists are interested in knowing whether any clear connection can be found between the specific "patterns of child rearing" and personality structures of a generation born and educated in the kibbutz.[10,12] The clinical psychologist asks whether developmental, behavioral, and personality disturbances found in kibbutz children are quantitatively (i.e., per number, intensity, or both) or qualitatively (i.e., according to symptom syndromes, etiology, and dynamics) different from those found in children raised within the traditional family structure.[1,8]

In this chapter I shall concentrate solely on the clinical aspects and mainly on those of a qualitative nature, analyzing the etiologic and dynamic factors involved.

Frequency in Distribution of Psychic Disturbances

Contrary to earlier observations,[1] the frequency of psychic disturbances among kibbutz children is about 10 per cent, which is equal to that in England and the United States, insofar as comparative statistics can be applied at all. Presently we have no standard definitions of clinical categories, assessment of the severity of symptoms, or choice of samples. Although we find within the kibbutz society all the symptoms, or syndromes, known in child psychiatry, we can point to relevant distributional differences.

In comparison with American figures, we find greater thumb-sucking up to and during school age and fewer feeding problems.[8] There do not seem to be differences worth mentioning in the distribution of enuresis, learning difficulties, aggression, and anxieties. It may be noteworthy, however, that in comparison we find relatively few cases of delinquency and almost no manifest homosexuality among boys. There is no lack in our material of any of the usual clinical categories, among which "behavior disorders," "behavior disorders with neurotic trends," and "preneurotic states" are the most frequent.

The fact that within the kibbutz movement the percentage of disturbed children, compared with other societies, is not considerably lower has caused much disappointment among leading kibbutz educators. They had hoped that the "scientific foundations" of this educational form, i.e., the transfer of motherly care and socialization functions from the emotion-laden atmosphere of the parents' home to "objective," professionally trained educators, would eliminate important pathogenic environmental factors.[3,4,5]

Clinicians will recall that when psychological and sociological theories, reinforced by the enthusiasm of a philosophy of life, are put into practice, temporary hypotheses and formulations are accepted as final and unchangeable truths and exaggerated in their use in a one-sided manner. The psychoanalytic theory of instinctual drives and the psychology of the unconscious (especially prior to the later findings of the psychoanalytic ego psychology) was subject at its beginning here, as in other centers of progressive education, to numerous misunderstandings which have since been rectified. It is, however, not only in theoretical errors and administrative weakness that pathogenic factors are to be found but, as usual, mainly in the dynamics of parent-child, educator-child, and parent-educator relationships (the last named more frequently in our social structure than in any other).

Genetic-dynamic Factors

It may be useful to name certain genetic-dynamic factors which we have obtained in the process of taking case histories in interviews with parents, educators, or both, as well as during the treatment of children and parents. Because we invariably seek to differentiate between etiologic factors at home (parents' rooms) and such factors effective in the children's house, we can now state that the former by far outweigh the latter, in spite of the fact that the child spends only about two hours daily in direct contact with the parents. This, in my opinion, proves that parents, even in the kibbutz structure, remain "effective" parents with all the conflicts involved in the parent-child relationship, which naturally can occur only on the basis of strong emotional ties. The borderline between pathogenic factors caused by the family and by the children's house cannot always be determined distinctly, especially when there are conflicts (as is frequently the case in our material) in the parent-educator relationship which constitute an important pathogenic factor. In such cases there is a discord in the interpersonal relationship in which both partners are involved.

We found that the most important pathogenic factors in the children's houses are the following:

1. A frequent change of nurses (house mothers) in early infancy.

2. A practice (now discontinued) requiring nonnursing mothers and mothers who have weaned their babies to leave the feeding to nurses (*metapelet*). These mothers, in addition to their disappointment at being deprived of a natural motherly function, were also being deprived of the warm contact with the child and the nursing situation as such.

3. Noisiness in the infants' home during nursing time—gossiping among nursing mothers, preventing the necessary concentration on the nursing activity and thus influencing the initimate relationship between mother and child.

4. The strict nursing schedule.

With the exception of the still regrettably frequent change of nurses in infant homes, the above-mentioned pathogenic factors appear in the case histories of children who have by now reached school age. They have mostly disappeared in today's infant homes. Other pathogenic factors in the children's home, not caused primarily by organizational shortcomings but rather by the personalities of the educators, are the following:

1. Pedantic *metaploth*, with distinctly anal character trends, in whose groups either enuresis (rebellion) or the opposite (enforced defense

mechanisms) appear as group phenomena. (In an extreme case we found enuresis in 70 per cent of one group of seven- to eight-year-olds, all of whom, of course, had come from different family situations.)

2. *Metaploth* who, stressing their "professional knowledge," consider mothers disturbing or even superfluous. For example, a *metapelet*, an extremely devoted, "self-sacrificing" worker, encountered in spite of (or, as we soon found out, because of) this devotion a very tense relationship with mothers. She revealed to us in a number of supervision interviews the frightful disappointment she had experienced as a child in her own mother, by whom she felt rejected, and her strong strivings at the time "to do better than her mother." This unsolved childhood conflict led to her attitude of constant abuse toward mothers, of accusations, and of identification of herself with the children, confronting their mothers as a "savior." Here the tension between *metapelet* and mother was caused by the unconscious competitive attitude of the *metapelet*.

Tension between *metapelet* and mother can also be caused, of course, by the mother's personality problems. For example, seven-year-old Danny suffers from severe nightmares and terrible separation anxieties. When the time comes for him to leave his parents at night and return to the children's house, heartbreaking scenes take place. The child clings to his mother, who excitedly tries to persuade him, begging and imploring him, to go back to the other children. Father keeps aside, muttering angrily. When Danny finally leaves, his mother, in a state of exhaustion, runs after him, crying: "Danny, you won't cry any more, will you? You won't be afraid . . . ," and as a result he bursts into tears all over again, cling-ing to his mother, unable to leave her. The *metapelet* appeals to the child's conscience: "This is not nice. What will the other children say?" etc., and she has difficulty in hiding her anger toward the mother, because she feels that it is the mother who does not want to let the child go. After a number of clinical interviews, the mother in cathartic reaction remem-bers a scene: the Nazis taking over her home village and she placing herself in front of her younger brother, but an SS man tearing him away from her. Up to that point she had not been conscious of the fact that her child's separation anxiety was in effect a reaction to her own separation anxiety, which had its roots in her experience.

The obvious solution in this case, namely, that the child should sleep beside his parents, is by no means easy to implement. The child lives in a very close social group of children, with strong tendencies toward conformity. At 5 a.m. he will tiptoe secretly back to the children's house, so that the other children won't find out that he stayed overnight with his parents. Further, as psychologists, we should accept that these parents have chosen this way of life voluntarily; presumably they do derive some satisfaction from it. We have here a real conflict between child and mother, which cannot be wiped out simply by advice. In the course of therapeutic interviews, we were able to help the mother to gain some insight into her own fears. The *metapelet* was helped to attain a more tolerant attitude toward the mother and to encourage the child to accept his nightly separations without pressure on his conscience.

Deeper personality problems, leading to disturbances in the parent role, are of course present in the kibbutz, as anywhere else: schizoid mothers with shallow feelings, unconscious hatred toward the child, or seductiveness as a result of marriage conflicts; overprotectiveness; identification of the child with husband, parents, and siblings; unplanned pregnancy interfering with other plans; or the child not being of the desired sex (such as a third girl after two previous girls), etc.

Such problems are, of course, not typical of kibbutz life and culture. What is characteristic in the kibbutz is the establishment of two emotional centers providing excellent opportunities to project the parents' inability to love and the resultant guilt feelings onto a worker in the children's house. Outside the kibbutzim such possibilities of projection are seldom available, because the emotional significance of educational institutions is much less important.

We have a further special problem in the kibbutz: the lack of professional distance between educators and parents. Educators are not salaried employees of the kibbutz. Besides their professional activities, they are first and foremost members of the same society. Sometimes one can overhear expressions, such as: "What, is this one going to be my child's *metapelet?* When she was seventeen, she was already chasing men"; or "She wants to teach me something? One has only to see how she carries on with her own children!" On the other hand, a *metapelet* may say about a mother: "She is always against me. Three times she has voted against my joining a special course in town." Everyday events which actually occur outside the educational framework may create tensions between parents and educators. Reasons for distrust on the part of a mother can be either objective (realistic fears) or subjective (caused by neurotic anxieties). In both cases and especially in the latter, the basic security of the child (the "balance of trust versus mistrust" in the terms of Erik Erikson), is likely to be affected. Mental health problems, growing out of such complicated interpersonal relationships, require the major part of our attention. They have led us to examine in detail the dynamics of parent-educator relationships in our therapeutic and supervising as well as in our teaching activities.

We find another problem involving the children of the educators themselves. These parents spend their time with other youngsters nearby, sometimes right in front of their own children. We have found in our material a pathogenic situation, now strictly avoided, in which a mother as *metapelet* works with a group of infants including her own. To avoid any signs of preference toward her own child (such preference being contrary to kibbutz philosophy), she tends to treat him less affectionately than the other children (for instance, feeding him last, etc.). These are some of the points of stress within the kibbutz society which may have pathogenic results, especially during an infant's first year.

There are also some very positive aspects to a child's life in the children's house, as, for instance, the opportunity for "corrective experiences." When mothers suffer from severe psychological disturbances, such as schizoid cyclic-depressive or obsessional disorders, the nurse may act as a warm mother substitute and thus be able to mitigate the harm otherwise done to the personality development of the children. Another form of corrective experience can be given in cases of anxious, overprotective, and overpossessive mothers through the care of a *metapelet* who loves the children without being as emotionally involved with them. This corrective influence depends to a large extent on the ability of the *metapelet* to avoid arousing feelings of competition, guilt, and hatred in the mothers toward herself if she is more successful. Our clinical help to *metapelet,* mother, or both is sometimes required to ensure a balance relationship.

The mental health advantages of these corrective influences in the children's house can be most significant during the second, third, and fourth years of a child's development. At this stage, the mother's attitude in connection with feeding habits, health care, cleanliness, and the independence drive resulting from growth and development of motor coordination and speech facilities is inevitably much more emotional than that of professional personnel in the children's house, who are primarily in charge of guiding the first social adjustments.

A pathogenic factor in the nursery (besides the aforementioned possible personality disturbances of educators) could be that toddlers in their groups of about six, always in their own age group, may have too little opportunity for the direct contact with grown-ups which is required to satisfy the "instinct of following," as J. Bowlby terms it. (The influence of this situation on the early speech development of kibbutz children has not yet been examined.) Further, constant living in the same age group during the phase of intense motor development leads to situations in which the weaker child or one whose rate of development is somewhat slower may feel "bullied" by stronger children and lack the necessary protection of adults; thus the "autonomy of the ego" (in Erikson's terms) may be impaired.

During the oedipal phase we find no particular pathogenic factors that are influenced by the specific kibbutz structure. There have been some optimistic expectations by the pioneers of kibbutz education (in line with the opinion of social anthropologists and followers of the neo-Freudian schools) to the effect that, by removal of the child from the parents' bedroom, possible damage caused by the conflict may be avoided. This has not occurred (at least not in those oedipal cases referred to our clinic). Even within the kibbutz social structure, parents definitely remain the basic and main objects of the child's sexual and aggressive impulses and his first objects of identification. Marriage problems, such as a lack of sexual or emotional satisfaction and a confusion of roles within the family constellation (for example, phallic mothers and passive, weak fathers), heighten a child's sexual and aggressive drives, anxieties, guilt feelings, and confusion of identification and make the "passing of the oedipal conflict" much more arduous. All this, in spite of the fact that the child lives most of the time away from the family atmosphere.

The oedipal child-mother relationship is quite often transferred by children to the kindergarten teacher or *metapelet,* whereas sibling rivalry is frequently transferred to other children in the group. These transference phenomena appear with greater intensity in the children's house of a kibbutz than in other kindergartens or nurseries. The fact that the children eat and sleep and are cared for physically all day long in the children's house encourages the transference of the family situation. While this particular setup considerably aggravates the educational situation in the kindergarten, it also promotes the possibility of reducing tensions caused by the oedipal conflict within the family; in particular, the only child can be helped to overcome his specific difficulties in the family triangle. The usefulness of such corrective experience is important especially in the area of sex education for preschool children. Here too, teachers can be much less emotionally involved than parents.[2,19]

In cases of family breakups caused by the death of one parent, there is a relatively good possibility of finding a parent substitute in the kibbutz. In cases of divorce, however, especially when each parent stays in the kibbutz and starts a new family, the feeling of confusion and deprivation for the child is very strong; he feels lost between the mother's and the father's children. For example, a child of a divorced family, who, in spite of his high IQ, had great difficulties in arithmetic, said: "I have one father and another one, one mother and another one, brothers from one and brothers from another. A confused family. Grown-ups confuse children." It became quite clear in the course of treatment that the accuracy needed for mathematics was in an unconscious conflict with this confusion. In cities, children and their divorced parents are not forced to confront each other constantly and have more of a chance to recover from the family catastrophe. Of course, the intensity of conflicts caused by such situations depends considerably on the educational, and sometimes the ethnic, background of the parents.

School Age and Adolescence

We meet another mental health problem in cases of school-age children referred to the clinic because of aggression against their peers or lack of cooperation. We ask ourselves whether this may not be an outcome of being forced to live with their age group day in, day out, at a phase of development during which they are not yet mature enough to benefit from the advantages of group dynamics. According to a basic learning theory, "those children who have been conditioned to 'cooperative living' are better able to to cooperate." We know quite well, however, that demands made in that sphere before the child is ready may also lead to frustration, to resistance, and even, after temporary resignation, to an increased tendency to regression.

A high percentage of cases referred to us involve learning difficulties at school age. This may seem surprising, since kibbutz classes are relatively small. Teachers are very much devoted to their work and well trained in the use of the "project method" designed to increase motivation in the learning process. Why, in spite of these favorable conditions, are learning problems so often encountered? The question arises whether the involvement by teachers in so many motherly duties may not have a pathogenic influence on learning activities. Teachers who have their meals with the children, put them to bed at night, and are there in the morning when they arise, perhaps after wetting, may become too closely involved in conflict situations, which would make it difficult for both children and teachers to switch over to a more objective learning atmosphere in the classroom. But let us not forget that in traditional school systems the lack of a positive emotional relationship constitutes one of the most important causes of learning difficulties.

Another mental health problem during school age in a kibbutz is the identity of the learning-playing and "everyday-living" groups. A child in town who is rejected by his schoolmates may yet enjoy a satisfactory status among his neighborhood companions or in some other group, as sociograms often show. We often found in our kibbutz material, however, that once a certain negative "public opinion" has been created about a child, it is usually long-lasting and the child has no other surroundings to which he can escape. This may have a pathogenic influence on the child's self-image and affect his future social development. The kibbutz school may, however, offer great mental hygienic advantages just because of this identity of the learning and living environment. A relatively weak student, who nevertheless proves himself a "good sport," who brings prestige to his group in games, etc., may attain a high social position, because this school does not evaluate him on the basis of learning capacities alone. As we know, the Gestalt psychological concept of the learning process has always criticized the separation of learning and living situations in traditional schools.

Another point in favor of the kibbutz school during preadolescence is that living in such a group, with its possibilities of identification with other group members, may help to loosen the infantile dependency ties and prevent severe conflicts with parents in adolescence.[13] Our recommendation for most preadolescents, to which age group the majority of our referrals belong, is educational help by a special educator of the kibbutz.

While the material available at our clinic on adolescents is considerably less extensive than that on children of elementary school age, we have noted the following pathogenic factors:

1. Girls (in some cases even during preadolescence, but more frequently during adolescence), as well as some more sensitive boys, suffer from an overorganized daily life. They have a feeling of weariness at being constantly with the crowd, without an opportunity of ever doing what they feel like doing or, now and then, just doing nothing. This increases the difficulty of their search for their own identity (Erikson).

2. Kibbutz youth, asking us for help, put much less emphasis on sexual troubles than nonkibbutz adolescents. They are more deeply troubled by problems of social adjustment, such as lack of popularity, inhibitions in social contacts, or difficulties regarding learning and work. When asked more direct questions about their sex life, they are never embarrassed or surprised but display a calm, matter-of-fact attitude, with expressions like: "There is nothing peculiar to it." "Everything is natural." "Our teachers have explained everything to us." In the course of therapeutic interviews, however, this factual attitude turns out to be on the surface only, and we encounter very strong defense mechanisms, repression, and denial. At first glance this may seem rather astonishing in view of the existing system of coeducation from birth through adolescence, with its atmosphere of frankness in sexual matters. We came to the conclusion that a philosophy of sex education which, on one hand, expects boys and girls to share the same bedroom (usually two girls and two boys) until the end of high school and, on the other, brings great pressure to bear on adolescents to renounce sexual relations during this educational period is apt to encourage the formation of overly strong defense mechanisms in order to withstand such seductive situations. These strong defenses may later lessen the capacity to enjoy pleasure in adult love and sex life. It is an interesting observation that love relations seldom develop between girls and boys growing up in the same kibbutz group (reminding us of exogamy in the clan). To quote one young lady: "I could never fall in love with a boy who sat right next to me on the pot all through my childhood." The sharing of shower rooms by boys and girls, once part of kibbutz sex education, has long been discontinued as the result of pressure on the part of adolescent girls.

The following positive factors must be pointed out: In these adolescent groups, there exists a spirit of good comradeship and cooperation between boys and girls, a spirit different from the crude and oversexed atmosphere generally prevailing in adolescent groups in other societies today. Girls are active, often holding important positions in the group, without the need for the long-lasting "tomboyism" so prevalent throughout Western urban culture. The kibbutz girls accept femininity in a much more positive way than did their mothers.

Kibbutz youth are often disappointed when the kibbutz is not always ready to accept and foster their specific talents and desires for professional training. A wrongly interpreted "democratic ideal" demands high school education for all youngsters up to the age of eighteen, so that the less gifted children, who are unable to keep up with the rest of the class in the theoretical curriculum, are dragged, perhaps with some outside help, from grade to grade, suffering from a feeling of "being a failure," although they could succeed and enjoy the satisfaction of accomplishment in other kinds of school curricula, for instance, trade schools. Other youngsters, after finishing the kibbutz high school (which does not supply matriculation certificates), who consider themselves able and ready for further studies at the college level, are not allowed to undertake them except in rare cases when their professional choice meets specific kibbutz needs.

It seems that the reasons for this state of affairs are not just economic but rather emotional, to be understood historically as a rebellion against the hypertrophy of academic professions among the Jewish people in the Diaspora and as an effort to put into practice the ideal of "the return to earth and industry." Although the "need for self-realization" in professional fields does not always find satisfaction, there are wide possibilities in the kibbutz for self-realization in the arts and other cultural activities, especially along social and political lines.

Of the highest advantage to adolescents in the kibbutz is the fact that they do not live in a "no-man's-land" (Kurt Lewin) nor in a "non-quite stage" (L. C. Lowrey) but in their own society with its own rights and duties, appreciated and furthered by the adult society surrounding them. The psychic reaction of the "marginal man" (Kurt Lewin), a feeling of frustration, insecurity, and aggression against parents and authorities, serving as a defense against insecurity, are found much less frequently in the kibbutz than in other Western societies, especially in cities. This may be one of the reasons why, fortunately, we have no serious juvenile delinquency in the kibbutz.

If good adjustments in the realm of work and love relationships are two of the most important criteria for mental health, we are able to say: kibbutz high school graduates are generally very well able to meet severe demands by the army and later at work. (The percentage of kibbutz members taking part in officers' courses is above average for the general population.) That about 90 per cent of kibbutz youngsters return to a kibbutz after the termination of compulsory military service proves that identification with their parents' generation is very strong.

Regarding the adjustment to more intimate situations, such as love and marriage, and to the role of parents, we do not as yet have enough material to make any definite statements. We hope that in the future conditions will be more favorable for systematic research into kibbutz culture and that we shall thus be better equipped to contribute not only to the field of the psychopathology of the child but also to that of general behavior and personality theory.[9,14,15]

Summary

We noted relatively small differences in the psychopathology of kibbutz children in comparison with nonkibbutz children. In addition, points of stress specific to kibbutz society were indicated; these may appear as psychopathogenic factors. Finally, we drew attention to mental health facilities available to the kibbutz society.

References

1. Caplan, Gerald: "Clinical Observations on the Emotional Life of Children in the Communal Settlements in Israel," in M. S. E. Senn (ed.), *Problems of Infancy and Childhood: Transactions of the Seventh Conference,* Josiah Macy, Jr. Foundation, New York, 1954, pp. 91–120.
2. Faigin, Helen: "Some Observations on the Young Children in the Kibbutz," *J. Abnorm. Soc. Psychol.,* 56:117–129, 1958.
3. Golan, Schmuel: "Collective Education in the Kibbutz," *Psych. J. Study Interpers. Processes,* 22:2, 1959.
4. ———: "Collective Education in the Kibbutz," *Amer. J. Orthopsychiat.,* 28:549–556, 1958; also in *Collective Education in the Kibbutz,* Education Department of the Kibbutz-Artzi Hashomer Hatzair, Israel, 1961, pp. 17–22.
5. ——— and Zvi Lavi: "Communal Education," in *Collective Education in the Kibbutz,* Education Department of the Kibbutz-Artzi Hashomer Hatzair, Israel, 1961, pp. 23–45.
6. Infield, Henrik F.: *Cooperative Living in Palestine,* Holt, Rinehart and Winston, Inc., New York, 1944.
7. Irvine, Elizabeth: "Observations on the Aims and Methods of Child Rearing in Communal Settlements in Israel," *Hum. Relat.,* 5:247–275, 1952.
8. Kaffmann, Mordecai: "Evaluation of Emotional Disturbance in 403 Israel Kibbutz Children," paper read at the 116th Annual Meeting of the American Psychological Association, Atlantic City, N.J., 1960.
9. Rabin, A. I.: "The Israeli Kibbutz (Collective Settlement) as a 'Laboratory' for Testing Psychodynamic Hypotheses," *Psychol. Rec.,* 7:111–115, 1957.
10. ———: "Personality Maturity of Kibbutz (Israeli Collective Settlement) and Non-kibbutz Children as Reflected in Rorschach Findings," *J. Proj. Tech. Pers. Assess.,* 21:148–153, 1957.
11. ———: "Infants and Children under Conditions of 'Intermittent' Mothering in the Kibbutz," *Amer. J. Orthopsychiat.,* 28:577–586, 1958.
12. ———: "Some Psychosexual Differences between Kibbutz and Non-kibbutz Israeli Boys," *J. Proj. Tech. Pers. Assess.,* 22:328–332, 1958.
13. ———: "Attitudes of Kibbutz Children to Family and Parents," *Amer. J. Orthopsychiat.,* 29:172–179, 1959.
14. Rapaport, David: "The Study of Kibbutz Education and Its Bearing on the Theory of Development," *Amer. J. Orthopsychiat.,* 28:587–597, 1958.

15. Schwartz, Richard D.: "Behavior Research in Collective Settlements in Israel," *Amer. J. Orthopsychiat.*, 28:572–576, 1958.
16. Spiro, Melford E.: "Education in a Communal Village in Israel," *Amer. J. Orthopsychiat.*, 25:283–292, 1955.
17. ———: *Venture in Utopia*, Harvard University Press, Cambridge, Mass., 1955.
18. ———: *Children of the Kibbutz*, Harvard University Press, Cambridge, Mass., 1958.
19. Winograd, Marilyn: "The Development of the Young Child in a Collective Settlement," *Amer. J. Orthopsychiat*, 28:557–562, 1958.

19. Children and Schools: A Reaction

Donald F. Buckle

There can be little doubt that the rigidity of forms of educational practice in ordinary schools accords ill with the aims of the mental health professions. The common compulsory school lies, in the child's life, between the flexibile, mental health–oriented nursery school and the democratic self-discipline of the university, distinguished by the high value it places on its task of providing the three R's and their modern extensions, consequently injecting organized and orderly facts and prejudice into children for the sake of making them adult workers, professionals, organization men. It is many years since the white hope of the progressives—the Eight-year Study [1]—faded into obscurity. Its findings hinted at heresy: that perhaps it was not necessary to pass examinations each year in order to study the next year's work.

What has this to do with mental health? In the obverse, it has to do with mental ill-health—not disease, perhaps not psychosis, but inhibitions, insufficiency of intelligence, depression, poor mechanisms of defense against anxiety, and acting out. All forms of anomalous development and all kinds of resistances to the influences of education can play their part later in potentially mentally unhealthy situations and may thus contribute to breakdown.

Large-scale, well-quantified experimentation in the field of comparative educational climates hardly exists. Deliberate milieu change in residential units for exceptional children has been made and observed, and there is a body of tangentially relevant literature about the social structure of workplaces. Ordinary schools, of course, do vary in their milieus, especially in dimensions of discipline and responsibility, but conclusions are usually unscientific—"the new headmaster is much better"—and are not transferable. New headmasters mostly do not repeat their good results in another

Especially prepared for this volume.

place; neither are attempts to imitate their practices usually successful. Schools for the maladjusted very often deliberately use the milieu for therapy, but their criteria are not those of educational success, which, for them, is a by-product. A far more sophisticated attempt to produce self-motivated achievement on the part of youths, with consequent positive educational results, is evident in Mr. Lyward's work, but this is a striking exception.[4] Unfortunately, unusual schools are frequently regarded as havens for the maladjusted (as they sometimes are), and the "progressive school" is stigmatized.

It is illogical that this should be, in view of the fact that the expressed aims of nursery schools are toward social development. *They* are concerned with the detection and treatment of minor handicaps, with the fostering of positive mental health, and with the prevention of faulty modes of adjustment.[5,14] They act as if these matters are important for good education, and they are well aware of the very many possible impediments to good learning. Perhaps we may now see more numerous comparisons of the long-term effects of these educational practices through the systematic use of epidemiologic techniques. A firm opinion exists in some countries that organized crèches and nursery schools produce more self-reliant adults, but the irony lies in doubt about values: are youths mentally healthy because they are more independent, or are they unhealthy because they are less conformist?

The definition of mental health is a current sport of the professionals. Laycock's [11] triad of a feeling of security, an interpersonal healthiness, and a flexibility in meeting life is reasonably standard. Differences of opinion (or is it value?) lie mostly in the elaboration of healthy social (mainly interpersonal) adjustment; here, discussion keeps within the Oedipus triangle and its proliferation, and social psychology (the relation between person and group) has not yet been fully appreciated. Perhaps it is characteristic of cultures with high intergroup tensions that they remain bemused by a neo-Freudian interpersonal psychology which is resistant to Kurt Lewin.

Sometimes it is said that we cannot define mental health because it involves value judgments. Why not, then, define value judgments? When we do, we see that this element of mental health is superficial and unimportant in comparison with Laycock's first and third areas: a feeling of security and a flexibility in meeting life. Aberrations in these areas are on the true psychiatric level.

I do not think that qualitative differences in psychiatric disorders have ever been demonstrated between countries and cultures; rather, the weight of evidence seems to me to be positively in favor of commonness of unsuccessful defense mechanisms. What differences exist are in the quantities of the expressions; for instance, differences in potentially ambivalent intrafamily relationships result in an intercountry difference between modes of conformity and rebellion, varying in individuals according to their social approval. So, Italians are stereotyped by foreigners as labile, Russians as social conformers, Frenchmen as individualists, and so on. But these are not dimensions of mental ill-health; it is only when an individual's repetitiveness or complex-determined conduct leads him to go too far on the scale, at either end, or to express the same feature too often that he has a quality of illness—in the sense that he will be led to further disturbance, to uncomfortable feelings about himself, and to inflexibility in meeting the ordinary demands of his life in the future. The psychological mechanisms are universal, but the way in which the social climate permits, inhibits, approves, or rewards them is peculiar to the milieu. If this concept is correct, we should find differences in rates of mental disorder in different milieus but not basic differences in their forms.

The study cited here by Nagler [13] is an important example that bears on this problem, and it supports the generalization that parent-child relations are most important for the child, as molding patterns of reaction which are carried forward into later situations. The data quoted strikingly confirm Sigmund Freud's ideas of psychogenesis and the universality of risks of anomalous emotional development in early infancy and hint at a conclusion that the wider social structures—the kibbutz and the educational milieu—are far less important. But the study is essentially nonstatistical and furthermore depicts only a narrow range of milieus.

Kahn's and Nursten's paper [8] is essentially psychiatric; that is to say, it deals with the analysis of rather severe cases whose disorders manifest themselves in school life (by refusing) but whose roots, prognosis, and treatment have little to do with the school. Yet they are characteristic enough of school medical practice and are typical of those childhood disorders which are first detected by parents or teachers and referred to child guidance centers. I do not propose to comment on the subject itself, which is dealt with much more fully in a later book by the same authors,[9] but to abstract certain attitudes from the article which exemplify modern psychiatric thought. The first of these has already been mentioned: the attitude that a school merely "provides an area where symptoms of different types of disturbance may be expressed." The importance of this attitude for therapeutic practice is obvious; as long as the children are sufficiently seriously disordered to be referred to a child guidance clinic, the apparatus for tackling the anamnesis and the parental guidance will be available. It may even, perhaps, be too much used—too many children may be referred. But where to draw the line? Is referral necessary for all children who express symptoms at school? If this were so, there would be little use for less elaborate mental health units and the type of work dominated by teacher guidance, as described by Klebanoff and Bindman,[10] would be ineffective. Of course, cases are different; some require the heavy guns of the organized child guidance clinic, while others can be dealt with more simply. To determine the method of therapeutic action a certain diagnostic process is necessary, but diagnosis and therapy should proceed together; it is faulty practice to push diagnosis too far without treatment (and it is uneconomic), and it is just as faulty to tackle every problem with a therapeutic interview without sufficient diagnostic cues about the case, his family, and his teachers. Perhaps the practical solution to this problem is to use the most experienced members of the mental health team in the front line, so that they may the more rapidly decide on effective and economic action.

The second attitude of Kahn and Nursten relates to their citation of the work of Adelaide Johnson. The influence of the series of her publications on child psychiatry is incalculable.[7] They describe a kind of psychiatric practice in which mother and child can be conceived as a treatable unity; they analyze—and help others to analyze in their practical work—the importance of the early mother-child relationship and the factors bringing about referral symptoms. Nowadays, with the modern confidence in family group therapy, paralleled by experiences with the conjoint therapy of marital partners and with marriage guidance, we are aware of the essentially collusive nature of all intrafamilial symptomatology, of the fact that the parent's part can only be understood in relation to his own childhood, and so on.[3] This collusive element is familial, and to the degree that similar unconscious transactions take place between teacher and child, they will be transferential (at least on the child's part) and usually not strongly structured. Thus, a consultant therapy which is directed only at the teacher will merely affect the child incidentally and accidentally. It is here that advice to the teacher, which relates only to the teacher's psychopathology, fails as *therapy* for disturbed children, even though it may be *preventive* for others.

What I am suggesting here (biased from the viewpoint of mental health promotion) is that schools should be primarily oriented toward undertaking preventive milieu therapy, that teachers should be primarily milieu therapists and secondarily instructors. To justify such a change in orientation, one must lessen the value given to academic knowledge in the early stages of school life and expect that the results of this reorientation will be to increase the gains from independent initiative in learning. Investigation on this point is typically backward, requiring a comparison of methods over long periods with matched samples, in different age groups and in different communities.

Perhaps the "good" teacher is always a milieu therapist; he creates an undisturbing atmosphere, and he reacts to each child in a mature, rational, adult manner, at the same time being conscious of, and sensitive to, each child's transferential attitudes. In such an atmosphere he can *also* instruct and evaluate his instruction and his pupils' learning.[2] The purpose of this plasticity of reaction on the part of the teacher is to permit development, to allow new forms of child-adult interaction to take place which are different from the intrafamilial child-parent patterns, and thus to avoid "structurization" of infantile patterns. The primary tactic of "prevention" in the mental health field is to allow normal development to proceed and, conversely, to avoid blockages; the secondary tactic, to correct fixations and their resultant anomalies.[6,12]

So much for an opinion; it helps to interpret the various problems and difficulties faced in the Massachusetts study.[10] The point is that what has been expressed here as a mental health philosophy *is an opinion;* true, it is probably not far from the basic outlook of the Massachusetts authors, but are these views held by the schoolteachers with whom they tried to work? I would be prepared to suggest that all mental health programs need to commence with attitude studies. In the situation of mental health experts influencing schoolteachers, the need for concurrence of aims is paramount. Such concurrence cannot be assumed, neither can it be adduced from a superficial examination; personal aims derive from one's social environments and from one's unconscious. It may well prove that profound clarification of a teacher's own aims in his teaching situation would be the best way to help him with all his pupils; perhaps this is best done in groups of teachers, because the group is an important determinant of each one's aims. The technique is an educational group process akin to group psychotherapy.

Has an outside mental health group the right to impose its views on bringing up children on a group of educators? Here is the dilemma: unless views are concordant, no effective teamwork can result, yet neither should prevail; others are involved. A liberal community may contain as many views as there are people; it is not yet a mental health team.

References

1. Aikin, W. A.: *Adventure in American Education,* vol. 1, *The Story of the Eight Year Study,* Harper & Row, Publishers, Incorporated, New York, 1942.
2. Bower, E. M.: "Psychology in the Schools: Conceptions, Processes and Territories," *Psychology in the Schools,* 1(1):3–11, 1964.
3. Buckle, D. F., et al.: *Family Mental Health in Europe,* WHO Public Health Paper, Geneva, 1965.
4. Burn, M.: *Mr. Lyward's Answer,* Hamilton Ltd., Publishers, London, 1956.
5. *Child Health and the School,* World Health Organization, Regional Office for Europe, Copenhagen, 1965.
6. Freud, A.: "Assessment of Childhood Disturbances," *The Psychoanalytic Study of the Child,* International Universities Press, Inc., New York, 1962, vol. xvii, pp. 149–158.
7. Johnson, A. M.: "Sanctions for Superego Lacunae of Adolescents," in K. Eissler (ed.), *Searchlights on Delinquency,* Imago, London, 1949, pp. 225–245.
8. Kahn, J. H., and J. P. Nursten: see Chap. 16.
9. ——— and ———: *Unwillingly to School,* Pergamon Press, Oxford, 1964.

10. Klebanoff, L. B., and A. J. Bindman: see Chap. 17.
11. Laycock, Samuel R.: see Chap. 15.
12. Lebovici, S.: "La prévention en santé mentale chez l'enfant: Reflexions à propos du Séminaire de Copenhague sous les auspices de l'Organisation Mondiale de la Santé, Copenhague," *Psychiat. Enfant*, 2:197–226, 1959.
13. Nagler, Shmuel: see Chap. 18.
14. Wall, W. D.: *Education and Mental Health*, UNESCO, Paris, 1955.

part five

Approaches to Social Problems

20. Project Re-ED: Reeducation of Emotionally Disturbed Children

W. W. Lewis

Introduction

Project Re-ED is a way of helping children. The wisdom of individuals and social arrangements taken from a variety of places and professional backgrounds have contributed to this new type of social institution. The basic idea is quite simple: children can be helped by living with sensitive, vital adults who care about children. There is nothing new about the idea, stated at this level of abstraction. It is as old as the motivation to help troubled children, but the particular arrangement of people and responsibilities in Project Re-ED may be somewhat unique.

A Re-ED school is first of all a *school*, with a treatment program that is educational in orientation and a staff who are essentially teachers— teachers who *teach* children how to trust, how to have faith in the future and in themselves, as well as to read and to do arithmetic.

From the beginning, four basic assumptions have guided the planning of the Re-ED schools and their programs: [3]

1. The problem of providing for emotionally disturbed children is a critical one requiring bold measures. Society will not continue to tolerate the assignment of disturbed children to detention homes, to hospitals for adults, or to institutions for the mentally deficient. The social need for imaginative planning is acute.

2. The United States does not have and will not be able to train a sufficient number of social workers, psychiatrists, psychologists, and nurses to staff psychiatric facilities along traditional lines. It will not be possible in the foreseeable future, with the manpower shortage becoming increasingly acute, to solve the problem of the emotionally disturbed child by adhering to limited patterns. The problem must be redefined if it is to be solved.

Especially prepared for this volume.

3. For effective work with children, the worker's personal attributes weigh more heavily than his professional knowledge and technical skills. Fully adequate programs for the reeducation of emotionally disturbed children can be developed by (a) emphasizing the selection of workers; (b) providing condensed, highly specific, functional training; and (c) backstopping the workers' day-by-day activities with a dependable system of consultation by top-level professional personnel.

4. The model provided by education, with its emphasis on health rather than illness, on teaching rather than treatment, on learning rather than fundamental personality reorganization, on the present and the future rather than the past, and on the operation of the total social system of which the child is a part rather than intrapsychic processes exclusively, may provide an effective as well as a feasible approach to the problems of a substantial number of emotionally disturbed children.

History

Some of the early momentum for Project Re-ED came from a study of resources for mental health training and research in the southeastern United States, conducted in 1954 by the Southern Regional Education Board (SREB) and the National Institute of Mental Health.[4] The study highlighted the problem of inadequate services for emotionally disturbed children, particularly residential treatment facilities. There simply were no such facilities in the region, so that when a child's problems became so grave that the community was compelled to find a residential placement for him, it was likely to be grossly inappropriate, such as placement in a detention home for delinquent and neglected children or an adult ward in a psychiatric hospital. At the time the SREB report was published, the solution seemed to lie in increasing the output of training programs in psychiatry, clinical psychology, and psychiatric social work. It was not long, however, before George W. Albee published a national survey of mental health manpower trends that questioned the validity of this solution. His firm conclusion was that the country was faced with a continuing shortage of personnel in all mental health professions that was so serious that it could not be remedied in the foreseeable future simply by increasing the present patterns of mental health services.[1]

During the same period, Nicholas Hobbs, the principal investigator for Project Re-ED, had been studying the institutional patterns of caring for emotionally disturbed children in Europe. What seemed to be required, in making up the serious deficit in facilities for the residential treatment of emotionally disturbed children, was a completely new approach to the staffing patterns currently being used in psychiatric facilities. Two institutional patterns, used in Europe for many years, suggested what has now become the staffing pattern in the Re-ED schools. One residential treatment center for emotionally disturbed children, near Glasgow,

Scotland, is staffed by workers called "educational psychologists." They are teachers who are given on-the-job training and who are responsible for around-the-clock therapeutic care of disturbed children. A similar staffing pattern was observed in France, where residential programs for several kinds of exceptional children are staffed by personnel called *"éducateurs,"* a professional group with relatively little formal training but extensive training on the job in pedagogy, group dynamics, psychodynamics, and other skills required in an around-the-clock therapeutic program for the children. The essential elements that seemed transposable to residential care for children in this country were (1) staffing by persons requiring less extensive professional preparation than those in the mental health disciplines; (2) careful selection of workers on the basis of individual qualities indicating a potential for effective work with children; (3) intimate around-the-clock learning and living in which small groups of children are supervised by these personnel; and (4) frequent consultation with, but not supervision by, mental health specialists.

The project was eventually organized as an eight-year demonstration, supported in its initial stages by a grant from the National Institute of Mental Health, but with the states of Tennessee and North Carolina gradually taking fiscal responsibility for the demonstration schools. The George Peabody College for Teachers assumed responsibility for the administration of the entire project as well as the training program and the program of research designed to evaluate the effectiveness of the demonstration.

The Schools

During the school year 1962–1963, Cumberland House Elementary School in Tennessee and Wright School in North Carolina began to operate on a limited basis, staffed by the initial group of carefully selected teachers who had gone through a special one-year training program, including some placement in England and Scotland. During the present school year, 1963–1964, both schools have a nearly full complement of teacher-counselors from the first two years' training programs. The expected capacity operation of forty children at each school has not been reached because of limitations imposed by lack of space. Each school is organized into groups of eight children, who live and attend school together and who are the responsibility of two teacher-counselors. The general pattern that has been followed in both schools is a five-day-a-week residential program, with children returning to their homes on the weekends. The two teacher-counselors are responsible for designing and carrying out an intensive treatment program for each child, based on his needs, presenting problems and the common objectives shared by the child's family, the referring mental health agency, and the Re-ED school.

The program is intentionally an educational one, emphasizing conscious, specific, and usually rather concrete goals toward which the individual child and his teacher-counselors work. The emphasis on psychotherapeutic treatment for inner conflicts, unconscious or intrapsychic problems, is purposely minimized. A child's responsibility in the socialization process is to learn the valued attitudes and behaviors of his family, school, and community. The purpose of the Re-ED demonstration is to explore the extent to which direct educational programming can be effective in modifying behavior in children identified as emotionally disturbed.

The Re-ED treatment pattern assumes that a basic validity exists in the traditional child-rearing arrangements in our culture and that, on the whole, they are effective and wholesome for a child's development. A disruption of child-rearing functions, as manifest in the identification of a child as emotionally disturbed, is looked upon as a disturbance within all the systems influencing that child. If the disruption in the child-rearing systems for a child is not completely enervating, the relief provided by a fairly rapid shift in symptoms or in demands on the child may allow the systems to recover their potential for growth and continue the socialization process relatively unaided. With this working hypothesis in mind, goals are set for children at the Re-ED schools that emphasize things like reading skills, learning to tolerate sitting in a classroom for extended periods of time, trusting adults, and living with peers with a minimum of conflict. In many ways, the approach to a child's problems may be thought of as social, as opposed to psychiatric treatment. The Re-ED strategy is to look at the effects of the child's behavior on an overt, symptomatic level and to see in what specific ways his behavior creates conflicts with the social systems of which he is a member. Then an attempt is made to construct a sequence of learning experiences that will influence, quite directly, the area of concern in the child's behavior.

The treatment program begins with a referring agency: child guidance clinic, family service agency, school, or other community agency involved in the identification or treatment of emotional disturbance in children. The Re-ED school is not seen as a sufficient or autonomous treatment facility but as a resource for agencies in the community already working with children. In most cases the agency referring a child to a Re-ED school will continue to work with the parents while the child is enrolled in the school and will resume major responsibility for the child on his return home. The admission conference between the referring agency and the Re-ED school reviews the history of the child's problem, any treatment attempted to date and the current status of the child, his family, and his school. Preliminary treatment goals are established at the conference, with an emphasis on specific changes that can be made rather quickly in the child's behavior or his natural environment, within the realistic limits imposed by the intent to return him home quickly, usually within four to six months. Planning for the child's release, including additional community resources that need to be mobilized (or placement outside his home, if that seems required), is initiated at the admission conference and forms an integral part of the treatment pattern. While these plans remain flexible, to allow for the unpredictable in human and institutional behavior, the thrust is forward, anticipating future behavior rather than explaining past events. There has been a gradually diminishing concern with the kind and degree of pathology in making the decision to enroll a particular child. When the schools were first opened, rigorous use was made of exclusion criteria like severe psychosis, brain injury, and mental retardation. As the confidence and skill of the staff have grown, the admission decisions have come to reflect a judgment that a child can respond in specified ways to the group-centered educational program. This attitude has resulted, of course, in the admission of children with a wide range of diagnostic labels, although each child has some unique strengths that can be exploited.

Following the admission conference, the child is assigned to a particular group, and specific preparation for his enrollment begins. He visits the school, with his parents, and meets the children and teacher-counselors with whom he will be living for the next few months. The teacher-counselors begin to outline a specific program of remedial education and social living experiences, based on their analysis of the details in the clinical and educational records on the child. In addition, they prepare the other children in the group for the coming of the new child, so that on the day of his enrollment he will be received warmly, on the basis of realistic expectations, including whatever problem behavior he is likely to present to the group.

The school day typically begins about nine o'clock, proceeds until noon, with time out for a recess period, and resumes after lunch until about three o'clock, when the recreation period begins. The school day is heavily loaded with instruction in the basic academic skills of reading, arithmetic, and use of language. The placement of children in groups is based more generally on social behavior than on educational development, so that much of the instruction in basic skills is individualized and the content determined by the social utility of a skill for a particular child. Units of instruction that will support heterogeneous educational abilities, however, such as preparing for a field trip to the Great Smoky Mountains National Park, are also a vital part of the school curriculum.

The nonacademic part of the school day also emphasizes the learning of skills which have social value for children of elementary school age but which, for some reason, have not been developed. The ability to kick a football, for example, or to roller-skate, swim, cook, or ride a bicycle may have a social utility as great as arithmetic skills in a child's reintegration into his normal school and home environment. Thus, a program of planned instruction, reflecting an assessment of a child's need for socially adaptive skills, is extended beyond the bounds of the usual school day. This is true also of the evening program, which emphasizes the skills required in living harmoniously with a group of peers and the adults to whom a child is responsible. It is one of the important strengths of the Re-ED staffing pattern that the afternoon and evening hours, including the homely child care tasks of eating, dressing, and getting ready for bed, are supervised by sensitive, competent personnel. While much of the interaction at this time is not planned in any specific sense, it is a time that is rich in opportunities for learning skills in social living and exploration of personal feelings. The way an adult responds to a child's refusal to eat or to go to bed or his strong impulse to hurt another child can make an important contribution to the child's social and emotional development. The intensity and intimacy of group living provide opportunity for personal growth that is not encountered elsewhere.

Each child's progress toward his goals is reviewed periodically, along with the progress being made in planning with the child's family, school, and community resources. As soon as a judgment can be made that the child is functioning just well enough or that the systems in his community are changing their tolerance thresholds enough, or both, to support his behavior without undue conflict and with a reasonable prognosis for his continued healthy development, plans will be made for him to return to his own home and school. During this time the teacher-counselors become more active in working with the child's parents and home school teacher. The Re-ED staff, the referring agency, the child's family, his school, and the child himself are all actively involved in planning the return.

Observations

Perhaps the simplest way to convey a flavor of the program at the Re-ED schools is to sample the anecdotal recording that is done from time to time by a member of the research staff. Each recording focuses attention on a single child. For example, Bill is a member of a group of boys who call themselves the Confederate Aviators. Besides Bill, there are six boys in the group, ranging in age from ten to twelve. The classroom has individual desks and chairs for each boy, all facing the front of the room, where the teacher's desk and blackboard are located. The observation was made during Bill's third month of residence. Both teacher-counselors, Mr. Brown and Miss King, are in the classroom.

9:00—As the observer enters the classroom, Mr. Brown is just beginning an arithmetic lesson. Miss King is seated next to the desk of one of the boys, toward the back of the room, looking with him at a book. Mr. Brown is at the blackboard, working examples to show how to multiply decimals by 10. Bill is at his desk, watching quietly and sucking his thumb. After Mr. Brown has worked through several examples, Bill gets up from his desk and climbs on top of a bookcase next to it. Miss King says quietly: "Get down, Bill." Bill climbs off the bookcase and sits down at his desk again. He picks up a pencil, walks across the room to sharpen it, and returns to his seat. As he sits down, he turns sideways in his chair and leans back against the bookcase. He seems inattentive for several minutes, apparently lost in his own thoughts. He turns back to his desk, takes out a ball of clay, and rolls it on his desk into a long cylinder. He breaks off a small piece of the clay, rolls it into a ball, and then flattens it out by pounding with his fist on top of the paper on which he had been doing his arithmetic. He sticks the pencil point into the clay, which adheres to the paper, holds it up and turns around to the boy behind him, saying: "Look, David." David smiles, and Bill turns back around in his seat and begins pounding the clay on his desk. Mr. Brown, interrupting his explanation for a moment, says: "Bill, I don't think you understand this yet. Perhaps you ought to listen." Bill gives Mr. Brown his attention, but when Mr. Brown turns back to his explanation at the blackboard, Bill turns to Allen, the boy who is reading the book with Miss King, and says, "See, Allen," holding up the paper with the clay and pencil once again, and then, "Look, Miss King," waving the paper at her. Mr. Brown interrupts his explanation again, comes over and stands beside Bill, and says: "Maybe I'd better take it for now, Bill." Bill is reluctant but gives the clay up as Mr. Brown assures him that he will return it after the lesson is over. Miss King moves her chair forward from Allen's desk to Bill's. Bill reaches his arm across her shoulder, saying: "How are you today, Miss King?" Miss King smiles at Bill. He turns back to his desk and begins copying arithmetic problems off the board, as Mr. Brown continues his explanation. Miss King continues to sit quietly beside Bill as he works through the arithmetic assignment. After he finishes the problems, he turns and hands his paper to Miss King with no comment. He watches as she begins checking the problems. She hands the paper back, saying: "Good, Bill." Bill looks up at the blackboard and begins copying new problems. He seems to be listening carefully as Mr. Brown talks. After he has worked several problems, he begins to say audibly: "Let me see—6 from 24." He scratches his head and begins writing on the desk. Miss King says: "Now, you have to borrow 1 from 2." Bill again scratches his head, beats his elbow on the desk, and begins to suck his thumb. "1?" he says questioningly. Miss King says: "Good." They go through several other problems in the same fashion; then Miss King sits back, watching, while Bill finishes. Then she pats him on the back and says approvingly: "Very, very good." And in a louder voice to Mr. Brown: "Bill got his all right." Mr. Brown calls back across the room: "Very good, Bill." Bill looks up at Mr. Brown and, pointing to his ankle, says: "When we get back to the house, will you put a cast on here? I fell on it, and it sure hurts, Mr. Brown." Mr. Brown says: "Dr. Chasen will have to do that, Bill." Bill says: "No, not that kind; one of those elastic things—you know—that pull up." Mr. Brown says: "We'll see if it still hurts later."

9:30—Mr. Brown finishes the arithmetic lesson and begins moving around the room, helping individuals as they work on their assignments. Bill finishes the problems he has written on his paper and, without comment, puts the paper inside his desk and gets up. He kicks off his shoes, walks over to the teacher's desk, where Miss King is now seated, saying, "Hey, a camera," and picks a camera up off the desk. Miss King says: "That is my camera, Bill. I'd rather you didn't play with it." He puts it back down on the desk and returns to his seat. He sits quietly looking around the room for a minute or so and then gets up and climbs onto the bookcase. He lies on top of the bookcase with his feet against the wall and pushes himself back toward the other end of the bookcase. Then he rolls over on his stomach and watches the observer for a few minutes. He sits up, still on top of the bookcase, as Miss King approaches him, places her hand gently on his shoulder, and asks him to return to his seat. He jumps down, goes back to his desk, sits down, and pulls out a book. Bobby pulls his seat over next to Bill, making no comment, apparently just wanting to see what Bill is doing. Bill opens the book and says to Miss King: "Why is the sky like a good loaf of bread, Miss King?" She answers: "I don't know." Bill says: "Because it's white when it rises." Allen looks up from the book he is reading, saying: "No, Bill, it is because it's light when it rises." Bill says, "Oh yeah," gives a big grin, and turning toward Allen, says: "That's right, Allen. I forgot." Bill begins to write something on a piece of paper, apparently copying out of the book. Allen says: "Miss King, can I go to the pet shop today?" Bill looks up and says: "Me, too." Miss King says: "I can only take two." Bill looks up again and says: "Take me—me and Allen." Then he returns to writing on the pad of paper with apparent interest. Allen says: "What are you writing, Bill?" Bill says: "Jokes." He puts his pencil down for a moment, as if in deep thought, then holds up his foot by the ankle, and says: "Oh, my ankle." Then he picks up his pencil and returns to his writing. He continues writing for several minutes, Allen continuing to watch. Bobby offers a Life-Saver to Allen. Bill says: "I want one, too." Bobby gives him one. Bill says, "Thanks," and smiles, picks up the book, and says to Miss King: "What is the best thing out?" She shrugs her shoulders. Bill says: "A fire." She says, with obvious amusement: "That's a good one, Bill." He resumes writing, continuing for several minutes, then looks up at Allen, who is still watching him, and says: "You want to write some?" Allen shakes his head no. Bill says: "Miss King, my ankle sure is sore." Miss King says: "Maybe it will feel better soon." Bill resumes his copying out of the book. After several minutes he stops writing and reads another joke to Bobby, who shrugs his shoulders, apparently not sharing Bill's amusement.

9:45—Bill says: "Miss King, can I play my record now, please?" Miss

King says: "I think so, Bill," and comes over to the bookcase, gets the record player and the record, carries it across the room, and puts it on a large table. As she plugs in the record player and gets the record out of the folder, Bill seems still to be absorbed in copying the jokes out of the book. After another minute or so, he puts the pencil down, looks up, and says: "I've got five jokes down, Miss King." She walks over to him and says: "Put your name on it, Bill," pointing to the paper. Bill writes his name across the top of the page. He leaves the paper on his desk and gets up and walks over to the table where the record player is playing the record he has asked to hear. He picks up the folder for the record, the name of which is "Twisting around the World," puts the folder down, returns to pick up his chair and bring it over to the table where the record player is, sits down, and begins to suck his thumb. He picks up the record cover again, still sucking his thumb, looks at the folder for a couple of minutes, and replaces it on the table. He notices a curtain rod in the corner of the room near the table, gets up, and retrieves it. He stands up, holding it like a cane, and hobbles across the room. Mr. Brown says: "Come here a minute, Bill." Bill limps over to him. Mr. Brown is holding a paper on which Bill had been writing at his desk. He asks Bill what it is; Bill takes it from him and reads aloud in a very soft voice. After he finishes, Mr. Brown pats him on the shoulder and says: "That was pretty good, Bill." Bill looks across the room to the table where the record player is, noticing that Bob and Allen are sitting down to put together a jigsaw puzzle of the United States. Bill hobbles across the room, still using the curtain rod as a cane, sits down in his chair at the table, and begins to watch very quietly, sucking his thumb and stamping his foot in time to the twist music. He watches for several minutes, not saying anything to Bob or Allen, and then gets up and hobbles back across the room, leaning on the curtain rod. He fishes his shoes out from under the desk with the curtain rod and steps into them. He returns to the table, still using the curtain rod as a cane, hangs the rod on the edge of the table, as one would with the handle of a real cane, and sits down again. He puts his thumb in his mouth and continues to watch the boys with the puzzle.

10:00—Miss King says: "Everyone sit down at his own desk." The other two boys get up from the table and return to their own desks. Bill continues to sit alone at the table, picks up one piece of puzzle that has not yet been fitted in, and turns it over and over in his hand, inspecting it very carefully. Miss King watches him for a moment and then says: "Bill, please sit down at your own desk." Bill puts down the piece of puzzle, picks up the curtain rod, and, still using it as a cane, hobbles back to his desk and sits down. Miss King says: "Remember, we were talking about money yesterday. Now why do you think all of us need money?" Bill calls out: "You got to have money to get things at the store." Miss King says: "But why do we need money? Why can't I just trade my shirt or blouse or shoes for a car or a bottle of milk or anything I want at the store?" Allen, Bill, and Bobby say: "Oh, no!" Miss King sits down at her desk and says: "Well, just for fun, let's pretend that we don't have any money and we have to trade things. What do you have, Allen, that you could trade?" Bill calls out: "I ain't got nothin' to trade." As the discussion continues, he picks up the curtain rod and places it across his desk over a piece of paper, and begins to draw his pencil along the edge of the rod, making a straight line on the paper. Miss King looks at him and says admonishingly: "Bill." He places the curtain rod on the floor under his desk, rests his feet on top of it, puts his elbows on the top of the desk, and begins to suck his thumb. The discussion about bartering continues for six or seven minutes, during which Bill continues to sit in the same position, apparently not listening to what is going on. As Miss King brings the discussion to a close, Bill reaches under his desk for the curtain rod, stands up, and hobbles to the front of the room where Miss King is sitting. He puts one arm around her shoulder, hugs her gently, and looks at her with an innocent grin, saying softly into her ear: "Can I have my clay?" Miss King says to him quite gently: "Sit down for just a minute, Bill, we are not quite through." Without protest, he hobbles back across the room to his desk, sits down, and hangs the curtain rod on his desk by the handle.

The Teacher-Counselor

It will be clear from the brief outline of the Re-ED program that the success of the treatment stands or falls on the strengths of the individual teacher-counselors. The two teacher-counselors living with a group of children have almost total responsibility for the welfare and development of the children in their group. They live, eat, work, and play together from the time the child's parents bring him to the school on Sunday evening to the time the child returns to his home on Friday afternoon. The program is intense and demanding but richly rewarding, particularly for a person who has grown accustomed to the structure and compartmentalization of teaching in a public school. The teacher-counselor is a teacher, spending several hours in the classroom with a group of children each day, but he is also a recreation supervisor, counselor, and parent substitute at other times during the day. As a teacher, the teacher-counselor has the goal of developing and maintaining motivation toward the usual academic accomplishments of children in elementary school. Emotionally disturbed children often have specific educational deficits that require remediation and generalized anxiety responses to school that require careful cultivation of positive attitudes. To provide meaningful, focused learning experiences for children in this context requires unusual commitment to the task as well as creativity and resourcefulness in a teacher.

Liaison with Home and School

The Re-ED strategy requires that a close liaison be maintained between the Re-ED school, while it is working with the child, and his family and home school. For this reason, there are two professional roles in addition to that of the teacher-counselor that call for particular mention. One is that of the social worker, whose task is to coordinate, with the referring agency, the entry of a child into the Re-ED school, the continuous contact with the child's family during the time he is in the school, and the planning to return him to his home. She is alert to factors in the family constellation that require attention so that the child will be able to resume membership in that family, particularly as these factors affect the timing of the child's reentry. While a child is attending a Re-ED school, the social worker has primary responsibility for coordinating agency communication, parent conferences, and the exploration of additional community resources required to facilitate the child's return.

The second special role is that of the liaison teacher, an experienced public school teacher who has gone through the Re-ED training program. His responsibility is to maintain contact with the schools from which children come to Re-ED and to which they will return. The liaison teacher takes much the same stance toward a child's home school as the social worker takes toward the child's family. Initially, he helps assess the nature of the child's problems, both social and educational, in the home school before the child is enrolled in the Re-ED school. During the child's enrollment, he maintains contact with the home school and plans, with the administrator and teacher in that school, the timing and style of the child's return. Like the social worker, he is responsible for following the progress of the child after he has returned to his regular school. The importance of the role of both the social worker and the liaison teacher in the Re-ED school is derived from the clear intention to influence the child-rearing systems as well as the child, in a broad treatment pattern that includes many variables impinging on the child's life, following his release from the school, as well as the time he is there.

Mental Health Consultation

The role of the mental health specialist has not been made explicit thus far in this discussion of the Re-ED schools. The Re-ED position on the mental health specialist's role is that a teacher-counselor should have easy access to the body of information represented by the mental health disciplines but in a counsulting relationship rather than a supervisory one. There has been a self-conscious effort to construct a consulting situation in which the two teacher-counselors take the initiative in setting goals for a child or a group of children and use consultation to devise techniques that will move them toward their designated goals. The consultant brings to the interaction specific knowledge of the child being discussed, both from direct observation and from records, as well as his background of professional skills, but no authority to make decisions in program planning. Decisions must be made by the two teachers and are clearly defined as working hypotheses to be tested in the program and continued or discarded on the basis of feedback from the child's behavior. This procedure is an attempt to meet one of the compelling problems of the mental health field, that is, to make the most effective use of the very limited number of people who have extensive training in the behavioral sciences and who have traditionally approached problems of emotional disturbance in a direct service relationship. The relatively heavy investment in consulting time is designed not only to provide teacher-counselors with whatever help they may need in solving problems of the moment but also to furnish a learning experience that will allow them to develop into behavior specialists in their own right. The ground rule, requiring that teacher-counselors make and take responsibility for decisions regarding children's programs, encourages learning at a level that probably cannot occur when a staff member is acting on the recommendations of a supervisor.

Follow-up of Students

Evaluation of the effectiveness of the treatment program at the Re-ED schools is, like the treatment program itself, being directed toward change in specific behaviors in children. Follow-up studies of the effectiveness of treatment of emotionally disturbed children have typically attempted to assess gross improvement or adjustment. Approaching the evaluation of treatment at this level of abstraction has not convincingly demonstrated the effectiveness of traditional treatment methods.[2]

In view of the specific changes being attempted in the Re-ED treatment program, it is necessary to approach evaluation in a specific way. The assessment of change in children who have been through the Re-ED schools is directed toward relatively simple, concrete measures of the child's social and academic effectiveness, such as reading-achievement scores, attendance records, and measurements of the child's social-stimulus value. In an attempt to direct the assessment to a level of concreteness commensurate with the treatment, assessment procedures are focused on educational and social skills and on the consequences of these behaviors as manifest in the judgments of the natural evaluators in a child's life: his parents, teachers, and peers. Each child receives a standard battery of tests and interviews on entry to the school, his parents and teachers are asked to describe their reactions to his behavior by means of questionnaires, and a sociometric test is used with his classroom peers. The educational tests and interviews are readministered just prior to his leaving the Re-ED school, and the social-stimulus questionnaires are readministered after he has been back in his home environment for two to three months. To date, the number of children who have been back in their own homes long enough for a follow-up is relatively small. Therefore, any evaluation of Re-ED treatment must be quite tentative, since it is based on an impressionistic analysis of a few cases.

Summaries from the records of children who attended the Re-ED schools during the first year of operation and who have been home long enough, usually two to three months, for a follow-up study to be made, are available on request to the author.

Parents of Re-ED children have been quite pleased with the progress they have seen while their children were at the school. In many cases their positive attitudes may be as much a function of change in themselves, most of them having been engaged in counseling relationships with another agency, as of change in the child. The compelling impression, however, is that parents do see things as much better, whatever the reason. While parents' assessments are based on comparisons of behavior in the same child at different times, teachers who make follow-up assessments of former Re-ED students often have not seen a child before he comes to them. Therefore, their assessments tend to be more normative, based on comparisons of the former Re-ED child with his present classmates. It seems encouraging, therefore, that many of the classroom teachers, on follow-up, report that the former Re-ED students are "average" in their classes. It is especially encouraging since many of these children were at the bottom of their classes before coming to the Re-ED schools. Objectively, there is little indication that the "average" performance of former Re-ED students in their own schools is due to marked acceleration in measured achievement. On achievement-test measures of school performance, the Re-ED children hold their own on a month-for-month basis or move ahead slightly but do not make radical improvement. The major change may be a social rather than an academic one. A child who has learned that school is a place where he can find basic satisfactions and who, in addition, has learned to sit in a classroom and attend to his assignments probably has a much better chance of being perceived as an "average" student than if he were actively resentful or disruptive. As was suggested by parents' perceptions, the implication is that some disturbed children can be reintegrated into their natural setting after brief residential treatment and relate more effectively to the child socializing agencies in their culture without major personality changes.

One of the intriguing effects of the apparent successes of Re-ED treatment is that one is compelled to seek new conceptual models in order to interpret the process in a self-consistent fashion. The medical model used in psychotherapeutic treatment obviously is not applicable. The solution to children's problems is not sought in a rearrangement of internal pressures that are reflected only secondarily in behavior. The behavior is approached quite directly, as an important object of treatment, regardless of the underlying cause. The use of stimulus-response learning theories is probably no more appropriate, however, since the precise patterns of response and reinforcement are difficult to discern in the complexity of an extended human encounter, such as that between teacher-counselor and child. Modern educational theories, with their emphasis on individualized instruction, intrinsic motivation, and experimential learning, may be most relevant. Their emphasis on learning in the cognitive domain may make them somewhat incomplete, however, and suggest a need to supplement them with educational theory from other sources. At this stage in the development of a new social institution, it seems proper to remain optimistic that with experience we shall become more articulate in discussing the process of reeducation at a level of theoretical concepts. For the moment, it is satisfying to see the development of institutional arrangements that bring helping adults and troubled children in a confrontation which encourages significant personal growth.

References

1. Albee, George W.: *Mental Health Manpower Trends*, Basic Books, Inc., Publishers, New York, 1959.
2. Levitt, E. E.: "The Results of Psychotherapy with Children: An Evaluation," *J. Consult. Psychol.*, 21:189–196, 1957.
3. *Project Re-ED: A Demonstration Project for the Reeducation of Emotionally Disturbed Children*, George Peabody College for Teachers, Nashville, Tenn., 1963.
4. Southern Regional Education Board: *Mental Health Training and Research in the Southern States*, a report to the Southern Governors' Conference, Atlanta, Georgia, 1954.

21. The Inpatient Psychiatric Treatment of Children in Europe

Donald F. Buckle, Serge Lebovici, and J. Tizard

Introduction

Most European countries possess a reasonably well-structured organization for the treatment of adult psychoses, but there are serious gaps in their health services for child psychiatric disorders. The Regional Office for Europe of the World Health Organization has endeavored to improve this position in two principal ways: (1) through providing training in the form of consultations, courses, and fellowships; and (2) by convening a series of small, highly organized international seminars to discuss key problems in this field. These seminars usually comprise about fifty participants, most of whom are nominated by European member states. Three such seminars were held on child guidance, in 1952, 1956, and 1960, while two were held on problems of subnormal children, in 1957 and 1959. In 1962 a seminar was held on mental health and the family. The aim of all these meetings has been to provide, by means of discussions, a form of mutual education for the participants through the appreciation of one another's work and points of view. The Seminar on the Inpatient Psychiatric Treatment of Children was convened as a part of this program.

A modern community requires a complex system of medical, social, and educational services for children, including specialized institutions to provide continuous psychiatric treatment in residential care for those whose individual needs demand such a regime. Typically, treatment in resi-

Adapted from the report of a seminar convened in October, 1963, in Frankfurt am Main, by the Regional Office for Europe of the World Health Organization in collaboration with the government of the Federal Republic of Germany. Single copies of the full report, including full discussion of the roles of different staff members, are available for distribution to persons officially or professionally concerned and may be obtained on request from the WHO Regional Office for Europe in Copenhagen, Denmark.

dential care integrates the functions of a home, of education, and of psychiatric treatment.

The purposes of the seminar were to study and discuss indications for the admission, treatment, discharge, and follow-up of children admitted to residential institutions because of psychiatric disorders. The forty-six participants, coming from twenty-one countries, included child psychiatrists, special educators, psychologists, nurses, and psychiatric social workers. One main working paper was taken as the broad basis for discussion. The present report is not a systematic account of the various discussions but rather a summary of the main problems in regard to child psychiatric institutions in Europe, based on the working document and on the various views expressed.

Residential Services Provided by the Community

Some General Considerations

Organized residential services for children are needed in any community. Homes must be provided for those without families of their own, and so must medical treatment, psychiatric care, or special education, as the case may be.

The choice of sending a child to a nonresidential day center, a foster home, a larger residential center, or a hospital will always be based on an assessment of his individual needs and the ability of the community, through its institutions, to meet them. Discussion of this subject would be easier if it were possible to group residential institutions in distinct categories: homes, boarding schools, or hospitals. In fact, this cannot be done, for the good reason that the children in them have complex needs.

A child requiring long hospital care needs the stimulus and love normally provided by a family. His proper development requires the interplay of the kind of reactions that occur within a family. He needs formal education as well as education for living. All these things should be provided in his treatment, sometimes, perforce, within the hospital or the residential center, which in some measure must assume the role of a family.

Residential schools for special classes of children—the academically subnormal, the maladjusted, and the delinquent—also require to integrate three functions: those of the home, of special education, and of psychological treatment. In practice, emphasis on the three different ingredients varies considerably from school to school. In larger centers, some residential staff act as house parents, others serve as educators, and still others provide specific forms of psychological treatment: remedial education and psychotherapy. Smaller institutions fulfill the three functions with less specifically specialized staff, trained in "special education" or "orthopedagogics." Here, "education" and "pedagogics" embrace all those methods which enhance the development of the child in every aspect, using knowledge and techniques deriving from the study of child development, family relationships, educational methods, social psychology, and psychotherapy.

Between the special school and the psychiatric hospital for children lie a variety of children's residential centers, some with more and some with less medical emphasis and all with some educational provision. A study undertaken by the United States Children's Bureau in 1952 was able to define residential treatment centers as "institutions for the treatment of emotionally disturbed children, in which the planning for the child is based upon clinical study, and in which treatment is carried out accordingly." [2] It may be added that the treatment should include the provision of a therapeutic environment.

There are special developmental problems for children growing up without the usual parental relationships.[1] Certain forms of depreviation can retard emotional and intellectual development. Consequently, many, though not all, authorities believe that a child without a family or a child who must be parted from his family should, as a rule, be placed in a foster home rather than in a large institution. In fact, any "home" which cares for deprived or neglected children faces considerable technical problems in providing for all their needs. The prevention of psychiatric disorders in these children is the concern of both the mental health and the child welfare professions.

In any discussion of institutions and the psychiatric treatment of children in them, general problems of child and adolescent psychiatry inevitably arise and have to be considered. The subject itself is one involving therapeutic method and must be discussed in the light of the increasing importance now being assumed by outpatient care. Moreover, the kind of relationship to be maintained between child welfare services in general and diverse institutions, inpatient and outpatient, manned by psychiatric and psychologically trained personnel must be constantly borne in mind.

Institutional needs in the case of subnormal children can be fairly precisely assessed, but it is much harder to do so for other types of children. Generally speaking, however, countries that are better off in educational resources find it easier to limit the range of psychiatric institutions required. In the same way, where the cultural level of a population is high and where general medical practitioners, social workers, teachers, and child care workers are well informed, it is far easier to do preventive work. With improving cultural levels, intervention by the child psychiatrist may become premature, and psychiatric care may well become less needed, so much so that, under ideal conditions, the psychiatrist would more frequently act in a purely consultative capacity.

Developing countries may well be able to avoid the mistakes made by those with services of longer standing and can embark on something in the nature of social experiments. An accurate study of educational and pediatric resources in the community should, however, be made. Certain priorities should be established. In principle, outpatient and residential care should be associated under common professional direction. The advantage of this association is to prevent a too fragmented and individualized treatment taking place and to ensure an ideal of comprehensive treatment of the family as a unit in itself.

Facilities in European Countries

In preparation for the seminar, each of the member states of WHO in the European region was asked about the extent and type of provision made by institutions, hospitals, and homes that provide residential care for children with psychiatric abnormalities. The inquiry specifically included children who were delinquent or in danger of delinquency, those who could not be educated within the normal school program, children with character and other psychiatric disorders, and the mentally subnormal.

The national administration of all these types of residential centers varies. Some centers are dependent on ministries of health, others on ministries of social welfare, and still others on ministries of education or ministries of justice. Consequently, their history, purposes, and procedures differ, even when their clientele is manifestly similar.

All countries have some children's psychiatric institutions, which are normally medical, usually within the country's health services. Many have children's psychiatric wards in psychiatric and pediatric clinics. Nearly all countries list some children's wards in their psychiatric hospital systems. Separate psychiatric units for children exist in all countries and are probably on the increase. It is not always clear which children are sent to these establishments. Their population is usually heterogeneous, with a common factor of emotional disturbance. Children with psychosis, mental defects, or sensory or motor handicaps may be included.

All countries have special residential establishments for subnormal children. Those for the severely subnormal are always under medical direction; centers for the mildly or moderately subnormal may not be so. Special establishments for epileptics are uncommon.

The situation with regard to observation centers is not at all clear. A few countries have designated observation centers under medical control; others have observation centers of one kind or another, sometimes for special classes of children, with arrangements for consultant psychiatric advice.

As distinct from the medical establishments, all European countries have special schools or homes for children with educational or behavior disorders. It is possible to classify these into three groups:

1. Special schools for children who are educational failures. Often they are primarily for the mildly subnormal or for the handicapped. They may include children who are emotionally maladjusted or mildly delinquent. It should be noted that there is a considerable overlap of types of children in special schools and in psychiatric inpatient establishments. Usually special schools are reported as having psychiatric consultation available, but rarely are they under medical direction. In a number of cases, there is no psychiatric consultation available, even when maladjusted children are treated.

2. Many countries have schools and institutions for the emotionally disturbed who present behavior disorders, often including "predelinquents." They are usually not under medical direction, and the amount of psychiatric consultation available is variable.

3. Nearly all countries have schools or institutions for frankly delinquent children. Psychiatric consultation or treatment is available in some of these but not in others.

Extent of the Problem

The largest class of mental disorder in children for which some services are already provided throughout much of Europe is mental subnormality. The principles governing the treatment of the mentally subnormal are relevant to the problems encountered among children suffering from other kinds of disorder. To turn, however, from the fairly clear epidemiology of mental subnormality in children to the epidemiology of behavior disorder is to enter a world of conjecture. Diagnostic criteria are ill defined, and the reliability of diagnosis has scarcely been examined. There is a marked lack of agreement about classification and terminology, and few data exist on the prevalence of symptoms in representative age groups of children. In consequence, we are still obliged to rely largely, for our knowledge about symptoms and their apparent significance, on information collected by clinicians working in child guidance centers, who inevitably draw heavily upon their personal experience with a selected group of children. In particular, our knowledge about the need for residential units is very inadequate. In order to plan services, however, it is necessary to be able to make an estimate of requirements, and general surveys of children in need of psychiatric treatment are relevant to this problem.[4,5,7]

In many instances, psychiatric problems in children may be transient; the proportion that require prolonged, intensive treatment is small, and it is difficult to decide the extent to which such children can or should be treated by centers which, because of shortage of staff, cannot even cope with children of minor severity or better prognosis.

The frequencies of certain specific disorders have been studied: epilepsy, cerebral palsy, defects of sight and hearing, and other clinically definable entities can be counted through community surveys. The extent of behavior disorders, however, is less easily assessed in this way, our knowledge being based on administrative or functional criteria: complaints of misbehavior, appearances at court, worries of parents, and so on. Schizophrenia in children has perhaps been underestimated in the past, being absorbed into the category of mental deficiency, but there are still no criteria of this disorder that are acceptable, even for the purpose of recommendations on the size of medical services.

Types of Center

A residential center, being one in which children spend the night, differs in the whole nature of its approach from the day school and the day hospital, from which children go home to sleep.

A convenient distinction between institutions is by *duration of stay*. Certain "observation centers" provide only for short stays of up to one month, either for temporary removal from the home in case of emergency or for diagnostic purposes. In the latter case, it is by no means sure that a few weeks allow sufficient time for the proper observation of the child. The sudden relief afforded him on admission makes it the more difficult to diagnose the environmental relationships in which he has been living. Nevertheless, clinical observation can be carried on, even if there is no very clear idea as to the social elements of his behavior disorder. Short-stay centers raise problems about the commencement of therapy; opportunities for the necessary transfer to other specialized long-stay establishments may be lacking. The difficulties involved in short stays often lead to the idea that too brief a period is undesirable and that it is better to combine short-term and medium-term residential centers, for periods up to about six months, or to avoid the setting up of short-stay centers altogether.

A type of short-term therapeutic holiday camp for the handicapped and socially deprived has been described.[12] In some instances, experience in regard to holiday camps for adolescents and for subnormal children has been favorable, but when it is simply a matter of moving a whole center to a holiday camp, no special therapeutic results occur.

In long-stay centers, children make more permanent relationships with their environment, continue their education, and receive appropriate treatment. These centers should clearly be separate from those designed for shorter periods of observation and treatment.

Institutions vary in the *comprehensiveness of care* they offer. To sum up some points already discussed, a child has four types of need which should be met:

1. He needs a home, i.e., a place where not only his material requirements for food, clothing, and shelter are met, but one in which he can

associate with parents and with other children to form relationships which will enhance his development.

2. For proper education, i.e., to play and use his leisure time constructively and happily, he needs other children with whom to associate in these activities.

3. In the majority of cases, even with long-term stay, a child needs contact with his parents and family; he needs to retain and develop contacts and interests outside the institution, so that when the time comes for him to leave, he will be better able to mix readily in the community.

4. When a child comes into care for psychiatric reasons or when he has psychiatric or psychological problems, he needs appropriate specific treatment.

When homeless children come into care—for social rather than psychiatric reasons, though many of them have psychiatric problems—they are in many countries placed in foster homes. There they are in contact with other children who live in families, retaining links with their own relatives, making new contacts with other families and with the community, and having their medical problems serviced through the resources of the community. Rather than create a comprehensive residential system, with its own separate educational and medical services, each need is dealt with by ordinary community resources. The practical efficacy of this kind of foster home provision has been questioned in some countries.

The size of the residential unit, varying from the intimate foster home to the 1,000-bed hospital for the mentally subnormal, will partly determine which needs can be most adequately met. Perhaps larger institutions can more easily provide resources for a variety of treatment, but if they are too large, the provision of something akin to family life may be lost. It was clear from the discussions that the size of institutions is a question in which national custom weighs. It is, however, generally recognized as advisable to keep institutions from becoming too large. A total of sixty beds is generally recognized as a maximum for a unit which engages in active therapeutic measures; even this is regarded by some as too large.

Where early detection and treatment are guiding principles, the value of setting up residential centers for children below school age is evident, with facilities for residence for their mothers, when appropriate. Fully equipped centers with ample facilities for making a complete assessment and for continuing treatment on a day hospital basis are required. Even when disturbances are apparently neurologic, the associated psychological conditions, whether established or incipient, call for psychiatric examination. Interest is more and more focusing on the specific pathology of adolescents. This suggests the need for highly flexible therapeutic and educational units which include provision for vocational training and a consideration of employment available after leaving the institution.

For psychotic children—schizophrenic and autistic children and those with very serious behavior disorders—separate establishments are sometimes set up where early diagnosis can be made and special therapeutic methods applied. Residential centers for serious cases are essential, if only to avoid placing children in adult mental hospitals. The treatment of schizophrenia among adolescents appears to be taking on greater and greater importance, indicating a need for new types of specialized therapeutic centers for them.

In spite of disagreements between some authorities on the kind of facilities to be provided for delinquents, the need to maintain special establishments for this group is generally recognized; group and milieu therapies are particularly appropriate. It is doubtful whether the maintenance of special residential centers is advisable for epileptic children.

The idea of maintaining a number of specialized residential centers is not universally accepted. Fairly broad opportunities for the early hospitalization and treatment of various clinical groups of children are necessary, particularly in hospitals and children's neuropsychiatric centers. Furthermore, it is generally agreed that residential centers and outpatient services should be closely associated and even that these two ways of handling psychiatric problems may be dealt with by the same technical units.

Placement

The severity or nature of the child's disorder is rarely the most important factor actually considered in relation to his admission. Probably the only circumstance that obliges a child to come under residential care is that he has no home of his own. Few children are in that unfortunate position, and even when they are, there is always some choice in the type of substitute home which might be made available to them. The family's material circumstances are, unfortunately, sometimes a determining influence.

It is not always sound policy to assume that a family crisis calls for immediate placement in an institution. This may often lead to relieving the burden on the family too quickly and giving it the impression that there is nothing more it can do to help the psychiatric services to extricate it and the child from the dramatic situation which has developed. Timely intervention by a social worker may avoid useless and expensive uprooting of the child. The need for admission to a residential institution should be determined by the nature of the child's disorder, taken together with the assessment of his family's ability to cope with his disorder emotionally and socially.

Criteria for Placement

Many grossly disturbed and defective children require to be removed from their families less for their own than for their family's good. In these cases, especially, it is necessary to estimate the effects of the child's removal upon his family (parents and siblings), as well as the changes which may result in the child himself, remembering that a separation which entails a complete and prolonged loss of personal contact between family and child will almost inevitably make it difficult for the family to have him home again.

The amount and quality of outpatient psychiatric services influence the demand on inpatient services. Where inpatient services are more highly developed and outpatient services are lacking, there will be pressure to admit a child into residential care, because only in this way can anything at all be done for him. When adequate dispensaries and day care services exist, the need for inpatient services is very much reduced.

Assuming that adequate alternatives to residential care are possible and that the family has satisfactory housing and living conditions, certain indications for residential treatment can be adduced. The first group of indications relates to the family. Either there is no family or it is incomplete, in a state of crisis, or judged to be incapable of such modification as is essential for the proper therapy of the child or to tolerate his remaining at home. A second group of indications involves assessment of the child himself, pointing to the need for complex psychiatric treatment, perhaps combined with special educational techniques, for a form of social therapy which cannot be given in his family, or for placement under social control in the interests of society.

In judging an individual case, it is not necessary to hold too rigidly to the view that residential treatment is something of a last resort, to be undertaken when treatment at home or in the open community is not available. The possible difficulties dependent on separation from the family should not weigh too heavily. Certain temporary separations from the family may often constitute the only way to enter therapeutically into a situation of family crisis. This is especially true when the reactive behavior of parents and child toward each other is part of a process of development which is aggravating the disturbance.

Generally speaking, older children support separations from their families better than younger ones. Indeed, many adolescent children benefit considerably by being given the opportunity to form relationships with other adults. This is the principle behind the ordinary boarding school. Even though an excellent behavioral adjustment may be made to a residential school, however, and even though there may be many opportunities to learn from other adults and from other children, a prolonged separation from the wider life of the community may in the end be deleterious.

The Center and the Family

The day hospital for children with psychiatric disorders, where the child stays only for the day and goes home at night, obliges his parents to retain far greater responsibility for his life than when he is in a fully residential center. The continued pathogenic effect of the family environment calls for intensive psychosocial activity in collaboration with parents, and new methods of treating the family as a whole may well evolve. Single centers offering inpatient care, day hospital care, and child guidance are well placed in this respect.

Separation is indicated when disturbance in a child is intimately bound up with that of his parents and it has not been possible to modify it by external treatment; for example, when there is intense, persistent aggressiveness with an intractable autopunitive and sadistic-masochistic cycle or when there is a phobic neurosis in a child combined with a similar condition in the mother, who fears that she and her child will die if they are separated. Separation may also become necessary because of the admission to a psychiatric institution of the only parent able to look after the child. There will, of course, also be nonpsychiatric reasons for separation, such as illness of the parents, absence of work, or lack of accommodation.

Among reasons for separation owing to parental shortcomings, the following may be cited:

1. Habitual delinquency, prostitution, sexual perversions, or serious neglect of the child.
2. Maltreatment of the child by the parents (alcoholic, psychopathic, or paranoid parents).
3. Psychotic parents (deluded parents inducing delusions in the child).
4. Neurotic parents in serious disagreement, the child being used against each of the marriage partners in turn.
5. Serious obsessional neurosis, causing the child to live in terror of the least fault.
6. Intolerable pressure on the child, e.g., threats of abandonment, discrediting the therapists, and open or furtive opposition by the parents to the child's treatment, accompanied by threats.

Concerning the reaction of children to separation, in most cases, if the separation is opportune, relief is noted, particularly in the child's anxious reactions and in the labile symptoms of a phobia. His attitude to his parents is frequently idealized to a point at which confrontation with this process sometimes becomes necessary. In the light of reality, the child will readjust himself. Where deep-rooted pathologic attitudes are concerned and where psychotherapy is not effective, however, various complications may be evident:

1. At the outset, either a keen desire may arise for identification with new parental figures and for integration in the new environment or there may be a temporary refusal of all change.

2. Later, if the refusal persists, a child may retain a profound attachment to the old frustrating parental images, and it is not possible to secure either any real modification of his personality or a harmonious reconstruction of it. Progress remains superficial and temporary, and regression may set in immediately after the child leaves the institution.

3. In certain cases, a very uneasy inner compromise is reached—a kind of dual psychic structure in which new identifications are superimposed on the old ones or alternate with them.

As for the parents' reactions, while cases of chronic psychiatric disturbance and permanent social maladjustment will remain unchanged, some relaxation of neurotic anxiety often occurs, accompanied by feelings of guilt. If the parents are then approached, this may be an occasion for progress in their understanding, permitting the return of the child after a fairly short interval. Very often, however, parental pathology will remain the same; for example, a phobic mother will displace her affections to another of her children as a means of reassurance. There is often a serious risk that the treated child loses his place in the home and only finds it again when he is of an age to contribute to the family's material resources. The effects of separation, like those of every other therapeutic measure, should be followed for the whole period of its application.

Psychiatric Treatment in Residential Settings

Observation as a Preliminary to Treatment

If we exclude from discussion the most seriously disordered and the homeless and consider the frequent case of a child with a relatively severe behavior problem, the decision to admit him to a residential institution can often best be taken after a period of observation away from his family. Such a procedure carries disadvantages, in that the situation is atypical for the child, but it also has certain advantages.

In principle, this procedure derives from a modern appreciation of the possible positive advantages of residential treatment as distinct from residential custodial care. Until recent years, psychiatric institutions for children dealt almost entirely with the severely subnormal, outpatient child guidance centers being expected to meet the need for diagnostic study and treatment of children with emotional disorders. Intensification of the child psychiatric team's work has made hospital services necessary for this purpose—services which provide a more comprehensive treatment than that offered in an outpatient setting. Special centers or sections within larger institutions, set up purely for the observation of children, are not uncommon. The length of stay of children in these centers may vary from a few days to months. In most cases, the time spent in an observation center should be long enough to make reliable observations of the child's reaction to his separation from his old milieu and to the effects of the new one. Even if residential placement is, after observation, rejected as a solution of the child's difficulties, the deeper understanding of his problems brought about through the observation can only be of value to the process of diagnosis.

The child in an observation center will be available for a complete examination, physical and psychological. It may not be useful to repeat routine examinations which have been made elsewhere, but it will be possible to look into the data more thoroughly and perhaps to extend certain elements in both physical and psychological procedures. In many cases, the child's being in full-time care will provide the social worker with an excellent opportunity to understand the family relationships more fully through interviewing parents and exploring their reactions to the realities of the child's stay in the observation center and to the possibility of his being taken for long-term residential treatment.

Nevertheless, the reasons for examining the child in an observation center go beyond enabling the psychiatric team to accumulate data on him and his family. Other data, derived from observing and understanding the child's behavior in a new environment, are expected. Observational work may be done by all those who have contact with the child, especially those who are closely engaged in his daily care. In the hospital, this function devolves on the nursing staff. Observation may be continuous and will study the child's behavior in standardized situations within the center, noting the relations he establishes with various members of staff and with the other children.

Specifically, particular attention can be paid to the reaction of the child to separation from his parents, not only on his admission but on occasions when they have visited him in the center or after he has been home on leave. Study of his behavior may be made at different points in the daily life of the center: his behavior on getting up in the morning, his habits of cleanliness, his appetite, his independence in work, games, leisure, and school tasks, and the nature of his sleep. The study of a child's relationships to others in the center can include observation of interactions between him and other children, the effect the child has on different staff members, and the progress of these various relationships. Sociometric data may be of considerable value in this connection.

The various data are usually brought together in staff case conferences which lead to decisions as to the length of the child's stay, the types of observation in which a more discerning technique is required, and those therapeutic procedures that may be adopted immediately.

The Aims of Psychotherapy in Residential Centers

The aim of every treatment is to promote the development of a healthy personality. Very often a complete recovery will not be realized, and in many instances the aim can only be a partial recovery. Social adjustment may be a realistic though limited goal; other limitations may be unavoidable.

Treatment should always focus on promoting the unfolding of the personality, strengthening the child's capacity to knit sound relations with society. The basic aim of residential treatment is to readapt the child to society in such a way as to ensure that he can make full use of all his potentialities. In other words, the center should prepare him for the next phase on his way to maturity.

Children depend on their environment, and their helplessness can be very great, especially in the case of disturbed children. A healthy child can, to a certain extent, influence his environment: he can ask for help and can even force adults to help him. In an institution, however, the staff have to help the child develop an ability to fit into society and, at the same time, prepare the milieu so that it is fit to receive the child again. There is a paradox in this process, in that the institution, by creating a therapeutic environment—sometimes by means of an artificial family setting, sometimes by means of a group-life situation—offers the child a healthy community to prepare him for return to a less healthy society. In that environment—our society—it is the lay person who will judge the child's behavior, his adaptation, his work, and his emotions. Hence, the child has to be prepared to live up to the standards and expectations of society; otherwise he will be sent back to the institution in a short time. This is a problem situation that has to be faced, and sometimes a long stay in an institution must be accepted for the child, until he is old enough to make a place for himself in the outside world.

Therapeutic Climate and Milieu Therapy

The social structure of a residential center will be largely determined by the philosophy of its direction and the specific views held as to treatment. In a residential center sufficiently small to be run as a single social unit yet large enough to be able to offer different kinds of treatment, dealing with a clientele which requires action in all three fields (upbringing, education, and psychiatry), the child will naturally be grouped according to sleeping accommodation, classroom work, leisure pursuits, occupations, and so on. A deliberate grouping by "families" may be preferred. Whatever the precise educational philosophy adopted [9] and whatever school of psychiatry is favored, the modern residential center adheres to the principle of allowing and helping children to develop with professional guidance. Social therapies—psychiatric, educational, or social—are available, as prescribed for each individual child.

The concept of milieu therapy sees the therapeutic role of the center itself as an active one, involving the idea of changing and using this role in a deliberate and manipulative way. Thus, the center becomes a therapeutic instrument in the true sense of the term, not only because life is organized there in such a way as to ensure that the child has a regular timetable, mental and physical relaxation after work, and fruitful recreational and cultural experiences, but also because it acts as a therapeutic instrument in all situations—often unforeseen ones—arising in the course of group life. Opinions and practices may vary as to the importance of milieu therapy, but necessarily the milieu predominates in the life of the child.

The aim of milieu therapy is to treat each child through improving his relationships with his social environment, particularly the quality of his relationships, and to make the perceptions and reactions of each child more realistic. This goal is realized through action on the part of the whole center with its staff, and it is for this reason that the staff who care for children require special training. Their role may be called parental, and they are at the service of the children outside classroom hours and individual therapeutic appointments, at all times of the day and night. The guidance they provide in assisting the normal development of children in the course of their social education, through the constant interplay of relationships, constitutes the dynamic psychological milieu.

It is impossible to give uniform instructions for the establishment of a therapeutic milieu appropriate to all centers and types of children of differing cultural origin. Generally speaking, as distinct from rigid authoritarianism, a permissive climate is required, though not such as to exclude the methodical organization of each child's life in the center. Intensive studies of character and personality show the importance of firmness on the part of an adult staff member faced with aggressive conduct, especially with children who might otherwise be overcome by feelings of guilt. A climate of controlled freedom is a good general rule, although in individual cases a complete absence of restraining counteraction may serve at times to break a pattern of compulsive antisocial conduct. Although modern methods preclude a return to systems of automatic and regular punishment, a liberal and educational climate does not exclude the use of modern sanctions which are acceptable to the children and which provide standards whereby a child can measure his progress and learn self-control.

The degree of permissiveness and the type of interference which might be made in respect to a child's conduct should, ideally, be that appropriate to the situation, taking into account, principally, the effects on the child himself. Thus, each staff member concerned needs to have a deep appreciation of the anxiety and guilt factors in the child and of his previous reactions.[10] Such individual flexibility within a therapeutic milieu makes considerable demands on the staff.

In describing in greater detail the role of the therapeutic milieu in an institution, the following points should be stressed:

1. In the course of institutional life, child care workers maintain an atmosphere by their attitudes to one another and to the children, as well as by the specific measures they take.

2. Merely to promote the establishment of good relations between a child and adults in a therapeutic atmosphere will often in itself favorably affect the development of personality structure in those who have been seriously deprived. Their antisocial behavior often cannot be changed without the prior establishment of deeper relationships, afterward enabling psychotherapy to be undertaken successfully.

3. Within a therapeutic milieu, remedial teachers and psychotherapists cannot be so easily rejected as when they are working from an entirely marginal position.

4. The institution, in sometimes requiring the child to be checked, may give him occasion to regress, but the structuring effect of the milieu on the child's personality allows him to integrate his emotional experiences in correctional situations.

5. The formation of stable groups of children, engaging in group activities and enjoying the interplay of group life, will in itself provide a form of mutual enrichment and education.

To quote Amado: [3]

> It is human relations that act as a common denominator of the different therapeutic and remedial teaching methods used in establishments for maladjusted children. . . . If relations are right, the children's personalities can be beneficially changed by means of different techniques. If not, all attempts end up in failure. The relations between adults and children, and those between the children themselves, are inevitably influenced by the atmosphere of the institution. That atmosphere will largely depend on the relations between the head and his staff. A director can never give too much attention to his attitudes, reactions, and the motives behind them, which will become evident in the very way he runs the place. The way he behaves with his staff will be reflected in their behavior with the children. Taking this outlook to its logical conclusion, we may add that it will be reflected in the way the children behave towards each other, as well as in each child's attitude toward himself.

Individual Psychotherapy

The planning of institutional treatment should avoid piling one specialized form of psychotherapy or educational procedure on top of another.

The importance of the phenomenon of transference in psychotherapy and in education requires that the different elements of a child's program be ordered in a hierarchical pattern.

It may be appropriate at this point to remark on the dangers of offering too many forms of individual treatment (psychotherapeutic and educational) to any one child, who thus may be so extensively occupied that his group experiences and the developing effect of the center's environment may be too limited. At the same time, too many forms of individual treatment will serve to multiply and complicate transference reactions. In such cases, it is useful to focus the treatment program on one person—psychotherapist, educator, or remedial teacher—and to consider carefully the timing of the various procedures and their complementary effects.

Group life can increase the resistances initiated by different contacts with different staff members. Thus, some children may stake their prestige in an obstinate struggle against the latter's endeavors. The whole purpose of the center should be known by all to be therapeutic, thus facilitating the application of specific forms of treatment.

A strong emphasis on the psychotherapeutic nature of the center itself sometimes carries the implication that individual psychotherapy, in its stricter sense, may not be applied or, if it is, not necessarily to all children. Without embarking on a technical discussion of the indications for individual psychotherapy, it would appear logical to suggest that, in any institution with frankly therapeutic aims, individual psychotherapy should be given to all who require it.

Special psychotherapists who work within the center are responsible for a limited number of patients, but as the work of all the staff must be psychotherapeutic, it is difficult to outline boundaries between an individual psychotherapy and psychotherapeutic actions attributable to various staff members.

The complications to which the introduction of individual psychotherapy within the establishment can give rise have often been noted. Children may feel singled out in front of their comrades and may refuse to attend treatment sessions. Their attitudes may be complicated by prestige factors and by group phenomena that make them want to remain unnoticed. If care is not taken to prevent it, other staff members working all day at the center may experience interference with their general program and educational methods.

There are certain technical problems in applying individual psychotherapeutic methods in residential settings:

1. The transference relationship initiated with the psychotherapist may be limited and complicated by the proximity of different child care workers, who may also become objects for transferential effects. The

psychotherapist needs to make his interpretations in the light of this rather special situation.

2. When family relationships are deeply disturbed because parents have not played their role or have disappeared, the psychotherapeutic relation will not be unreservedly transferential. The new reality, in which the child seeks to convince himself that he will not be abandoned by his psychotherapist or else evades him in order not to experience the abandonment which he already knows too well, may be important. A solid, trustful relationship needs to be built up before any real psychotherapy can commence.

3. When children are treated for disorders which manifest themselves principally in their behavior, the psychotherapist must become accepted before any useful progress can be made by individual methods.

4. Some children, under psychotherapy, become particularly excitable, and their regressions create problems in the institution. To some extent, we are witnessing a useful change in the clinical picture—a change in the direction of disturbance and excitement as the psychotherapeutic course progresses. If this is not understood, it may activate tensions between psychotherapist and child care staff, who, after all, are in charge of the children and have to deal with these disturbing effects. There is need for further study of the psychotherapeutic methods applied in residential establishments and their effects on relationships between child care workers and psychotherapists, so that their mutual difficulties can be better understood.

5. Children undergoing psychotherapy may find themselves in some difficulty in making a clear distinction between, on the one hand, their opportunities for expressing themselves as they please in sessions with the psychotherapist and, on the other hand, the necessary restrictions set upon their freedom for the satisfactory running of the institutional community. To revolt against general principle is obviously, for them, a way of giving active expression to their transference and a way of dealing with the anxiety aroused in connection with the freedom experienced in psychotherapy.

6. The privileged position of the psychotherapist in whom a child confides may give rise to other difficulties within the wider therapeutic team of the institution. Opinions vary as to the degree of confidence which should be maintained with individual psychotherapeutic data. Traditionally, and with good cause, ordinary psychoanalytic therapy demands perfect professional secrecy. However valuable this principle may be for psychoanalytic sessions, it may militate against the ability of the psychotherapist to participate usefully in case conferences at which decisions are taken about other therapeutic measures for his individual patients. Some therapists, therefore, hold that the need for good and unrestricted teamwork is paramount, assure their patients of professional secrecy *within*

the staff group, and conduct their psychotherapy with this understanding.

7. Although certain drug treatments are rightly considered adjuncts to psychotherapy, the resulting complications of transference relationships may call for special interpretation and management.

Group Psychotherapy

It would seem natural that psychotherapy should be exclusively or predominantly arranged around groups, since the life of the children in centers is organized on a group basis. Experience shows, however, that the treatment of special "therapeutic groups" in institutions by the usual method of closed group psychotherapy is far from easy. Generally speaking, group structure is dependent on the personality of the individuals who constitute it, as well as on its organization. The adult member of staff tends, at first, to structure a children's group in contrast to himself and then, in the best examples, around himself as an identification model.

Thus, it can be said that the child care worker already responsible for a group ought to be its real psychotherapist. When special group psychotherapists work with the already structured social groups in a center, there is a risk that the respective roles of psychotherapist and child care worker will be confused. In the group psychotherapeutic method described by Redl [11] under the term "life-space-interview," a qualified psychotherapist or a child care worker already in the group intervenes as incidents occur, so as to reduce tensions or to make interpretations that each child must know in order better to understand the life of his group.

Group psychotherapy can, however, be organized with therapeutic groups of children drawn from different institutional groups. Whether the methods used are verbal, psychodramatic, or occupational, this kind of therapeutic group can be treated as an entity as long as it remains closed. In the case of open groups of variable membership, it is more important to confine the group work to a study of interpersonal reactions relating to specific problems or to the specific reactions of the group to the behavior of one of its members.

Other problems are involved in applying the usual methods of group psychotherapy under routine conditions of institutional life. For instance, should the child care worker normally responsible for the group be included in the therapeutic group? His presence cannot fail to produce complex reactions, but his absence may permit the expression of aggressive attitudes to him which would be much better controlled in his presence. Moreover, children belonging to a group can be embarrassed by the fact that their deeper interpersonal problems have been aired in the presence of all and sundry, since, after the group psychotherapy session, they are back again with the same group in their daily life. In practice, it seems easier to deal with acute problems that may arise within the child's social group by various methods that lead children to identify themselves with each other or with the child care worker in charge of them.[8]

Psychiatric Treatment in Hospitals

Children admitted to psychiatric clinics of universities or psychiatric wards in general or pediatric hospitals often have more numerous neuro-psychiatric problems or are more severely ill than those considered hitherto. Consequently, access to specialized equipment and laboratory methods appropriate to central-nervous-system examinations is of greater importance, and somatic therapies will have greater weight. In such types of clinics, the variety of the clinical material, its severity, and the rapid turnover of children admitted primarily for diagnosis put the accent on individual treatment methods, and unless a certain degree of homogeneity of cases can be arranged, the possibilities of milieu therapy must be disregarded. The fact that the accent is on "physical" disorder and "hospital" practice, however, should never lead to neglect of assessment or of treatment of the family as a whole.[6] Neither should educational needs be neglected: educational assessment, guidance, and trials of teaching and learning may well be just as essential to the diagnosis and treatment of these children as in long-term institutional cases.

The Psychiatric Team as Consultant in Pediatric Wards

There are certain typical situations which warrant comment. As long as the psychiatrist, with or without his team, is acting as a contributor to the diagnosis of a child, his work will be straightforward. But to embark on a long therapeutic endeavor with a child in a hospital, where the milieu is not under his technical control, may well present problems. Therapeutic action is limited to psychotherapy, on the one hand, and general advice about the patient's management, on the other. To carry such advice into effect requires a close teamwork relationship between the consultant and the pediatrician in charge and in the end leads to certain implications for the training of both pediatricians and nurses.

In the work of collaboration with pediatrics, child psychiatry contributes knowledge of mental processes; of interpersonal relationships, their management, and treatment; of child development, especially emotional and intellectual; and of the somatic processes—handicaps, illnesses, and "psychosomatic" disorders. Although some of this background lies in the field of psychology, a comprehensive appreciation of all the necessary factors will not be within the province of a professional psychologist alone, even in close collaboration with a pediatrician. For this reason, clinical work in the borderlands of pediatrics should preferably be carried out by a team which includes a psychiatrist, pediatrician, child psychiatrist, clinical psychologist, nurse, and social worker.

The Psychiatrist as Consultant to Residential Educational Establishments

Although it is common for residential special schools to employ part-time consultant psychiatrists, the practice, ideally, needs a more careful definition than is usually made. The psychiatrist cannot replace the child care worker or the clinical psychologist, who should be already on the school staff. Neither can he replace the general physician. He may, however, be employed as a part-time psychotherapist, as a consultant on general and special management within the school, or as a psychiatric consultant to staff members. The last-named role is often worth developing, as a staff member in need of help through discussion of his own personality may not be able to engage in such discussion profitably within the institution. Here, the privacy of the outside consultant in a preventive mental health role is of great value.

There will inevitably be children in special schools who need psychiatric examination and diagnosis. In such cases, it may be questioned whether a visit by a consultant psychiatrist will suffice. The patient should rather be referred to a child guidance center or to a child and family psychiatric clinic, where the full resources of a psychiatric team can be brought to bear on his problem.

The practice of employing a psychiatrist as a full-time member of the staff of a residential special school is unfortunately rare and seems, in many countries, to be precluded by economic factors.

Staff Roles

The roles of staff members were discussed in detail at the WHO seminar and are cited at length in its report. Only some highlights will be mentioned in this chapter. Consideration of the real and ideal roles of the different members of the staff is, of course, handicapped by the extreme variations encountered in practice. These variations not only result from the historical development and socioeconomic framework of the country concerned but also tend to reflect the administrative organization of the center and the kinds of patients served. Even though relatively clear roles may be assigned to staff members in a large and complex institution, in a small setting more than one role is assumed by most persons.

Staff communication, at all levels, is of paramount importance, particularly when the institution is sufficiently large to employ a wide variety of specialists. Many believed that at least one-fifth of each staff member's working time should be devoted to formal interstaff communication. The control of this process, the structure of meetings required for it, and the resolution of difficulties form a part of the management function of the director and are his responsibility even when this work is adequately delegated. It is difficult to see how this structure of communication can be kept if there is an unclear division of responsibility between psychiatric and administrative staff. It is also difficult to ensure an adequate process of communication where there are numerous part-time staff members. Even a part-time staff member working only one or two hours a week in a specific role, such as a dentist, might well require the opportunity regularly to attend staff conferences, so as to contribute observations and to receive guidance about his particular function in the center's community.

In many cases, placement of a child in a day center, as an alternative to hospitalization (or other residential care), carries the advantage that his parents are continually involved in his treatment. The corresponding disadvantage in residential placement is offset by special efforts to ensure that parents do not abandon their responsibilities. Consequently, preparation for the child's admission needs to be made in the light of a clear understanding of the purposes of residential treatment, its duration, and its probable outcome. While the child is in treatment, his parents will be required to continue their parental roles through visiting and other forms of contact. They will be required to maintain contact with the center's staff, and they may need active therapeutic procedures, individually, together, or in groups.

Much of this contact with parents will devolve upon the social worker. Thus, the social worker on the staff of a residential psychiatric institution for children requires special training in family dynamics and social casework method, normally a part of the specialized training of the psychiatric social worker. In many centers, the social worker's role is especially important, because he or she is the only person who has a real firsthand knowledge of the family. The link between understanding of the child's behavior in the center and his behavior at home is often entirely dependent on professional ability to observe, interpret, and communicate.

The psychiatric social worker's role is often an ungrateful one, simply because he is the link between the institution and society and may become the target for the criticisms of both. On the one hand, the parents are reproachful because they think the institution is not ideal, and, on the other, the child care workers make the social worker responsible for the undesirable behavior of the parents. In spite of his attempts to bring parents within the influence of the whole team of the center, factors of distance or of reluctance on the part of the parents may force his responsibility unduly. For these reasons, it is desirable to consider the possibility of several social workers working together as a team, so as to provide mutual support, with one of them sufficiently experienced to undertake a supervisory role in respect to the others.

Centers of the hospital type will naturally employ qualified nurses, but even those centers which are not under medical direction will require a qualified nurse on the staff to see that the principles of general hygiene are observed, to contribute to the health education of their community (both staff and children), and to cope with specific nursing care in case of illness, accident, immunization, and so on.

Just as they do with other members of the residential center's staff, children project onto the nurse certain roles which derive from their need for parental images. Her role can be particularly important in cases of emotional crises in the children, who may use the nurse and her "sickroom" as a relief from the anxiety engendered by aggressive emotions. Many emotionally disturbed children suffer from somatic complaints, tend to dramatize illnesses or accidents, often worry about their physique, or have feelings of unreality. Children who feel ill will go to the nurse as they might to their own mother. In this setting she may both comfort and, at the same time, educate the child in his understanding of bodily symptoms and processes. The assumption of parental roles demands the nurse's involvement at all times in the various forms of case conferences which are a part of the center's regular functioning.

The term "child care worker" is American and generally describes those members of the staff whose primary responsibility is for the around-the-clock care of the children. As their functions combine those of substitute parents and those of educators (in the wider sense of the word), their training must be oriented toward the development of skills which involve a high degree of knowledge and feeling in interpersonal relationships, as well as a grasp of educational principles.

The appreciation of the role of the child care worker as a social educator leads in French-speaking countries to the designation "éducateur." The term does not translate directly into English; "éducateur spécialisé" is worse, conveying to English ears a notion of narrowness in approach which is quite contrary to its intentions. In British countries these staff members are more commonly referred to as "house mothers" and "house fathers." As might be expected from the terminology, the éducateur tends to have a more precise training in pedagogics than his British counterpart. This profession is sometimes referred to as "orthopedagogics" or "Heilpädagogik." The latter term has nowadays a more technical connotation, somewhat related to remedial teaching, involving the more deliberate use of educational methods than is envisaged here.

From the foregoing comments, the role of the social educator will be seen to devolve to some extent on *all* adults in the institution. It is therefore usually considered desirable that administrative staff (secretaries, accountants, etc.) and nonprofessional staff in subordinate positions (kitchen staff, cleaners, etc.) recognize their potential involvement and the possibility of their assuming a high importance in the life of a child. The appreciation of this position demands the provision of some in-service training for all personnel.

Summary

Discussion of diverse practices in the inpatient psychiatric treatment of children in Europe reflects differences in operation and administration in aims relative to the prognosis of children and questions of treatment for specific cases.

Residential centers differ in size, in the kind of patients they take, and in their distance from and relations to the community they serve. They are dissimilar in the training and proportion of staff to the number of patients, in the way in which the staff are divided for giving care and treatment, and in their educational, recreational, and treatment programs. Attitudes to parents and attempts to return children to their own homes represent aspects of varying policies.

The stage is thus set for planned investigations into the effectiveness of distinct policies and for the formulation of criteria by which to judge the relative merits and disadvantages of different elements of institutional care and treatment. Not the least of these is assessment of the effects of residential treatment on families as well as on the children admitted and of comparable results with similar children who are treated solely in an outpatient setting.

No research is possible without careful planning and the assistance of specialized scientific research workers. It is only when the preliminary problems—delineating the milieu, assessing the changes in the children, and recording those data which are relative in quantifiable units—have been solved that precise research bearing on the direct effects of treatment can be undertaken. Progress in treatment methods will only be possible when its ingredients are specified rigorously and when experiments in treatment are so planned that the various outcomes can be compared with their expected goals.

References

1. Ainsworth, M. D.: "The Effects of Maternal Deprivation: A Review of Findings and Controversy in the Context of Research Strategy," *Deprivation of Maternal Care*, WHO Public Health Papers, no. 14, Geneva, 1962.
2. Alt, H.: *Residential Treatment for the Disturbed Child*, International Universities Press, Inc., New York, 1960.
3. Amado, G.: "Douze ans de pratique médic-pédagogique," *Psychiat. Enfant*, vol. 4, no. 2, 1962; see also G. Amado et al., *Méthodes psychologiques pédagogiques et sociales en psychiatrie infantile*, Monographie de l'Institut National d'Hygiène, Paris, 1961.
4. Davidson, M.: "Some Results of Surveys of Psychological Disorders in Children," unpublished WHO working document, EURO-103. 2/WP7, 1960.
5. Great Britain, Ministry of Education: *Report of the Committee on Maladjusted Children*, H. M. Stationery Office, London, 1955.
6. Howells, J. G.: *Family Psychiatry*, Oliver & Boyd, Ltd., Edinburgh, 1963.

7. Kirk, S. A.: *Educating Exceptional Children,* Houghton Mifflin Company, Boston, 1962.
8. Larsson, S.: "Introductory Report on Group Work and Group Therapy in the Treatment of Delinquent and Maladjusted Children and Young People," *Int. Child Welf. Rev.,* 13:119–137, 1959.
9. Mulock-Houwer, D. Q. R.: "Group Work and Group Therapy in Institutional Care," *Int. Child Welf. Rev.,* 13:112–118, 1959.
10. Redl, F.: *The Principles of Permissiveness in the Institutional Situation,* World Health Organization, Regional Office for Europe, Scandinavian Seminar on Child Psychiatry and Child Guidance Work, Copenhagen, 1952.
11. ———: "Strategy and Techniques of the Life-space-interview," *Amer. J. Orthopsychiat.,* 29:1–18, 1959.
12. World Health Organization, Regional Office for Europe: *European Seminar on the Mental Health of the Subnormal Child: Report,* Copenhagen, 1957.
13. References to the work of WHO in child psychiatry are cited in D. F. Buckle, "The World Health Organization and Child Psychiatry," *Proceedings of the Second European Congress of Child Psychiatry,* Rome, 1963; copies obtainable from the WHO Regional Office for Europe, Copenhagen.

22. A Community Program for the Retarded: The Hague

*President's Panel on Mental Retardation,
Mission to the Netherlands*

Introduction

The purpose of this chapter is to describe the program for the retarded in one Dutch city, The Hague. This program, which encompasses a whole complex of services, is probably more complete than any available to the residents of most other municipalities in the Netherlands. It does not, however, necessarily represent the optimum organization, since it reflects both historical accidents and the personalities of those who have been responsible for its continuing evolution.

The members of the mission spent considerable time with the leaders of the program in The Hague and were able to visit a variety of the local facilities. This report should not be considered exhaustive, however, since we were not able to visit all the facilities and organizations which contribute to this program.

The Hague is a compact, rectangular municipality of 600,000 people. Except in the historical central core, an elaborate urban renewal program is under way to rehabilitate the older sections of the city. Since the Dutch emphasize social as well as physical planning, the contemplated reconstruction will probably include new schools and agencies to serve the handicapped. The facilities visited by the members of the mission were found to be housed in old buildings adapted to new purposes. This was in contrast to the smaller communities we visited elsewhere in the Netherlands, where so many of the schools and workshops have been newly constructed within the past decade.

Published with permission of the U.S. Department of Health, Education, and Welfare from the *Report of the Mission to the Netherlands* of the President's Panel on Mental Retardation; adapted for this volume. Members of the mission were W. Wallace Tudor (chairman), Elizabeth M. Boggs, Charles B. Brink, John Melcher, and F. Ray Power.

Systems of Coordination

What makes The Hague's program particularly worthy of study is its systems of coordination. The term "systems" is used advisedly, for there are several, two of which were discussed in detail with us. The interaction between these two systems depends on both formal and informal factors. The interlocking directorate is clearly a consciously used device, as is the power of the purse. Almost all programs are heavily subsidized by the municipality. The initiative in identifying new needs may well come from a public official, who, nevertheless, finds it easier to secure additional funds from his governing body for allocation to a voluntary organization than for the proliferation of programs directly under municipal auspices. Thus, public and private agencies are interdependent and must establish machinery for coordination in order to expand or even to survive.

The emphasis is upon supplying a diversity of services. When these are properly utilized for the needs of each particular individual, they maximize the possibilities of maintenance of the retarded individual in the community. At the same time, residential care for certain children and adults is recognized. Efforts at qualitative and quantitative improvement of these facilities are stressed by public and private organizations.

The two agencies which have the greatest influence in bringing about coordination are the Division of Mental Health in the Department of Public Health of the municipality of The Hague, and The Hague Social-Pedagogic Center, a nonprofit, nondenominational private agency. These organizations share with certain denominational groups the function of continuing guidance and counseling of families (coordination around the clinical objective). In addition, between them they perform the major function of identifying, initiating, promoting, and evaluating worthwhile existing or needed services (coordination around the administrative objective).

City Mental Health Sections

There are nine sections in the city division of mental health. Several of these sections have some functions vis-à-vis the mentally retarded. Section 1 covers the intake of all referrals and handles classification and referral to other sections, as well as admissions to institutions. It also handles psychiatric emergencies on a twenty-four-hour basis and attempts to avoid unnecessary hospitalization of the mentally ill through preadmission review. Section 3 is for the mentally retarded.

Where institutional placement is required, most mentally retarded persons can be placed near The Hague, many going, for example, to the van den Bergh Stichting at Noordwijk (half an hour distant to the north). Patients can, however, be placed anywhere in the country. The processes of admission, care, and discharge are supervised by financial control.

Section 2's work includes the debile * person who becomes psychotic or otherwise grossly disturbed. Section 4 provides a probation service under psychiatric supervision to delinquent children and adults referred by the courts. In some cases a mentally retarded child or adult would be referred back to section 3; in others he might be continued under the supervision of section 4. The staff of this section includes two social workers who are especially assigned to work with the mentally retarded. The case load is not large, however, since in The Hague in 1964, out of 4,268 offenses, only 300, mostly minor, were committed by individuals identified as mentally retarded.

Section 5 provides a complete school mental health service. It follows up truants. If a child fails a grade or if it is suspected that he is mentally retarded or disturbed, this department does a diagnostic work-up. In effect, it engages in case finding and also counsels teachers. Four social workers, six psychologists, and three psychiatrists staff the section. Parents whose children are emotionally disturbed may be advised to take them to other treatment facilities or to private psychiatrists in the community.

Section 6 is an administrative department in the sense that all psychologists are assigned there while also serving the other eight sections of the division of mental health. Section 7 has to do with personnel. There are 13,000 employees of the city of The Hague, some of whom are debiles. In the event that any employee of the department of public health gets into trouble of almost any sort, it will inevitably come to the attention of the division of mental health, and if it is indicated, direct treatment for the individual will be given. This section screens all personnel, especially if there is a history of mental illness; in such instances it makes a recommendation as to whether to employ the individual or not.

In section 8 relations with the various private associations are handled. Varied services, including child guidance clinics, marriage guidance offices, sheltered workshops, and the like, are offered by the nonprofit private agencies and associations. Almost the entire financing of the private associations comes from government subsidy, much of it through the division of mental health. The city may pay a direct subsidy for personnel and even for the buildings and equipment, or it may purchase care on a per patient basis, depending on the nature of the service. Frequently the division will stimulate private organizations or associations to form or expand in order to deal with some emerging special problem. In all such instances, a member of the division sits on the board of these voluntary organizations. Through the fact of subsidy, the department and division are able to maintain quality control on the operation of the services.

* The Dutch use two terms to classify retarded children in special schools: debile and imbecile. In psychometric terms, debile covers a range with an upper limit of 80 and a lower limit of approximately 50 IQ.

Section 3 deals with the mentally retarded exclusively. It maintains cumulative records and offers consultation as necessary from the earliest identification. Practically all mentally retarded individuals six years of age are known to section 3 through the cooperation of the schools and to section 5. A master file is kept on them. Some cases of mental retardation under six and over thirty-five years of age may go unrecorded, although considerable efforts are being made to have physicians refer identified retarded children under six years of age. In addition, a substantial amount of interpretation has been given to parents' associations so that parents will bring retarded children to the attention of the division. The department of public health has some 13,000 records on mentally retarded individuals now living in The Hague. This is somewhat more than 2 per cent of the population. About half of these individuals are "active." Of this number, 545 are in care in residential institutions; 600 in family care, group homes, and foster care; and 3,898 in aftercare—these youth and adults are in their own homes; some may be in normal employment, in postprimary schools, or in workshops; 2,370 children are in special BLO * day schools. Section 3's responsibilities primarily concern those who are not in BLO schools, especially those who have left school and need help in social or vocational adjustment.

All police lists of arrests are received each day and are checked against the records in the office. These lists include all incidents, such as accidents, injuries, and minor offenses. In addition, the department receives lists of marriages, which are checked against its dossiers. When any of these events coming to the attention of the division involve a retarded person who is not in school, a visit is made to his home, usually by a social worker. There are twenty social workers in section 3.

In the absence of incidents or emergencies, visits are nevertheless made to the homes as often as is necessary in an effort to combat a tendency toward dependency. Visits diminish as the retardate improves. The patient may be encouraged to visit the social worker or psychiatrist in the office, and if he is considered to be socially adjusted, it will be strongly suggested to him that he need not continue his contacts with the social worker or psychiatrist but can return whenever he needs additional help. Parents of retarded children are as much clients of this section as is the retarded child or adult himself.

In brief, then, the division of mental health of the department of public health of The Hague performs five related functions within the total complex of local services to the mentally retarded. Four of these functions are basically coordinate. Although the workers of the division come face to face with the mentally retarded, direct service in the sense of

* Buitengewonn Lager Onderwijs is the section of the Ministry of Education which serves handicapped children. Local BLO schools, both public and private, are financed from tax funds.

medical or psychiatric care, education, training, vocational rehabilitation, recreation, etc., is not provided by this public agency. The five functions are (1) the maintenance of a registry of all known living mentally retarded residents of The Hague, whether receiving active service or not, with a cumulative case record of contacts and a service history on each; (2) a social management service to individuals, carried out by caseworkers especially trained to work with the mentally retarded and to offer individual counseling and referral for them and their families; (3) an information source for the professions and the public concerning the general complex of services; (4) administrative evaluation, in cooperation with key personnel in other public and private agencies, of the totality of services, leading to identification of new needs and stimulus to other agencies, usually voluntary, to initiate additional direct services; and (5) municipal subsidy of a wide variety of services offered by private nonprofit agencies.

Interagency Interaction

It has sometimes been said that any major institution is just the lengthened shadow of a man. In The Hague, postwar developments for the retarded are to a very considerable extent the shadow of two men, both dynamic, dedicated, determined, and prepared to differ with their colleagues. These two men, one in a public and the other in a private setting, have complemented each other in promoting a common philosophy, that of the continuum of care. This continuum is seen as composed of a variety of facilities appropriate to different age groups, degrees of retardation, and other specific differentiating conditions, which must be selected and threaded together, as required in each individual case, to serve the preschool child, the school-age child, and the retarded individual after he leaves school. These three periods are sometimes referred to as "precare," "care," and "aftercare," but in The Hague, at least, emphasis is placed on continuity of care.

This is not, however, to say that one agency is expected to play the dominant role in all phases and stages of the retardate's life. Quite the contrary; in fact, one of the striking things about the attitudes of authorities both in The Hague and in other parts of the Netherlands is the mutual acceptance of the complementary roles of the schools on the one hand and the other health and welfare agencies on the other hand. It is accepted as a fact that both educable and trainable children (debiles and imbeciles) can benefit by properly organized school programs under educational auspices and that during the period when these services are being offered the other agencies concerned with guidance, protection, and welfare can be relatively inactive, except, of course, in the case of individual children who may be surrounded by acutely pathologic social conditions. Schools, on the other hand, can operate with equal confidence that when a child is ready to leave school, there will be available to him the guidance and counseling necessary to assist him in further community adjustment in work, living, and leisure-time pursuits. This applies up and down the line from participation in competitive employment, normal leisure-time activities, and relatively normal living situations, through gradations in intensity of sheltering in any one of these three areas, to the possibility of complete sheltering in all three areas such as might be afforded in a residential institution. Because a spectrum of services is available, especially in the postschool period, both the schools and the various social agencies can go about their business with confidence that each of the others is doing its job. One does not hear arguments that the "imbeciles" are "no business of the schools because they will need continuing supervision and will become a concern of the mental health or welfare authorities."

Many of the programs in The Hague are operated on the premise that with good schools and other supportive services at least three-quarters of all imbeciles and even a substantial fraction of the idiots can be maintained for protracted periods or indefinitely in the community. As one official said, "It is a disgrace if the imbeciles must go to an institution." It has also been demonstrated that, with appropriate supportive care, even those debiles who show some behavioral instability, particularly in adolescence, need not always be sent out of the community but can often be rehabilitated to everyone's advantage by steps which will remedy, rather than accentuate, temporary problems of adjustment. Foster home or group home placement is advocated, at least on a trial basis, in most such cases. Group homes are described further under "Postschool Social Management and Community Care" in this chapter.

Provisions for Comprehensive Residential Care for Residents of The Hague

The records of the division of mental health show currently 545 persons of all ages as resident in "real" institutions. This represents a rate of about 9 per 1,000 of the total population. The authorities in The Hague recognize a further need. The waiting lists, since they have been carefully screened, cannot be conjured away. As a result, plans are afoot which will increase accessible capacity by several hundred. Specifically, an institution, Koonings Jaght, is planned under the sponsorship of The Hague Social-Pedagogic Center at Schaarsbergen. It will accommodate 400 school-age children and adults who cannot be satisfactorily maintained in the community. Monstra, the new institution for 300 to be developed near The Hague under the auspices of the League for Education and Care of Mentally Retarded Children, will also help to alleviate the shortage, together with the expansion of the Catholic institution, Nieuwenoord, at Baarn.

Preschool Community Care

It is admitted that even in The Hague the preschool link in the chain is currently the weakest. Case finding and referral depend largely on the cooperation of private medical practitioners, and only recently has an observation center or clinic, staffed for intensive diagnostic work, been inaugurated. Relatively little attention has been given to systematic assistance to parents with home training. The recent development under the auspices of The Hague Social-Pedagogic Center of a prekindergarten for children as young as three years of age constitutes a very positive step in strengthening services to very young children.

The same agency has organized several kindergarten classes for children from four to seven. These are carefully designed to perform the same function for children in this age group relative to preparation for entry into the BLO schools as do similar kindergartens for normal children in relation to the ordinary primary schools. Whereas kindergartens for normal children are now fully government-subsidized under the Ministry of Education, The Hague kindergartens for the mentally retarded are financed by parent fees, on a sliding scale, supplemented by a municipal subsidy for children of needy families. National legislation will be necessary in order to bring this program (which as yet has not been established widely throughout the Netherlands) under the special education section of the Ministry of Education and to authorize Ministry subsidy. Children in the prekindergarten may move on into these special kindergartens, depending on their maturational patterns.

Programs for Retarded Children of School Age

The vast majority of school-age children attend the BLO schools. Nearly two thousand debiles and about five hundred imbeciles are enrolled. During the period of school enrollment the teachers and school social workers have the primary responsibility for consultation and guidance to families, although the children remain on the register of the division of mental health. As already described, the division offers general school mental health services paralleling somewhat the department of public health's responsibility for school general health services. The mission did not visit any schools in The Hague, but reports from other visitors suggest that, except for having fewer modern buildings than more recently established programs, they offer the same high quality of education observed elsewhere in the country.

Many years ago vacation camps and homes for retarded children began to be established by private organizations in the Netherlands, especially for underprivileged retarded city children. Some of these now operate on a year-around basis, although summer is the peak time. Such opportunities are now also open to the retarded from normal-income groups. A stay at one of these vacation homes or camps serves the dual purpose of giving the retarded child (or youth, or adult) a healthy and stimulating change in the new environment while providing his family with an opportunity to go places and do things in which he probably would not be interested.

For the relatively small group of children and youth of school age who are not able to attend school at all, The Hague Social-Pedagogic Center has organized a day care program. Day care for the very severely retarded is a relatively new development in the Netherlands and is to be found in only a few communities. What is most impressive about the program in The Hague, however, is its acceptance of those with the severest disability. Several completely nonambulatory patients were observed who indeed required "total care."

Postschool Social Management and Community Care

The director of The Hague Social-Pedagogic Center estimates that 2.5 per cent of the total school-leaving cohort will be debiles, most of whom will have had the benefit of BLO education. Of these approximately 20 per cent can be expected to merge successfully with the general population and to utilize the social agencies and employment opportunities for normal persons without any further distinction. About 60 per cent of the total debile group will, he estimates, be able to engage in competitive employment with only occasional counseling or assistance from time to time, more particularly during the first ten years after school. It is possible that as many as 10 per cent of the group classified in school as debiles may require sheltering in the occupational component of their adult lives. An additional 10 per cent will be able to maintain themselves in competitive employment but will require somewhat more specific community support in relation to living and leisure-time activities. For example, a certain number of adolescent girls whose families have anxieties about them are identified from time to time. A number of these girls have been accommodated through the critical adolescent period in a group home (Die Saen Haghe) while participating in the post-BLO work-training program or in regular employment. Not only is this type of care relatively inexpensive during the time when it is actually given, but it also tides over the group served until the girls develop stability, without subjecting them to the additional retrogressive hazard of complete separation from their community.

Several group homes for working adults (men or women) are also operated in The Hague. One provides for men who are in competitive employment (mostly debiles), and one for those who are in sheltered employment (mostly imbeciles). A number of evening or "continuation" classes are made available by the Dr. Schroeder van der Kolk Association for the benefit of retarded youth and adults.

The Retarded Adult in the Community

The program for adults in The Hague is predicated on the assumption that the need for social support or sheltering in one aspect of one's life program need not automatically carry with it a requirement that sheltering be accepted in all phases. Use is made of a "psychiatric profile" in which there are three major variables or components: for work, living arrangements, and leisure-time activities. An individual who requires sheltered working conditions may nevertheless be able to live in a "free" or normal situation, especially if living with one's family is so regarded. He may also be able to make use of common or undifferentiated recreational facilities. On the other hand, another individual who is able to maintain himself in a competitive industrial position may require greater sheltering during afterwork hours. It will be seen that, between the extreme of complete independence in all three aspects and the extreme of complete dependence in all three aspects, there are six marginal situations involving a need for sheltering or social sustenance in only one or two of the three components. Barring aggressively antisocial behavior, the general philosophy is that such individuals should receive specific social support in the community and, indeed, that those who need support in all three areas may also be maintained in the community if they are able to function well enough to move physically and socially from one to another extramural activity during the course of the day. Only when the degree of sheltering required is marked in all components will a program self-contained in all respects (i.e., a true institutional program) be indicated.

Sheltered evening recreational programs for men and women are offered in The Hague on a weekly basis as a form of sustenance in the leisure-time aspect. These are open to persons working in competitive jobs or in the sheltered workshops, for example, whether they are living in group homes or the family home, whenever the individual retardate appears unsuited to participate in normal community recreation but can interact socially with his peers. Vacation homes and camps are also open to adults.

None of these homes or leisure-time programs would be of much value without constructive approaches to the employment problem of the retarded. The system of follow-up of pupils leaving school by the social-pedagogic or social psychiatric services is in full force and effect in The Hague. The social psychiatric component is provided mostly by section 3 of the division of mental health, as described earlier. The specialized employment services for the handicapped within the labor exchanges are also called upon; indeed, they have the legal responsibility of helping the handicapped find jobs in competitive employment whenever possible.

The Dr. Schroeder van der Kolk Workshops

No account of services for the mentally retarded in The Hague can be in any sense complete without a description of the group of sheltered workshops operated by the Dr. Schroeder van der Kolk Association. This program never fails to impress foreign visitors.

The association is a "general" one and has a board broadly representative of the various religious persuasions, the professions, the schools, the aftercare agencies, labor, industry, and government. It has a long history, having been established in 1923. In recent years services to the mentally retarded have been expanding. In 1957 there were two workshops (in two former school buildings) accommodating 325 mentally handicapped workers, of whom about one-third were mentally retarded. As of 1962 there are three shops with 475 workers, of whom approximately two-thirds are mentally retarded. A new especially designed building to accommodate a total of 700, is projected. The workers not classified as mentally retarded are mentally ill, most of them schizophrenics. These workshops are unique in the Netherlands in this respect.

All but twenty of the workers come to the workshop on their own, usually walking or by public transportation. A bus is provided to transport twenty workers who have complicating physical handicaps or who are for some other reason particularly disadvantaged.

A great variety of industrial activities may be observed, some quite complex. In fact, the various processes have been classified into six levels according to complexity. In the highest levels one finds power machines (some with special fail-safe devices) used in the manufacture of clothes, the assembly of bicycles, and so on. At the lowest level one group of very severely retarded men, who cannot qualify for the government-subsidized program, are nevertheless kept active and productive and even earn a few cents an hour on an ingenious device which enables them to glue plastic caps to corks to make stoppers for soft-drink bottles, for which a subcontract has been secured by the shop.

Considerable stress is placed on tempo. Conveyor belts and revolving tables, whose speed is variable but controlled, are deliberately used in order to put gentle pressure on the worker to maintain and improve his rate of productivity, to pace him, and to focus his attention. It is considered as damaging to give a worker a task substantially below his capacity as it is to require of him more than his capabilities permit. The multidimensional matching of the job demands to the capabilities of the individual is stressed.

Because every effort is made to screen out and place any mentally handicapped workers who can go directly into competitive employment without utilizing the sheltered workshop as a way station, relatively few of the mentally retarded move from sheltered to competitive placement.

The possibility is never discounted, however, and within the past year twenty workers were placed outside from the shops. In this connection it is interesting to note that, under an arrangement worked out with industrial and union leaders, a worker may be placed in open industry at a wage below the normal standard with the permission of a special board in the employment branch of the Ministry of Social Affairs. This arrangement permits the employment of otherwise adaptable persons whose principal defect is an inability to maintain the minimum normal speed in production. It is also possible for workers to be placed temporarily in industry at normal wages but without immediately acquiring union privileges and guarantees. Such provisional placement may be permitted for a period up to one year.

An Evolving Network

It will be seen from the foregoing observations that the range of specialized needs of the retarded has been recognized and analyzed in some detail in The Hague, that services are directed and conducted by professional and subprofessional personnel who specialize in work with the mentally retarded, and that the network of services is in continuing dynamic development. Seen in the large, the network is also notable for the attention given to balancing the isolating tendencies of needed specialized services against the shortcomings of nonspecialized, nominally "integrated," but inappropriate activities. The mentally retarded person is not provided with meaningless community living "opportunities" by being asked to sink or swim without supporting services. Wherever beneficial and to the degree beneficial with any particular individual, efforts are made to place the retarded person where he will have contact with normal society and normal social institutions. This is a delicate balance which is often misunderstood and hence upset by social planners. The maintenance of this balance and the near-completeness of coverage of the needs of the mentally retarded in The Hague are that city's proudest achievements in this sphere of social activity.

23. The Highfields Program for Delinquent Boys

Albert Elias

Introduction

Effective treatment of the juvenile delinquent in correctional institutions is a complex problem that has challenged, and oftentimes defied, the most sophisticated efforts of therapists and administrators ever since the welfare of the wayward child was singled out for specialized attention. Attempts to resolve this problem have had to contend with two crucial factors: (1) the continuous growth of the correctional population and (2) the social world of the inmates.

New methods of treatment have provided no assurances that their impact on the delinquent population will enable us to reduce this problem to manageable proportions. Delinquency, like adult crime, has become a social fact. It has emerged as a normal and inevitable consequence of a complex industrialized society, a situation long ago noted by Émile Durkheim. In his classic treatise on the rules of sociological method,[4] Durkheim stated:

> Crime is present not only in the majority of societies of one particular species, but in all societies of all types. There is no society that is not confronted with the problem of criminality. Its form changes; the acts thus characterized are not the same everywhere; but, everywhere and always, there have been men who have behaved in such a way as to draw upon themselves penal repression. If, in proportion as societies pass from the lower to the higher types, the rate of criminality, i.e., the relation between the yearly number of crimes and the population, tended to decline, it might be believed that crime, while still normal, is tending to lose this character of normality. But we have no reason to believe that such a regression is substantiated. Many facts would seem rather to indi-

A previously unpublished report, prepared while Mr. Elias was superintendent of Highfields Residential Group Center, Hopewell, N.J., U.S.A.; especially prepared for this volume.

cate a movement in the opposite direction. From the beginning of the [nineteenth] century, statistics enable us to follow the course of criminality. It has everywhere increased. . . . There is, then, no phenomenon that presents more indisputably all the symptoms of normality, since it appears closely connected with the conditions of all collective life.

If Durkheim is correct, and there is no reason today to question his observations of three-quarters of a century ago, we can make a corollary observation. As the population increases, we can expect a corresponding increase in the number of juvenile delinquents in correctional institutions. Obviously, this problem goes beyond the scope of correctional administration.

The constant search for new, experimental methods of changing delinquents into nondelinquents is, however, within the range of the field. In fact, it is the basic task of institutions for juvenile offenders. Under ideal conditions, the achievement of this aim is both difficult and costly, but it is much more difficult to accomplish in correctional institutions, where the culture and the informally organized social system of the inmates compete with the conventional culture and the formally organized social system of the administration for the loyalty and support of the inmates. Although we still lack systematic evidence for this kind of development in residential facilities for juveniles, common experience and recent social science literature suggest that, generally, the inmate social system serves to neutralize the effective implementation of treatment methods.[2] This situation is a direct consequence of the fact that the major influence on an inmate during his incarceration comes from the other inmates rather than the staff. A recent study,[7] describing this problem as it affects all total institutions, observes:

> There is a basic split between a large managed group, conveniently called inmates, and a small supervisory staff. Inmates typically live in the institution and have restricted contact with the world outside the walls; staff often operate on an eight hour day, and are socially integrated into the outside world. Each grouping tends to conceive of the other in terms of narrow, hostile stereotypes, staff often seeing inmates as bitter, secretive, and untrustworthy, while inmates often see staff as condescending, highhanded, and mean. Staff tend to feel superior and righteous; inmates tend, in some ways at least, to feel inferior, weak, blameworthy, and guilty. Social mobility between the two strata is grossly restricted; social distance is typically great, and often formally prescribed.

While this view of the relations between the social and cultural worlds of the inmates and the officials may be an overstatement of the case, it does represent a close enough approximation of the actual situation to warrant serious consideration, especially as it relates to the treatment of incarcerated offenders. The implication of this position is that a direct approach to the problem would be to develop methods of reorienting the character of inmate peer-group relationships in the direction of conventional goals and of decreasing the social distance and communication between staff and inmates. Needless to say, these suggested changes would have a very direct bearing upon almost every facet of an institutional structure and would inevitably require changes in other areas as well. One of the missions of correctional personnel and social scientists in this field is to explore possibilities for the establishment of treatment conditions within institutions that can gain the support of the inmate society. It is the purpose of this chapter to describe the various elements of Highfields, a correctional program that attempts to achieve these aims by utilizing a group-living experience for all the residents.

Evolution of the Method

Although it is difficult to delineate the impact of specific influences on the evolution of the Highfields approach, it is possible to point to a few of the most obvious ones. Initially, the stimulus for the establishment of the program was provided by a proposal, made in 1949 by a committee of judges, for legislation to permit the courts to impose short, fixed-term reformatory sentences of from three to six months. The New Jersey Department of Institutions and Agencies felt that the presence in the reformatories of men with this type of sentence would complicate the matter of handling the majority of inmates serving longer institutional sentences. It made an alternative proposal, suggesting the establishment, on an experimental basis, of a small unit for the short-term treatment of a limited number of selected delinquent boys, who would be admitted as a condition of their probation.[8]

A few months later, the New York Foundation offered to provide financial support for the project. To avoid the danger of perpetrating another of the many fads that have emerged and failed in the field of correction, an independent evaluation was undertaken by New York University, under a grant from the Vincent Astor Foundation. Moreover, support and acceptance of the program were secured from the juvenile courts and probation departments of the state. With Dr. L. W. McCorkle as director, under the general supervision of Dr. F. L. Bixby, the project admitted the first boy in July, 1950.[9]

Other influences, of a more general nature, were also instrumental in the establishment of Highfields. The originators of the program were very much aware of the work of Wills, Aichhorn, Redl, and others, who fostered the concept of intensive care of emotionally disturbed and delinquent children in a small group-living setting.[16] These men had urged and demonstrated that it was possible to involve the entire staff and population of the facility in the rehabilitation process. Moreover, it was recognized that small, open facilities, such as forestry and work camps, primarily for the more amenable male offenders, suggested concepts that could be incorporated in the design of the Highfields program.

A third factor playing an important part in the evolution of the program was the group psychotherapy movement, which had been emerging as a relatively new concept in various countries. During World War II, this movement received its greatest impetus, particularly in hospitals for soldiers with severe psychoneurotic ailments. This method was also employed in correctional facilities for military offenders, in the hope of restoring them to duty within the shortest possible time. In a very direct sense, the group therapy program at the Fort Knox, Kentucky, Rehabilitation Center, under Dr. Alexander Wolf, was influential in the development of Highfields. It was there that Dr. McCorkle, the first director, received his training in this field, and Dr. Bixby formed his interest in experimenting with this approach in New Jersey after the war.[1]

The work of the Chicago school of sociologists prior to the war also played a part in this program. These sociologists conducted comprehensive studies of the role of the group factor in delinquency which have yet to be matched by more recent social science research efforts. Shaw and McKay and Thrasher demonstrated the critical role of primary group experiences, particularly the peer group, among adolescent delinquents, while Burgess called attention to the fact that the delinquent was not only a mass of physical and personality traits but also a person with a social role and a status.[12] These studies provided theoretical and empirical support for much of the orientation that underlies the Highfields approach to delinquents.

Objectives and Assumptions

The principle objectives of the Highfields program are similar to the objectives of any correctional treatment program for juvenile offenders, namely, to change delinquents into nondelinquents. Implicit in this goal is a series of assumptions about the character of delinquency and the delinquent himself, adolescent peer groups, and the method of effecting stable changes in a conventional direction.[5]

Delinquency and Delinquents

There is no doubt that delinquents, like nondelinquents, are troubled by psychological stresses and strains of varying degrees of intensity. At Highfields the assumption is made that the delinquent's problem stems from his allegiance to and internalization of a deviant system of values and attitudes. He has formulated his relations with others and his conception of himself in terms that are in direct conflict with those of the conventional society. If this is the case, then the central task of the program is to achieve for each boy conformity with and acceptance of prosocial norms and expectations rather than delinquent self-conceptions and patterns of interaction.[11]

Frequently adolescent offenders, particularly those of middle-class origin, do not see themselves as delinquents but rather as unfortunate victims of an irrational system of social justice. To paraphrase Tannenbaum,[14] their evil has not been dramatized sufficiently to make offenders aware of the community's definition of them as delinquent. This definition must be taken into account by the boys themselves; otherwise the process of rehabilitation will be hindered considerably. They will avoid committing themselves to the program and thereby escape identifying with its aims. In a sense, unless they see themselves as delinquents, they will neither understand nor accept the need for change.

The other side of the coin involves boys who accept community definitions of themselves as offenders. Many delinquents are cognizant of the standards of conduct required by conventional society and may even be in agreement with them. This awareness is sometimes employed by offenders to evade the social controls that attempt to prevent delinquency. They design systems of rationalization to justify their commitment to a delinquent style of life. These techniques, such as denial of responsibility for one's acts and defining injury to the victim as rightful revenge, are used to neutralize treatment techniques as well. Nevertheless, the common awareness and possibly agreement by both delinquents and nondelinquents on the basic values of the larger society enhance the prospect of utilizing knowledge about these values in a rehabilitation program. It would enable such a program, for example, to pose realistic alternative ways of acting and defining behavior for the delinquent groups.[13]

The Peer Group

The transition from adolescence to adulthood is paved with much anxiety and even discontinuity. For the adolescent to achieve the status of a young adult, he must construct the identity around which he will organize his behavior. In other words, an adolescent must see himself reflected from significant others, both adults and peers. The latter appear to be very important in the construction of a new identity.[6] For example, the peer group provides support in his rebelliousness against his parents; it offers a form of group loyalty which extends beyond the family and prepares him to participate as a responsible member of society. The real shortcoming of the delinquent peer group as a socializing agency, however, is that it promotes and intensifies the isolation of the adolescent from the cultivation of significant relationships wih conventional adults and other adolescents. It is a self-defeating solution, because it creates and perpetuates social barriers that preclude experimentation with conventional roles and modes of adjustment.

At Highfields, the assumption is made that the isolation of the delinquent peer group can be counteracted by making accessible to the boy alternative roles and relationships for exploration. By using the adolescent peer group as a medium of change and a source of influence over its members, change as an end in itself can be legitimized by the group as acceptable conduct for its members.

Methods

The most obvious technique employed at Highfields to attain stable changes in the residents is to involve the total population in the same treatment program at the same time. This approach assumes that this is one of the most effective ways of intervening directly in the delinquent inmate social system, thereby creating a setting for the emergence and maintenance of a conventional inmate social system. Opportunities can be developed for assigning status to the boys on the basis of prosocial patterns of interaction that are independent of the system of allocating status within the delinquent culture. Communication between staff and inmates is regulated by the demands of a rehabilitation program rather than by the needs of administrative convenience. A climate is created in which the inmates and the officials are focused on a similar goal, namely, to make changing delinquents into nondelinquents a distinct and achievable end. It eliminates the common practice of evaluating the inmates in terms of surface conformity to institutional norms and makes it possible to define them in terms of conventional peer-group alignments, new self-conceptions, and commitment to a prosocial value system.[3]

Residents

At Highfields, an attempt is made to incorporate the stated framework in a residential treatment setting for a group of twenty male adolescent offenders.[10,15] These offenders are, for the most part, probation failures, who are selected by juvenile-court judges throughout the state of New Jersey. In selecting these boys, the judges, usually on the recommendation of the probation officers, are guided by the following criteria:

1. The boys must be between sixteen and eighteen years of age. This age group was included because in New Jersey the compulsory school age is sixteen years and the upper age in the Juvenile Court Act is eighteen years. Since we do not have a school program and we accept cases only from the juvenile courts, we are bound by this age level.

2. Boys who have previously been committed to a state training school are not eligible for consideration. In general, boys who were institutionalized have developed patterns of behavior and techniques of manipulation and surface conformity that make it difficult for the program to deal with them. The relatively short period of residence in the Highfields program requires that boys respond to the program elements in terms of their

personal problems almost from the start. Institutionalized boys have a strong tendency to react in terms of their prior experiences in the training school.

3. Boys who are severely handicapped physically, intellectually, or psychologically are excluded from consideration. Since the boys are required to work an eight-hour day, handicapped boys would be unable to participate as equal members with their peers in work assignments. No clinical services are provided, and seriously neurotic or psychotic boys could not be served.

Youngsters who seem to gain most from the Highfields program are those whose delinquency is influenced principally by a peer group. In general, these boys have fairly extensive histories of involvement in property offenses. A sizable proportion were involved in offenses against persons, and a third group were involved in offenses against public policy. In the overwhelming majority of cases, the offenses were committed in association with other delinquents. Very few of those admitted have any interest in formal education. In general they have succeeded in rejecting the school situation largely by getting into difficulty, usually over an extended period of time.

The length of residence in the program is relatively short, usually about four months. Release depends upon a variety of factors, including each boy's behavior and the evaluation of the staff and of the therapy group to which he has been assigned. Some boys do not complete their period of training and are returned to court for other disposition. They either run away and do not want to return, are serious psychiatric problems and require clinical attention, or are so threatening to the other boys or to the program itself that they must be transferred. All the boys, however, are admitted as a condition of probation rather than on a commitment basis, so that after release they are returned to the direct supervision of the probation department.

The Staff

There are six employees on the staff at Highfields: the director, an assistant director, a cottage couple, a work supervisor, and a secretary. The director and his assistant conduct group meetings and perform routine administrative duties. The cottage couple prepare meals, maintain the building in which the program is conducted, and supervise the boys who may be working around the house. The work supervisor takes the boys to and from work and, on alternate Sunday evenings, takes them to town to attend movies, call home, and buy refreshments. The secretary is in charge of records, correspondence, minor bookkeeping, the typing of reports, and related duties. Four of the six employees reside in the same building as the boys. The project is located on the former estate of Brig. Gen. Charles A. Lindbergh, who deeded the property to the state of New Jersey in 1941.

The only persons on the staff with professional training are the director and his assistant, who is usually a graduate in one of the social sciences, education, or social work. The other staff members, especially the cook, play a significant part in serving the boys as adult models and in socializing them in a conventional way. Because there are relatively few boys in residence, the staff can establish close and intimate ties with them. Although on rare occasions other staff members mete out punishment, the cottage couple have assumed this responsibility. At Highfields, punishment consists of additional hours of work around the house for getting involved in a situation that is defined by one or both cottage supervisors as an infraction. Since there are no fixed rules and regulations, punishment is rather arbitrarily assigned. The most severe punishment involves working in the back of the house, digging holes in the ground to bury refuse. A boy may be assigned to this job for one or more days. He does not get paid for this work. In practice, this type of sanction is employed as a means of social control by the cottage couple, but it is not a very effective device, because the boys quickly develop methods of manipulating the staff members. Such experiences can be fruitful, however, because they are discussed in the group meetings at night, where they are related to each boy's or each group's problems.

The Program

In contrast with the involved bureaucratic structure that is generally found in a conventional correctional facility, the Highfields program is relatively simple. The program consists of four principal features: (1) method of orientation, (2) work situation, (3) contacts with the community, and (4) guided group-interaction meetings. The overriding aspect of these features is that the peer group is employed as the principal instrument for change.

Method of Orientation

The usage patterns of the Highfields social system are based on the assumption that youthful offenders need an informal educational experience. Since there is little formal structure, there is no conventional system of rewards and punishments. Also, there are no rules and regulations as such, because usually in a correctional setting these become fixed as a result of experience in a tradition. As a consequence, the residents do not have to relate to these formal controls but rather to the situations and problems that develop in the course of their careers at Highfields. The norms and sanctions that do exist include only those which are considered essential for the maintenance of order, so that food is made available, health is preserved, and the right of each boy to participate in the program is maintained.

The admission procedure is short and simple. An admission card is completed, and the boy given an opportunity to ask questions. Afterward he is assigned to a room and given a job around the house. His orientation to the program is provided by the peer group. In this way he develops a perspective that is meaningful to everyone and not just to the staff. Moreover, this procedure sets the tone for other experiences and relationships.

Work

All the boys, with the exception of the KP who helps the cook, are taken by the work supervisor each morning to a nearby state hospital. Under the direction of hospital employees, they are assigned to various jobs in the storehouse, the garage, the butcher shop, the linen room, the farm, and anywhere else they are needed. Each boy who goes to work receives 50 cents per day, so that he may have funds for haircuts, refreshments, cigarettes, and similar items. No attempt is made to teach occupational skills; rather, the work situation is designed to provide an opportunity to develop conventional work habits.

Contacts with the Community

Contacts with the free community are frequent. Every boy is granted two 3-day furloughs at home during his residence. In addition, on Saturday evenings the boys are taken to nearby towns to attend movies, buy refreshments, and call home. On Sunday mornings, those who desire are taken to town to attend church services of their choice. On Sunday afternoons, they receive visitors, who may take a boy off the grounds provided a parent is present.

Method of Group Treatment

The third feature of Highfields consists of the guided group-interaction sessions, which are the core of the entire program. They serve as a means of stabilizing the lives of the boys and as the medium through which each boy can come to grips with his problems. In these sessions major emphasis is on the group and its development rather than on an exhaustive analysis of each group member. On arrival, each boy is assigned to membership in one of the two therapy groups. These groups meet in the director's office five evenings each week for ninety-minute sessions. Attendance is not compulsory. At these meetings group members have an opportunity to discuss issues and experiences of their own choosing.

Every group is closed to new members when it reaches a certain size, usually eight to ten boys. Every group, therefore, has a history of its own, for it has a beginning and an end. Since new boys are assigned to the "old meeting," they have an opportunity to witness and get involved in the discussions of the "old boys" and thereby to learn by a process which can be likened to that of participant observation. In this way, too, they are oriented not only toward the techniques of participating in the group sessions but also toward Highfields as a whole, because it is in these sessions that the significance of Highfields becomes apparent. Through the process of informal orientation, every group is able to internalize the culture of Highfields and also to transmit this culture in turn to other new groups as they arrive.

During the group sessions, the leader plays a fairly active part in the proceedings. He attempts to support and assist the group toward awareness of its problems, as well as to make interpretations of the interactions between members.

It is our impression that each group proceeds through a series of stages in its development, from an aggregate of strangers, who have little or no interest in each other, to a closely knit primary group, whose members are able to relate to one another in a significant way. Although not all groups adhere strictly to this pattern, they all do so to some degree. A brief, oversimplified outline of this process might be presented as follows:

During the initial stage there is no discernible group structure. There is much random, restless behavior. The members engage in two major types of activities: (1) they seek information about each other, the staff, and Highfields; and (2) they test the situation by engaging in hostile, defensive behavior, such as scapegoating and paying lip service to conventional standards.

The second stage is characterized by the development of awareness of themselves and others, as well as the formation of cliques within the larger group. Delinquent social roles and self-conceptions are revealed. A great deal of tension is generated around revealing oneself and one's feelings about other members. The group begins to experiment with the establishment of rules to govern their conduct in the meetings. From the point of view of the individual boy, this second stage involves discovery of "his problems" and learning how to "trust" the meeting. He is beginning to identify himself with the other members and to define the meeting as "our group," in opposition to the "old group," which consists of all the other boys in the house. Moreover, he recognizes that demands are being made on him to help make group decisions. Oftentimes, at this point, the members start to formulate their strategy for dealing with the most basic issue at Highfields, namely, to change or not to change.

The third stage is a critical period in the lives of most boys. For the group it means that clique ties are broken and identification with the larger group is demanded by other boys. For the individual member it means that his problems are carefully analyzed and his choices challenged, particularly when he begins to experiment with new social roles in an attempt to find one that is satisfying to him and at the same time acceptable to the group. The discussion of these issues is characterized by an expression of intense hostility, particularly toward the group leader; defenses are breached, and much frustration is experienced. The outcome of this struggle is a high degree of group solidarity and mutual identification. For most boys it means that a crucial choice is to be made, namely, that in order to survive in the free community the boy must change his values, attitudes, and behavior. He is also learning that he "helps himself by helping other group members." This process involves reforming oneself by attempting to reform others. The delinquent accepts the common purpose of the group, identifies himself closely with other persons engaging in reformation, and assigns status to others on the basis of conventional behavior. He becomes a genuine member of this group, and, hopefully, at the same time he is alienated from his previous delinquent-group affiliation.

The final stage is a period of intense, concentrated activity. There is a direct assault on each member's problems and an expression, in action, of confidence in the group's ability to resolve any difficulty. There is minimal dependence on the group leader. The members review each other's roles, interpersonal relationships at Highfields and at home, and their present and past behavior. And, of course, the group begins to send its members home.

Adjustment in the Community

The problem of determining whether or not the Highfields program reforms the boys who are exposed to it is a difficult one with which to deal. The same situation exists for any correctional institution which attempts to evaluate the effectiveness of its program in these terms. One of the obstacles is to find a set of criteria which can be applied to measure the type and degree of reformation which has taken place; in effect, to tell the story of persons who have failed to reform and of those who have changed from delinquency to nondelinquency. Probably one of the most searching and challenging problems in the field of correction is to find a method of demonstrating that reformation, when it does occur, is due to institutional treatment. In other words, do changes in attitudes and conduct occur because of institutional experience and treatment or in spite of them? Even in the case of the recidivist, when the discharged boy returns to delinquency and eventually is recommitted to a correctional facility, did he fail to reform because of the failure of the institution or was his failure the result of factors in the free community unrelated to his institutional experience? These problems, which require further study, are beyond the scope of this chapter.

Two commonly employed measures of whether or not reformation has taken place are the recidivist rate and the success rate. They are not entirely satisfactory. For example, a boy who is returned to the community and experiences rearrest without conviction, has no visible means of support, associates with other probationers and parolees, and gets involved in minor infractions of the rules of probation but does not get convicted and sentenced is regarded as a success. Although they are gross methods, however, these measures do shed some light on one important aspect of the problem of determining the kind of adjustment in the free community that has been made by boys who were released from a correctional facility.

Highfields has been the object of two evaluation studies. The first was limited to a comparison of a Highfields experimental group with a reformatory control group of boys, who were sent to each facility from the same juvenile court. The control group included only boys who were committed to the reformatory during the period *preceding* the opening of Highfields. The second study was a five-year follow-up comparison of Highfields boys with a control group of reformatory inmates who were committed *after* Highfields opened. Both studies reached essentially the same conclusion: that the Highfields program is not only a more effective correctional form for selected offenders than the traditional reformatory program, but that it is also a less expensive method to administer.

Summary

The notion that the delinquent peer group might be used to facilitate delinquency rehabilitation has been explored in this chapter. The assumptions guiding the Highfields project are discussed, and the program is described. Perhaps in few other fields of human endeavor has man been so cautious of change as in correction.

References

1. Abrahms, Joseph, and L. W. McCorkle: "Group Psychotherapy at an Army Rehabilitation Center," *Dis. Nerv. Syst.* 8:50–62, 1947.
2. Clemmer, Donald: *The Prison Community*, Holt, Rinehart and Winston, Inc., New York, 1958; McCorkle, L. W., and R. Korn: "Resocialization within Walls," *Annals*, 293:88–89, 1954; Sykes, Gresham M.: "The Corruption of Authority and Rehabilitation," *Soc. Forces*, 34:257–262, 1956; Cloward, R. A., D. R. Cressey, G. H. Sykes, and S. L. Messinger: *Theoretical Studies in Social Organization of the Prison*, New York Social Science Research Council, New York, 1960, p. 15.
3. Cressey, Donald R.: "Changing Criminals: The Application of the Theory of Differential Association," *Amer. J. Sociol.*, 61:116, 1955.
4. Durkheim, Émile: *The Roles of Sociological Method*, 8th ed., The University of Chicago Press, Chicago, 1938, pp. 65–66.
5. Empey, L. T., and J. Rabow: "The Provo Experiment in Delinquency Rehabilitation," *Amer. Sociol. Rev.*, 26(5):679–696, 1961; McCorkle, L. W., and A. Elias: "The Essexfields Program for Youthful Offenders," *N.J. Welf. Reporter*, forthcoming.
6. Erikson, Erik H.: "Ego Identity and the Psycho-social Moratorium," in H. Kotin-

sky (ed.), *New Perspectives for Research on Juvenile Delinquency*, U.S. Department of Health, Education, and Welfare, 1955, pp. 24–50.

7. Goffman, Erving: *Asylums*, Anchor Books, Doubleday & Company, Inc., New York, 1961, p. 7; see also Lloyd E. Ohlin, *Sociology and the Field of Correction*, Russell Sage Foundation, New York, 1956, pp. 14–20.

8. McCorkle, L. W., A. Elias, and F. L. Bixby: *The Highfields Story*, Holt, Rinehart and Winston, Inc., New York, 1958, p. 173 and Appendix A.

9. *Ibid.*, pp. 10–11.

10. *Ibid.*, chap. 10.

11. Ohlin, Lloyd E., and William Lawrence: "The Role of the Inmate System in the Institutional Treatment Process," unpublished paper, New York School of Social Work, Columbia Unversity, New York.

12. Shaw, Clifford R., and Henry D. McKay: *Social Factors in Juvenile Deliquency*, Government Printing Office, Washington, D.C., 1931; Burgess, Ernest W.: "The Delinquent as a Person," *Amer. J. Sociol.*, 1925; Thrasher, Frederick L.: *The Gang*, 2d ed., The University of Chicago Press, Chicago, 1936.

13. Sykes, Gresham M., and David Matza: "Techniques of Neutralization," *Amer. Sociol. Rev.*, 22: 664–670, 1957.

14. Tannenbaum, Frank: *Crime and the Community*, Ginn and Company, Boston, 1938, p. 19.

15. Weeks, H. Ashley: *Youthful Offenders at Highfields*, The University of Michigan Press, Ann Arbor, Mich., 1959 .

16. Wills, W. David: *The Barnes Experiment*, George Allen & Unwin, Ltd., London, 1945; Aichhorn, August: *Wayward Youth*, The Viking Press, Inc., New York, 1935; Redl, F., and D. Wineman: *Children Who Hate*, The Free Press of Glencoe, New York, 1951.

24. Institutional Social Education of Severely Maladjusted Girls

Asger Hansen

Introduction

It is the purpose of this chapter to describe a frame of reference and discuss a methodology for the pedagogical-psychological treatment program for severely maladjusted girls conducted at the Viby Statsungdomshjem in Denmark. Our small institution has room for twenty-five girls, between fifteen and twenty-one years of age, who live in three sections, housing five, six, and fourteen pupils, respectively. One of the sections contains two isolation rooms, which are used when a pupil is considered dangerous either to herself or to others.

Referral to Viby is made through the municipal boards for children and youth welfare, usually following three to five unsuccessful placements in other child and youth welfare centers. After a review of the total case record by the Viby staff, recommendations are forwarded to the directorate of the National Child and Youth Welfare Authority, which must approve any actual commitment. The decision to transfer a pupil to Viby is generally based on the observation that (1) previous sanctions and treatment methods have not had any corrective effect on social behavior as observed during parole or (2) the pupil is so difficult to handle and presents so many disciplinary problems that work with other girls is severely handicapped. It will be apparent that negative factors play a major role in referral to Viby.

It is very rare to find a pupil whose deviant social behavior cannot be traced back to early childhood. While about 90 per cent of the girls have never had a legitimate occupation, ending in prostitution or semiprostitution, this evident symptom of asocial behavior is not their most noteworthy characteristic. It should be noted that about 50 per cent have been trans-

Adapted from a paper previously published in *Nordisk Psykologi*, 14 (7):305–316, 1962.

ferred directly from psychiatric hospitals or wards where they had stayed from two to fourteen months. Only 20 per cent of the Viby girls have not had previous psychiatric treatment.

In terms of traditional diagnostic labels, the majority of the girls may be described as psychopathic personalities. At Viby we do not insist on making such a diagnosis but leave it to individual judgment to use such terms as "insufficient character," "character disorder," "ego weakness," "impulse-ridden," "drive-directed," or whatever might be preferred. It is characteristic for the pupils to have an extremely short latency period between impulse and reaction, so that contrary inhibiting tendencies do not occur in time to prevent behavior motivated by immediate impulse gratification. The existence of this personality disturbance, frequently noted in so-called "psychopaths," does not exclude the simultaneous existence of expressive, neurotic symptoms. The initial impression, however, is that of marked insufficiency of character, leading to a kind of asocial behavior which results in commitment to Viby.

The Pedagogical-psychological Approach

For a description of the nature and background of the character disorders presented, several frames of reference, none of which can claim to be valid in and of itself, are available. The legitimate use of a certain frame of reference depends, however, on the purpose for which it is employed. Since it is my intention to give an account of what I call "pedagogical-psychological treatment of the total personality," it has seemed more appropriate to describe character deviation within the concepts of social psychology, but it should not be assumed that this frame of reference is the only one applicable.

From a social-psychological view, personality may be seen as a genetic formation experiencing many of the conditioning processes noted in learning. While numerous different theories have been presented on the development of personality and ego formation during the first years of life, there appears to be general agreement that a certain security and stability in the environment facilitate the inevitable conflicts between the infant's unregulated needs and environmental demands for adaptation.

Behavioral rules, as defined by adults, are mediated through reward and encouragement, as well as through disapproval and punishment. It may be supposed that these rules are initially experienced by the child as unmotivated pressures and demands from the outside. Gradually, growing identification with adults results in an internalization of accepted norms and rules, so that these finally are experienced as personal value judgments concerning good and evil, right and wrong.

The structural organization of these value judgments grows into a frame of reference on the basis of which an individual adopts his attitudes and behaves in actual life situations. Through these attitudes and through this behavior, he expresses what we call his personality. The identification of the child with the adult is an essential condition for the establishment of the social learning process, and it seems that frequent shifts in identifications objects and disrupted emotional contacts have a damaging effect on the course of the learning process.

A 1960 test sample of residents from Vejstrup Statsungdomshjem (which has now been incorporated into Viby Statsungdomshjem) showed that only two of nineteen pupils had so-called "normal" homes in which both father and mother were present during the entire childhood. The other seventeen came from broken homes which had experienced separations, divorces, or deaths.

Combining this background information with our knowledge that during their previous commitments these pupils had been subject to frequent changes from institution to institution and in this way had experienced constant shifts in parents' substitutes, it is understandable that the identification process had not influenced the social learning process in the best way. It is even conceivable that the instability in the identification objects prevented the emergence of the identification process itself. One practical consequence of this observation should be that the prevailing tendency to move a child from one institution to another be avoided whenever possible.

The frequent prevalence of broken homes is too rough a criterion for adequate characterization of home life. We therefore tried to ascertain the methods of child rearing used in the nineteen cases included in the Vejstrup test sample. On the basis of records and interviews with the pupils, each and every one had to be described as having experienced a deviant upbringing.

As a rough estimate, we classified the methods of child rearing into four types which seemed to cover the whole material:

1. Extremely authoritarian upbringing with beating and punishment at the slightest provocation, practiced from earliest infancy.

2. Indulgent upbringing in which weak parents tried to buy the acceptance of the child, probably because they were unable to provide a deeper emotional contact.

3. Capricious, unstable upbringing in which the child at one moment was indulged with tenderness and at the next rejected and punished. In such a setting it is impossible for the youngster to predict adult reactions on the basis of his own behavior.

4. Indifferent, careless upbringing in which the child was neglected emotionally and materially, with nobody taking responsibility.

In descriptions of the learning process, the effect of motivation has been the subject of much interest. It is common to distinguish between negative and positive motivation, depending on whether disapproval and punishment or encouragement and reward have been used as motivating factors. In this connection, it may be pertinent to note a distinction made by the Danish psychologist Kurt Palsvig between what may be called motivation-supporting and motivation-infringing effects on personality development. This distinction is often contrary to traditional concepts.

A few examples might be illustrative. One morning in 1960, an intelligent seventeen-year-old girl reacted with a violent emotional and aggressive outburst to a minor disappointment. I was called at about 10:30 A.M., at which time she was breaking windows and furniture in her room. When she saw me, she demanded in a very excited way to be placed in the isolation room. I explained to her that I found this solution of the problem very poor, but as she insisted with growing excitement, I gave in and took her to the isolation room.

At 4:30 P.M. that afternoon she wanted to have a conversation with me. During about 1½ hours we discussed very thoroughly her basic situation. She spoke quietly without affective overtones. There was a long history of a well-established hostile relationship with authorities, primarily with her father but also with all representatives of social agencies, including teachers, police, child and welfare workers, etc. She showed a good understanding of the fact that, when frustrated, she reacted with regression to an infantile pattern of defiance. We talked about the normal stubbornness of small children and compared her own behavioral pattern with this tendency.

Toward the end of the conversation, which occurred in an atmosphere of very good contact, she asked if she could now leave the isolation room. I answered in the negative, about as follows: 'You knew that I did not like to use the isolation room, but you forced me to it. I do not use this room for petty disciplinary nonsense. If I really have to use it, it will be for at least twenty-four hours. I consider you a grown-up human being, and grown-up people have a right to be reacted to in a grown-up way. This implies that you cannot play truant with respect to the consequences of your own behavior. Had you been the little child of four we talked about just now, I should have taken pity and removed you at once, but you are an adult, and therefore you have to be isolated until 10:30 tomorrow morning.'

Her reaction to this explanation was a very quiet "thank you," after which she equally quietly went back to the isolation room. Later on she told me that on this occasion, for the first time, she felt respected as an adult human being and not treated as an irresponsible child. This example should illustrate the use of negative moderation (punishment) which, as far as I can see, had a supporting and not an infringing effect on the personality.

An example of the opposite can be taken from my previous work at the ward for the treatment of criminal psychopaths at Herstedvester. A borstal boy who had been referred to Herstedvester for observation was extremely emotionally attached to his grandfather, who apparently was the only human being toward whom he felt any close ties. One day he was visited by his mother. She sat in front of him, opened her big bag, and looked at him with the roguish smile used at Christmas time when gifts are exchanged and unwrapped. Suddenly her facial expression changed, and she said: "Little Carl, mother has something very sad to tell you. Grandfather died the day before yesterday." Then she smiled again and continued encouragingly: "But, don't worry. I have a new camera here, and I know you always wanted one." A camera in exchange for the human being he loved, coupled with an implicit demand not to "behave stupidly" as he used to do when something did not go his way!

Returning now to the four child-rearing methods mentioned earlier, at least three seem to be characterized by motivation infringing on the personality, namely, the authoritarian, the indulgent, and the capricious upbringing.

Considering the social technique of which the Viby pupils are capable, it is obvious that it represents an age level far below their actual chronological one. It is remarkable that the technique is mastered with fluency and has become automatic, but the technique has very few variations and is primitive and immature relative to the pupils' age and general physical development.

If it is correct that, with respect to learning social behavior and social norms, the pupils have been exposed to primarily personality-infringing motivation, we can anticipate a tendency to inhibited social development. We also must be very careful which kind of motivating factors to use in treatment. Unfortunately, available professional literature offers few ideas and little inspiration for work with character disorders.

Pedagogical-psychological Treatment

With rare exceptions, experts have agreed that the kind of clients here described are so deviant that, for a variety of reasons, treatment has not been considered feasible. Most psychiatrists and psychologists have preferred to leave the problem to others, refusing even to tackle it on a theoretical basis.

The reason that trained psychotherapists have declined their services is mainly that classical psychotherapy, as developed on the basis of Sigmund Freud's theories of the neuroses, is considered inappropriate. It is hardly surprising that a method of treatment in which one of the main goals is to remove inhibitions is not an adequate approach for the treatment of people whose major problem is too great a tendency toward an uncontrolled instantaneous satisfaction of needs.

Describing the Viby treatment method as pedagogical-psychological implies that the aim is to educate or, in some cases, reeducate. This means that in our daily work we have to maintain a certain level of demands with respect to social behavior, observation of norms, work standards, etc.

To place an unstable, "spineless" personality in an environment in which everything is relative and uncertain, in which the possibilities to choose seem overwhelming, will, generally, only result in cultivating the symptom of spinelessness. If a laissez-faire attitude has provoked this symptom into a conflict demanding solution and if, as part of our duty, we help with the solution of this conflict, we have only undertaken symptomatic treatment of the most superficial character. Of course, our level of demand cannot possibly be absolute. As our clients come to us with very different personality structures, intellectually as well as emotionally, the approach has to be adopted to the possibilities and conditions of every single individual. This might seem a very simple assumption, but it is frequently difficult to administer, because it offends the often rather undifferentiated concepts of justice in the majority of the pupils. For example, it might be hard for girls in a work group to understand that a single member could get full credit for less work than others.

To administer this heterogeneous level of demand, it is necessary that the staff have sufficiently close contact with every pupil to survive conflict situations. In this goal we meet another difficulty, since contact with other people is a basic part of the problem of character insufficiency. As one result of their early frustrations, pupils are often afraid and generally quite incapable of engaging in lasting contacts. It is characteristic for them to develop a certain contact rather quickly, and the inexperienced staff member will often be seduced into believing this relationship to be deep and valid because the pupil seems to load it with emotional intensity. After the member has experienced several times the quickness with which pupils can sever relations for seemingly insignificant reasons, however, the joy over the first overwhelming, spontaneous contact becomes more reserved.

In our work with the Viby pupils we do not try to hide this state of affairs. Our most important therapeutic tool is an effort to try to orient the pupil toward reality, and only in very extraordinary cases is this demand compromised. This reality orientation has, however, no chance of leading to something positive if it is accompanied by a didactic, condemning attitude, underlining the excellence of the staff member (personality-infringing motivation). At the same time that the pupil is presented with, and perhaps realizes, her problem, it is necessary that she also realize her need for help and support and that this support be given in a way in which she feels herself accepted. All this seems like a very commonplace observation, taken directly from a popular textbook on child rearing, but for the ego-weak, "spineless," and self-devaluating girls this basic acceptance is the *sine qua non* for the next step in treatment, namely, the "straining" of the clients.

As mentioned earlier, our level of demand is not an absolute entity. We generally try to work right on the borderline of the personality strength of the pupil with respect to demand and also with respect to showing confidence, rendering facilities, etc. In our daily institutional life we meet again and again an outspoken "demand" from our pupils that we solve a certain problem or conflict or impossible situation by authoritarian interference. Sometimes the pupils seem to ask for advice, and at other times it appears that they want to provoke sanctions of a more or less punitive nature. While demands seem to depend on the nature of the conflict or situation, it is characteristic that the pupils want a solution from outside, do no wish to assume responsibility, and prefer to let authority dictate.

Usually, we do not yield to the demand to interfere. As a result, we often succeed in converting an external conflict into an internal, individual one. When we decline to provide solutions, however, as pedagogues we are obliged to help the pupil to analyze her problem and understand her own reaction patterns and behavioral choices. We also have to help her perceive the realistic possibilities for a resolution of her problem and to assist her to understand and foresee the consequences of her decision.

It is incumbent upon us to make honest use of our experience and the knowledge we have about a pupil's earlier situations, what she told us about her previous life, and what we have observed during her stay at Viby. But, with this, our obligation is usually fulfilled. The decision and the choice must be the pupil's own. Each single conflict in which she finds herself is a problem situation, and the effectiveness of learning depends on the degree of self-activity with which she has been forced to solve the problem.

We try to implement our idea of pedagogical "straining" of the pupil but have to admit that it is not always possible to do so. A few pupils have broken down in such situations, and once a psychogenic psychosis resulted. Also, it is not only the "straining threshold" which determines how far we can go. Sometimes consideration for the pupil group limits our activities. Group pressure occasionally forces us to avoid pedagogical measures which in our opinion would be best for an individual pupil.

If we lay aside all becoming modesty and try to view disciplinary activities at Viby as representative of the different punitive theories, it is obvious that the pupil group, almost without exception, represents the classical punitive theory, which prescribes that the severity of punishment should fit the crime, regardless of circumstances. In contrast, the staff has a closer affinity to the positive punitive theory, which gives greater consideration to the person than to the actual criminal behavior. It is not uncommon that the pupil group is more deeply offended by a break in norms (no matter by whom) than the staff and that the pupils demand stricter and more rigorous sanction than we should find desirable.

In our pedagogical treatment we are, to some extent, forced to take group standards into consideration. If certain social norms have been established in a group of pupils, we cannot permit transgressions without comment. A too yielding or too permissive attitude on our part would lead to corruption of the system of social norms. There is a limit to the degree to which "justified wrath" can be frustrated. We have to conserve and further elaborate the sense of justice which is so essential.

In earlier paragraphs I have several times referred to conflicts, and this has been with good reason. In our pedagogical treatment we simply cannot do without conflicts, even if these are very tiresome for the pupils and the staff. During conflicts we obtain insight into the motivations and "behavioral mechanisms" which have resulted in students' hostile attitudes toward social norms. Through concrete and actual knowledge we get a chance to belabor and change these mechanisms. The decisive factor in whether a conflict is productive or not depends on the ability to profit by it in treatment. Conflict for the sake of conflict is irrelevant.

While we still maintain that in our pedagogical treatment we aim toward the establishment of a social learning process, there seems to be considerable evidence that the receptivity of the pupils is increased during affectively provoking situations. For example, many have been the times when, months later, I have been told verbatim what I had said to a pupil on such an emotionally loaded occasion. Often this was followed by the observation: "It is strange that I remember this so vividly, because I was so angry at that time that I experienced everything in a sort of mist."

There is no doubt that what we in Viby, and for that matter people in other Danish pedagogical treatment institutions, call treatment is an elaboration and extension of the traditional treatment concept. We find that we cannot limit treatment to the therapeutic interviews that occur between a client and a psychiatrist or a psychologist. We prefer to use a treatment concept very close to that enunciated by Dr. Georg K. Stürup, chief psychiatrist of the ward for the treatment of criminal psychopaths at Herstedvester. He usually says that treatment is the sum total of all the goal-oriented influences any staff member directs toward the client to facilitate the insight needed for adaptation to the ethical demands of our culture. It is necessary that this treatment concept be placed in the foreground, day and night, in the sections, in the workshops, in the hobby rooms, and in school, as well as on the station. When we succeed in this effort, we shall have created a truly therapeutic climate.

It is quite possible that our treatment does not result in "happier" people. Perhaps the "spineless" charming client has a much easier life as a psychopath than as a "nice member of society." I shall not here go into the ethical justification of a rational and utilitarian goal setting such as ours. Let it be an open question if the more or less neurotic member of society has a more dignified life than the free-floating psychopath, whose uncontrolled behavior unceasingly provokes society into placing limitations on her personal acting out.

The creation of a therapeutic climate depends on the relationship existing between the group of pupils and the staff, among the pupils themselves, and between management and staff. Sometimes one has the impression that the greatest problem in an institution is staff. Besides differences in personalities, staff members are further subdivided into salary grades, seniority, educational levels, and institutional duties. To create collaboration amidst such a heterogeneous group on a certain treatment scheme for a single pupil or more generally, everybody responsible for implementing the scheme must have been coresponsible for planning it. Otherwise the necessary loyalty cannot possibly be expected.

Daily staff conferences on each pupil are a necessity for effective teamwork. Even if there is a treatment program for a single pupil, it does not exist in a vacuum. New observations and fresh knowledge demand program revisions or even reformulation, and, if so, the staff members involved in the original plan must be involved again and accept the new plan.

Before they come to us, our pupils have usually experienced the consequences of disagreements between parents and other adult authorities, often to excess. In many cases they have learned to manipulate conflicts with eminent skill. It is our duty, in the way we try to influence them, not to allow repetition, because they would only mean a further fixation on a more primitive level of problem solving.

With very few exceptions (August Aichhorn, F. Redl, and, in Denmark, Georg K. Stürup and Torpe), a general defeatism has long prevailed among experts on treatment of early-acquired personality and character disorders in children and youths. It seems to me that one main reason has been the reluctance to accept or understand that an entirely different treatment concept, other than that of classical psychotherapy, is needed. Psychiatrists and psychologists have largely declined to work with these groups because traditional therapeutic tools have been found inapplicable. There has been reluctance to experiment. One consequence has been that the whole field has been more or less surrendered to amateurs. Because of special gifts and the strength of their own personalities, some of these amateurs have produced eminent work, but, to the extent that such endeavors have depended primarily on an individual personality, it has been impossible for others to forge ahead in the absence of a theoretical foundation. At Viby we have tried to fill this void with our pedagogical-psychological rationale.

Summary

The approved school for girls at Viby, Aarhus, is a treatment center administered by the National Child and Youth Welfare Authority. The girls referred for treatment are among the most deeply maladjusted in the age group from fifteen to twenty-one; the majority have records of three to five unsuccessful placements in child welfare institutions, and 80 per cent have at some time been under observation or treatment in psychiatric clinics or hospitals.

On the assumption that social behavior and adjustment patterns are conditioned by processes similar to learning, an attempt is made to offer a systematic description which might assist in laying a foundation for treatment methods of character deviants (psychopaths) who have frequently been considered relatively insusceptible to therapy.

The treatment approach is described as a dynamic combination of pedagogical and psychological methods. Although the description deals primarily with treatment in an institutional environment, there is reason to suppose that similar viewpoints, with certain modifications, may be used in ambulatory treatment. This assertion is based on experiences with aftercare, which is regarded as an essential and integral part of the total treatment program. Emphasis is also placed on the need for highly developed teamwork among the staff members, which is so essential for creating an institutional treatment atmosphere.

25. Innovation and Experience in Mental Health: A Commentary

Henry P. David

Introduction

Innovation and experience are primary ingredients and principal products of progress in most fields of human endeavor, including the broad area of mental health. They are of little avail, however, unless they are communicated and shared with others similarly coping with common concerns. In the world-wide search for effective and practical approaches to social problems, we have much to learn from each other. To facilitate the sharing of innovation and experience is the primary objective of the contributions to Part Five.

All of the chapters in this section deal with children or adolescents in Europe or the United States. Among the contributors are physicians, psychologists, an educator, a sociologist, and, in the case of the President's Panel on Mental Retardation, a team consisting of specialists and particularly qualified laymen. It is immediately evident that in choosing work with disturbed, retarded, or delinquent youngsters, we are entering, as Charlotte Babcock [2] expressed it, "a multidisciplinary field of ever changing complexity." The uncertainties and unknowns are such as to demand a mature and dedicated attitude to not always rewarding tasks. Ingenuity and innovation must frequently be matched by patience and endurance.

In the Introduction to this volume, I reviewed the development of the third revolution in mental health [6] and the sober appraisals of future manpower needs and limited resources by George W. Albee [1] and Henri Collomb.[5] Among the programs described here, some are still in a stage of innovation, while others can point to a decade or more of successful experience. None are high-cost demonstration projects, involving an elite staff and a refined selection of case loads. To cope with the realistic problems of manpower and funds and to work toward the goal of eventually

Especially prepared for this volume.

extending mental health services to all people in need and not only the privileged few, we must endeavor to begin adapting to local circumstances knowledge gained from the innovations and experiences of others, regardless of origin, professional bias, or cherished tradition.

Emotionally Disturbed Children

The first contribution to this section, describing Project Re-ED, presents a particularly unique innovation. Five-day residential centers for emotionally disturbed children, the Re-ED schools consider themselves primarily schools. With an avowedly educational orientation they attempt to substitute a public health-mental health model for the traditional clinical one in providing a service for disturbed children.

The momentum for Project Re-ED stemmed in part from observing the work of educators, pedagogues, and educational psychologists in France and England. The project draws on a source of manpower (or womanpower) that is in reasonably good supply without compromising on the quality of the individual who works with the child on a twenty-four-hour basis. Teacher-counselors make and take responsibility for decisions that may or may not be reviewed with mental health consultants. Perhaps most important, there is a relative deemphasis of deep intrapsychic processes, of fundamental personality reorganization, and of the usual clinical objective of attaining a "cure." Rather, primary emphasis is on learning and the public health goal of getting into a reasonably functioning order the circumscribed social system of which the child is an essential part. As Hobbs [6] describes it, this means that every attempt is made "to get the child, the family, the school, the neighborhood, and the community just above the threshold with respect to the requirements of each with respect to the other." When it is judged that the system has reached a level of functioning so that the probability of its successful operation exceeds the probability of failure, the child is returned home.

To be widely adoptable, the public health effort must be economically feasible. It is generally estimated that the existing clinical model for the residential care of disturbed children in the United States costs from $25 to $80 per day, with an average of around $50. Hobbs suggests that Re-ED schools can be operated for around $12 to $15 per day per student. The average length of stay is generally four to six months. It is evident that Project Re-ED is a promising innovation deserving further consideration as an approach to working with emotionally disturbed children and conceivably preventing even more serious difficulties in adult life.

The summary report by Donald F. Buckle, Serge Lebovici, and J. Tizard of the WHO Seminar on the Inpatient Psychiatric Treatment of Children in Europe is packed with useful suggestions. The public health approach is apparent in the broad representation, which included child psychiatrists, special educators, psychologists, nurses, and psychiatric social workers. The representatives came from twenty-one European countries, both Western and Socialist, and spent a week discussing indications for the admission, treatment, discharge, and follow-up of children admitted to a variety of residential centers because of psychiatric disorders. Approaches, standards, and medical provisions differed, but all facilities made at least some endeavor in continuing education.

Discussion of diverse practices in European psychiatric residential centers tended to reflect differences in operation and administration, from exclusively medical to nonmedical direction with psychiatric consultation. There were variations in size, in the kinds of patients accepted, and in distances from and relationships to the communities served. Dissimilarities were also noted in the training and proportion of staff to number of patients, in professional education, and in psychiatric treatment. The stage is thus well set for potential studies designed to evaluate the merits and disadvantages of differing elements of institutional care, the roles of staff members, and the effectiveness of multiple therapies.

While there was a consensus on institutional needs and programs for subnormal (retarded) children, it was far more difficult to reach readily implementable recommendations for children with behavior problems. Apparently countries with greater educational resources find it easier to limit the range of psychiatric institutions required. It was noted:

> Where the cultural level of a population is high and where general medical practitioners, social workers, teachers, and child care workers are well informed, it is far easier to do preventive work. With improving cultural levels, intervention by the child psychiatrist may become premature and psychiatric care may well become less needed, so much so that, under ideal conditions, the psychiatrist would more frequently act in a purely consultative capacity.

It is always hazardous to generalize, but there are perhaps some notable differences between European and American approaches to services for emotionally disturbed children. While there tends to be much less concern with basic research and program evaluation in Europe, there is also a broader range of services more widely available to all socioeconomic strata. There are shortages in specialized facilities and trained staff, but the fundamental philosophy seems to be more one of accepted public responsibility for troubled children. This is reflected by steadily increasing fiscal support, less emphasis on formal training, and a greater willingness to experiment with people who demonstrate warmth and aptitude for work with children.

Among postwar innovations, the most important perhaps may be the readily expanding use of small residential units. These homes or schools generally house from eight to forty children in a familylike setting. Often located in a rural area, they place primary emphasis on milieu therapy and an educational orientation. There are usually one or two trained professionals (in mental health, education, or both), with several devoted care-takers and students who receive on-the-job training. To a perhaps undue degree, these programs tend to depend on the continuing leadership of key individuals.

In 1963, Paul Penningroth, an experienced mental health professional, made a sophisticated survey of children's services in selected European countries.[8] His summary conclusions are worthy of note:

> Europe has gone a long way to help the disturbed child. The range of services provided, the devotion of the personnel, the willingness to create whatever new services are needed, and the emphasis on prevention were both impressive and inspiring. It is hoped that our country, whose financial, technical, and human resources far outstrip those of any other nation, can use them on behalf of disturbed children with as much, or even more success.

Mental Retardation

The historic document on *National Action to Combat Mental Retardation*,[9] the report of the President's Panel on Mental Retardation, is as much a part of the third revolution as the report of the Joint Commission on Mental Illness and Health, *Action for Mental Health*.[7] Although major public focus has tended to be on the biogenetic aspects of retardation, a redefinition of the problem appears to be occurring in recognition of the preponderant involvement of social and educational influences in the total picture. There are a refreshing vigor and activity in the parent and other citizen groups concerned with retardation, which augur well for innovation and sharing of experiences.

For a commentary on the comprehensive community program for the retarded in The Hague, it seems most appropriate to cite some of the observations of the Mission to the Netherlands by the President's Panel,[10] from which The Hague report was excerpted. The American visitors appeared to be particularly impressed with the practical demonstration of the philosophy of "differing in need but equal in human rights" which permeates the Dutch program for the retarded. There is repeated emphasis on the extent and usefulness of social-psychological and social-pedagogic services, the cooperation of labor and business with government, and the comprehensive yet highly flexible community facilities. The same philosophy was also well expressed by N. Speijer's [11] discussion of the social integration of the retarded at the 1963 Annual Meeting of the World Federation for Mental Health: "Our task is to minimize his disability at every point in his life, so that he can reach the highest degree of social integration possible."

It would be difficult, I believe, to find a more eloquent statement of the practical and social utility of the Dutch program for the retarded than the conclusions reached by the Mission to the Netherlands:

No state in the United States can say that it offers special education to so many of its retarded children, that its employment opportunities and follow-up services are so generally available and so effective in the adjustment of so many of its retardates to community living, working and leisure time opportunities, that its opportunities for sheltered employment for those who are truly disabled below the competitive level are so widespread and on such a firm ongoing footing, and that the quality of care offered to its more severely retarded in its institutions, existing and planned, represents such a good approximation between what its leaders believe and what it is prepared to do.

Juvenile Delinquency

Among the most baffling social maladies of the century is that of juvenile delinquency. If adolescence is the period of apprenticeship for one's adult role, then in G. M. Carstairs's [4] view there can be little doubt that this apprenticeship is not working very smoothly at the moment. He observes that, in 1961, there were nearly three times as many men in British prisons as in 1938 and nearly half of all the indictable offenses were committed by youths under the age of twenty-one.

There is little doubt that juvenile delinquency is a world-wide phenomenon, although it may vary qualitatively and quantitatively from country to country. The United Kingdom has its teddy boys, France its *blousons noirs*, Sweden its *raggare*, Germany its *halbstarken*, Japan its thunder boys, and the Soviet Union its *stilyagi*. As Roul Tunley [12] noted in his global survey, juvenile delinquency may flourish in the most Western democratic and in the most Socialist of societies. Sweden had the highest known rate: 3 per cent of its teen-agers passed through the courts. This compares with 2.3 per cent in the United States (1.8 per cent if traffic violations are deducted). In Japan the rate of delinquents brought before the courts has risen from an imperceptible low prewar rate to 1.2 per cent, with a rate of climb steeper than that of the United States. Teen-agers commit 21 per cent of Japan's total crimes, compared to 12 per cent of those in the United States. Similar trends are observable in Israel, where the number of arrested juveniles has doubled in the past decade.

The only agencies reporting national figures on juvenile delinquency in the United States are the Children's Bureau of the Department of Health, Education, and Welfare and the Federal Bureau of Investigation. Although there are varying methods of collecting data, these separately gathered statistics both show strong upward trends, far in excess of the normal population rise. There is, however, at least one significant difference between juvenile statistics in the United States and other countries. Nearly everywhere else, a youngster is brought to court and tried only if he breaks a law whose violation by an adult would also constitute a crime. In the United States, the definition of juvenile delinquency has become so all-compassing that children enter the statistical records for such behavior

as truancy, stubbornness, leaving home, curfew violations, etc., none of
which would be considered a law violation requiring court action in most
other countries.

Regarding the long-discussed "causes" of delinquency, the evidence is
becoming increasingly clear that it is less a product of poverty, lower
socioeconomic class, and slums. Rather, juvenile delinquency appears to
be the price of progress on the road to an industrial affluent society.
United States statistics support the view that delinquency is more likely to
increase in a time of prosperity than during a depression. Moreover, it has
been noted that in largely agricultural, nonindustrial economies, juvenile
delinquency appears to be generally nonexistent. And, if it does exist, it
may go unnoticed for lack of resources to cope with it. As Phon Sangsingkeo observed in Chapter 5, in developing countries the major catalyst
appears to be swift social change, the rapid destruction of long-established
traditions and customs, and the conflict of rising expectations with an
inability to provide social services.

When it comes to "doing something" about juvenile delinquency, the
literature reflects a plethora of approaches, from individual psychoanalysis to severe punishment. It is also evident that many well-intentioned
social endeavors have had little impact on the climbing delinquency rate.
Such measures as building housing developments, creating playgrounds,
organizing boys' clubs, reducing the number of working mothers, mending
broken homes, and sending everyone to child guidance clinics have not
had far-reaching effects. American and European experience does support
the view that an impact can be made by providing meaningful jobs for
teen-agers, by lowering the school-leaving age for those entering vocational training programs, and by qualitatively strengthening the youth
work of police and parole agencies.

In terms of group residential programs with disturbed youngsters, the
two projects presented in this volume are particularly noteworthy. The
Highfields program in New Jersey, summarized by Albert Elias, has been
operating for more than a decade on the assumption that previously non-
institutionalized delinquent boys can be helped if given a chance to live in
homelike surroundings, work at something useful during the day, and
participate in "guided group interaction" at night. Two evaluation studies
have demonstrated the favorable results attained; only 23 per cent of the
boys had subsequent difficulties with the law. The average length of stay
is about four months, with a cost of approximately $700 a boy.

The Viby program for severely maladjusted and delinquent girls,
described by Asger Hansen, has a more individual and more pedagogical-
psychological orientation than Highfields. Most of the "pupils" are on
probation, usually on a charge of prostitution, have had three to five placements in other institutions, and have been considered failures in previous
psychiatric treatment. It is quite likely that the Viby girls tend to be more

severely emotionally disturbed and more pathologic than the Highfields boys. The average stay is longer, and the staff-student ratio higher, with a concomitant increase in costs per girl. According to Paul Penningroth,[8] initial results appear promising, especially when considered with the alternative of a lifetime in either prison or hospital.

The Highfields program was an innovation in working with delinquent boys. As cited by Elias, several evaluations were made and communicated during the past decade. Nevertheless, the Highfields concepts have not been widely adopted outside New Jersey, although a number of its features are being incorporated into other programs abroad. While less is known about the Viby program, it too has not found many echoes. Similarly, other approaches to correctional work with delinquents, successfully innovated abroad, including youth hostels, aftercare homes, and halfway houses, remain to be widely explored in the United States. Clearly, if we are to discharge our social responsibility to troubled adolescents, imaginative innovation and wider adaptation of proved methods of rehabilitation deserve a higher priority.

Reflections

Why is it, one may ask, that numerous worthwhile projects, whose effectiveness and relatively moderate cost have been convincingly demonstrated, are not widely adopted? And, conversely, why is it that services once initiated tend to perpetuate themselves, regardless of social utility? Is there a truth in the charge that one of the reasons for lag is the strongly individual orientation built into most training programs for the mental health profession? As David Vail [13] has commented: "The mental health practitioners of today are not born, they are made. If their outlook is stunted, it is not because of limitations of personality, but because they are trained that way." He continues with the prediction that significant steps forward will not be made until "training programs re-gear themselves to turn out not market entrepeneurs but public servants, oriented toward the solution of public problems and committed to the public good."

If we are to innovate effectively, our attention and energy must be directed increasingly to social action and prevention. In discussions at the 1962 International Congress of Child Psychiatry, a sociologist, Orville G. Brim, Jr.,[3] observed that both somatic and psychosocial causes of mental disorders in children tend themselves to be products of the larger social environment, including its organization, methods of education, and cultural tradition. He suggested that greater emphasis be placed on a concern with broad groups in the population rather than specific individuals. This is also the primary recommendation of the WHO Scientific Group on Mental Health Research, whose *Summary Report of Suggested Priorities* is presented in Chapter 26. And, as Leon Eisenberg has phrased it so well in Chapter 6, "If not now, when?"

In reflecting on ways to speed the third mental health revolution, the growing problem of communication comes to the fore. Innovation and experience must not only be shared; the sharing must reach those in a position to implement and adopt new knowledge. It is up to all of us to make certain that the responsible voice of mental health is heard, that meaningful priorities are established, and that the best possible program receives the effective support of society's decision makers.

Summary

Bold innovation, shared experience, and effective communication are essential ingredients of the third revolution in mental health. As is so clearly evident in the chapters of this section, new procedures, new roles, and new professional responsibilities are being developed in many parts of the world in a coordinated attack on the social problems of emotional disturbance in children and youth, retardation, and juvenile delinquency. We have much to learn from each other.

References

1. Albee, George W.: *Mental Health Manpower Trends,* Basic Books, Inc., Publishers, New York, 1959.
2. Babcock, Charlotte G.: "Having Chosen to Work with Children," unpublished paper read for the Extension Division of the Child Therapy Program, Institute for Psychoanalysis, Chicago, 1964 .
3. Brim, Orville G., Jr.: "Changing the Social Environment to Prevent Mental Disorders in Children," in D. Arn Van Krevelen (ed.), *Child Psychiatry and Prevention,* H. Huber Verlag, Bern, 1964.
4. Carstairs, G. M.: *This Island Now,* Penguin Books, Inc., London, 1964.
5. Collomb, Henri: "Psychiatric Teaching and Research in African Medical Schools," *Int. MH Res. Newsltr.,* 6(4): 11–15, 1964.
6. Hobbs, Nicholas: "Mental Health's Third Revolution," *Amer. J. Orthopsychiat.,* 34:822–833, 1964.
7. Joint Commission on Mental Illness and Hearth: *Action for Mental Health,* Science Editions, Inc., New York, 1961.
8. Penningroth, Paul: *A Study of Programs for Emotionally Disturbed Children in Selected European Countries, 1963,* Southern Regional Education Board, Atlanta, 1964.
9. President's Panel on Mental Retardation: *National Action to Combat Mental Retardation,* U.S. Department of Health, Education, and Welfare, 1962.
10. ————: *Report of the Mission to the Netherlands,* U.S. Department of Health, Education, and Welfare, 1962.
11. Speijer, N.: "Social Integration of the Mentally Handicapped Adult," in H. P. David (ed.), *Population and Mental Health,* H. Huber Verlag, Bern, 1964; Springer Publ. Co., New York, 1964.
12. Tunley, Roul: *Kids, Crime and Chaos,* Harper & Row, Publishers, Incorporated, New York, 1962.
13. Vail, David J.: Education and Service . . . Two Wings of Advance," *Minn. MH Newsltr.,* November–December, 1964.

part six

Resources

26. Mental Health Research: A Summary Report of Suggested Priorities

*WHO Scientific Group on Mental Health Research**

It is generally recognized that most mental disorders have multiple causes. As little is known of the causes themselves, progress is slow, and a better understanding of the pathologic processes involved can only be arrived at step by step. Examples of partial advances made in this field include chromosome studies of the syndromes associated with mental retardation, studies of inherited defects in enzyme systems, identification by electro-encephalography of certain psychoses previously classed as schizophrenia, pharmacological studies of the activity of certain brain constituents (acetylcholine, histamine, catecholamines, etc.) and psychotropic drugs, the application of conditioned-reflex theory to the study of human and animal behavior, and the identification of factors associated with the occurrence of particular psychomatic disorders.

In marked contrast to the slow gains in etiologic understanding, there have been radical changes in both the volume and the character of the work done by psychiatric services over the last twenty years, not only in countries with highly organized services but also in some developing countries. In Taiwan and Nigeria, for instance, psychiatrists have started to reorganize their treatment services so as to exploit the special cultural characteristics of the society which they serve.

Adapted with permission from the *WHO Chronicle,* 18:330–383, 1964.

* The First WHO Scientific Group on Mental Health Research met in Geneva on April 6–10, 1964. The members were J. de Ajuriaguerra (Switzerland); D. Bovet (Italy); L. Eisenberg (United States); R. H. Felix (United States), chairman; O. V. Kerbikov (U.S.S.R.); T. A. Lambo (Nigeria); C. A. Léon (Colombia); T. Lin (Taiwan); P. D. Sivadon (France), vice-chairman; and E. T. O. Slater (United Kingdom). The consultants were G. M. Carstairs (United Kingdom), rapporteur; W. A. Caudill (United States); N. E. Miller (United States); B. A. Lebedev (U.S.S.R.); and J. Tizard (United Kingdom). The secretariat consisted of P. Baan (WHO), secretary; D. Buckle (WHO Regional Office for Europe); J. M. Moser (WHO); and M. Pfister (WHO).

In spite of the advances made, firm scientific foundations are still lacking on which to build practical programs of prevention and therapy, and the WHO Scientific Group on Mental Health Research considered that basic research relevant to mental health problems should now be given the attention hitherto devoted almost exclusively to physical health. Aware as it was of the enormous task that has to be accomplished, the group wished first to emphasize that it would be necessary to form small groups of experts to work out the details of research projects. The group confined itself to listing such projects in descending order of priority.

Epidemiology

The group considered that absolute priority should be given to the promotion of epidemiologic research on the distribution of mental disorders in different countries and on the effectiveness of curative and preventive services in these countries. For surveys to be internationally comparable, WHO assistance was essential in two crucial undertakings:

1. The development of a classification of mental disorders internationally acceptable and capable of uniform application. Steps toward this end would include studies of diagnostic variations between psychiatrists from different countries when presented with a similar pattern of symptoms and the preparation of glossaries to clarify the diagnostic procedures currently in use in different countries.

2. The development of standardized procedures for case finding and for the assessment of the severity of illness. Here, too, it might be expected that systematic recording of symptoms and behavioral disturbance would lead to the recognition of objectively identifiable syndromes.

WHO should promote and give technical assistance to epidemiologic field studies:

1. Surveys of defined populations to ascertain psychiatric morbidity and the distribution of particular diseases in subsections of the population studied.

2. Collaboration in other surveys so as to include a count of mental disorders in studies of cancer or cardiovascular disease, for example.

3. Surveys of high-risk groups (inhabitants of areas where certain diseases are endemic, widows and widowers, retired persons, children of schizophrenic parents, etc.):

4. Studies of suicide and attempted suicide.

5. Studies of changes in psychiatric morbidity with the passage of time in relation to changes in the social environment.

6. Longitudinal studies designed to reveal the "natural history" of various types of mental illness and, in particular, to assess rates of spontaneous recovery, which must be known if the effectiveness of preventive or curative interventions is also to be assessed.

7. Finally, the training of research workers. This is an essential task, since traditional psychiatric instruction very often attaches too little importance to the initiation of psychiatrists in methods of research. In developing countries it seems that young psychiatrists suffer especially from the lack of methodological instruction and from the scarcity of libraries subscribing to all the specialized reviews. WHO could be of particular service in this field if its Mental Health Unit were to constitute a reference center offering advice on the drawing up of research projects and giving bibliographical guidance on the subject for study.

Social Psychiatry

Advances in this field can be made only by the use of operational epidemiologic research, focusing not on the study of entire populations but on the operation of existing medical services. Operational research seeks to answer such questions as the following: What kinds of patients avail themselves of psychiatric help? What treatment was given to them? What was the result? This form of research is of particular importance for countries where psychiatric services are at an early stage of development and where their operation is still fairly flexible.

WHO assistance in operational research might cover the following items:

1. Aiding national authorities in collecting uniform data on patients treated in psychiatric establishments.

2. Training personnel for the analysis and tabulation of data on mental patients.

3. Setting up cumulative case registers embracing all forms of psychiatric care.

4. Disseminating information on clinical research (descriptive studies of patients exhibiting particular syndromes, cohort studies of patients in defined diagnostic groups, controlled trials of new drugs, and other forms of therapy).

5. Studies of community attitudes toward mental illness and psychiatric treatment.

6. Studies of the utilization of psychiatric services by different sectors of the population.

7. Comparative studies of contrasting patterns of the organization of psychiatric care (for example, in a psychiatric hospital, a general hospital, and a psychiatric day center; or aftercare by public health nurses as contrasted with aftercare by a psychiatric staff).

The scientific group unanimously agreed that if WHO were to create an international center for the collection and analysis of data on mental morbidity and on the use of psychiatric services, this would provide excellent opportunities for the prosecution of many of the above-mentioned research proposals as well as for the training of personnel in methods of recordkeeping and statistical analysis.

Cultural and Environmental Factors

Throughout the deliberations of the scientific group, emphasis was placed on the cultural and environmental factors affecting mental health. "Culture" is here taken in the anthropological sense of a people's way of life (their social, economic, and political organization and characteristic patterns of thought, emotion, and personal relations), while "environment" refers as much to physical surroundings as to general living conditions (overcrowding or isolation, pollution of water and air, architecture and spatial arrangement of psychiatric hospitals, and so on).

The great diversity of cultures in the modern world constitutes, as it were, a natural laboratory in which to study the effects on human behavior of many crucial variables. As these cultures are undergoing rapid change, it is important to gather data relevant to mental illness and health both before and as such change takes place.

Before such studies can be effectively carried out, however, social scientists need to be trained, with the assistance of WHO, in mental health research and in the development of more accurate research techniques. WHO might then convene a group of experts to plan comparative studies of the effects of particular cultural influences. Suitable topics for research would be the relation of family structure and group value systems to mental health and illness.

Genetics and Mental Disorders

Discoveries, such as the causation of mongolism by chromosomal abnormality or the effect of genetic polymorphism in normal populations on the individual capacity to metabolize and inactivate psychotropic drugs, are of very great interest to psychiatric research workers. There again, WHO should grant training fellowships to young research workers in the techniques of chromosome analysis and the biochemical study of abnormal metabolites.

It is especially important to remember the links connecting genetics with biological psychiatry and epidemiology. It would be interesting to select one of the smaller nations and to determine all forms of mental disorder and all known genetically determined abnormalities in that country. The basis for such a scheme already exists in such countries as Denmark, Norway, and Switzerland. In Denmark it would be possible to ascertain the exact number of cases of hemophilia, for example, or the exact number of twins. The duplication of the Danish system in another small country, if possible one with a very different culture and genetic background, would facilitate research into the etiology and epidemiology of mental disorder and disease, into cultural anthropology, and into social psychiatry and intrafamilial psychodynamics.

The scientific group also stressed the importance of carrying out studies on particular groups whose genetic composition had been influenced by unusual patterns of mating (e.g., polygamy and polyandry) or by inbreeding due to isolation.

The Mental Health of Children and Old People

The mental disorders of childhood should be made the subject of more comprehensive and better-directed research. WHO might give assistance in the following fields:

1. Cross-sectional and longitudinal studies of the development of intellect and personality in normal children as influenced by environmental factors (cultural background, nutrition, educational opportunities, family patterns, etc.). Any studies of personality development should include consideration of the critical period of adolescence. The question is one of capital importance, as defects of intelligence and personality affect not only the health of individuals but also the welfare of the community.

2. Prospective and retrospective studies on child care outside the family (foster homes, children's nurseries, etc.).

3. Operational research on children treated by psychiatric services. The comparison of results from different countries would provide the basis for a better evaluation of such services.

4. Studies of the repercussions of family planning on the mental development of children.

The mental disorders of old age are an increasingly important problem. The scientific group considered that WHO should promote studies on the prevalence of mental disease among the elderly in different societies, on social factors (including family and community attitudes), and on the possible influence of genetic and nutritional factors and of cardiovascular diseases in relation to degenerative changes in the central nervous system.

Conditioned Reflexes and Learning Theory

Research on conditioned-reflex activity is of vital interest to the study of mental health and disease, as it helps us to understand the nature and dynamics of the physical processes in the brain, to establish links between the internal laws governing higher nervous activity and environmental influences, to integrate the data obtained by other methods in an overall picture of man's behavior under normal and pathologic conditions, and to devise psychiatric treatment based on sound scientific knowledge. Conditioned-reflex research has been pursued most thoroughly in research institutes of the U.S.S.R. In some other countries, notably Britain and the United States, research workers have been concentrating on the application of learning theory (as developed by Edward L. Thorndike, C. L. Hull, B. F. Skinner, and H. J. Eysenck) and communications-systems theory to the understanding of human thinking, feeling, and behavior. This research has led to the development of theoretically based (as distinct from purely empirical) therapeutic methods.

WHO should, in the view of the scientific group, provide training fellowships to facilitate the study of both conditioned-reflex therapy and behavior therapy based on learning theory in centers where these techniques are being actively employed and arrange for consultants to be sent to research institutes beginning work in this field. Finally, the dissemination and exchange of information on the research that is being carried out in these fields—through translation of the existing literature, publication of general reviews, and international meetings—are highly desirable measures.

Besides these important questions, the group discussed many others concerning research to be done in biological psychiatry, psychosomatic disorders, psychotherapy, alcoholism and drug abuse, the repercussions of industrialization on mental health, and forensic psychiatry.

27. Mental Health Grants: International Progress and Problems

Henry P. David

Progress in mental health requires trained people and financial support. A judicious combination of these ingredients is essential for the development of any program, whether local, regional, national, or international. That advances in training, research, and professional services have been greatly stimulated by the increasingly available fiscal resources of the postwar era is clearly demonstrated by the contributors to this volume.

Another promising aspect of the present decade is the growing awareness that mental health—and illness—know no national boundaries. As one result, international and interdisciplinary exchanges and communication are increasingly hurdling linguistic and ideological barriers. It is the purpose of this chapter to cite some sources of current information on individual educational opportunities abroad, particularly those catalogued by UNESCO and the Institute for International Education. The role of WHO in fostering exchanges, training, and collaborative research will be noted. The contributions of American foundations and the international program of the National Institutes of Health (United States) are described as one example of the recognition of similar interests and complementary resources among colleagues in many lands. Concluding this survey is a brief discussion of problems and pitfalls in preparing and evaluating a grant proposal.

Study Abroad

Encouraging the "exchange of persons" has always been one of the major aims of UNESCO, the United Nations Educational, Scientific and Cultural Organization, whose headquarters are located at 9 Place de Fontenoy, Paris vɪɪe, France. This is clearly apparent in the fifteen editions of *Study Abroad*,[12] a quadrilingual reference guide published by UNESCO since 1948. The 1964–1966 edition lists more than 130,000 individual op-

Especially prepared for this volume.

portunities for subsidized international study and travel in more than 100 countries. Fellowships and scholarships are available in nearly all fields of learning, including the mental health professions. The sixteenth edition, for the period 1966–1968, will be published at the end of 1965. UNESCO cautions that persons wishing to apply for a specific award have all the stated qualifications and begin initial inquiries at least one year in advance.

In recent years, the focus of UNESCO's attention has been shifted from matters concerned purely with the exchange of persons to more general questions of international relations in the fields of education, science, and culture. In 1964, UNESCO published the first edition of the *Handbook of International Exchanges.*[13] It provides details on the activities of 272 international organizations and more than 5,000 governmental and non-governmental institutions and agencies in 126 states and territories. The Index of Cultural Agreements includes more than 4,000 bilateral and multilateral agreements to which these states are parties. Readers are presented with a wide range of information in English, French, Russian, and Spanish. There is also a section on organizations offering advisory services and practical help.

American citizens may qualify for United States government scholar-ships provided by the Fulbright-Hays Act. Grants are available for pre-doctoral graduate study, professional training, or research. Details may be requested from the Institute for International Education, 809 United Nations Plaza, New York, New York. Grants for university lecturing and postdoctoral training or research are administered by the Conference Board of Associated Research Councils, 2101 Constitution Avenue, N.W., Washington, D.C. Each of these programs has its own application form, and competitions are conducted independently of each other. In any given year, however, a candidate may apply to the Institute of International Education or to the Conference Board but not to both.

The Institute of International Education, founded in 1919, is a private nonprofit organization which develops and administers programs of edu-cational exchange for foundations, private organizations, governments, colleges, universities, and corporations in the United States and abroad.[6] Approximately six thousand students, teachers, technicians, and specialists from more than 100 countries study or train through these programs each year. Through its counseling and information services and its publications, the institute assists thousands of individuals and many organizations with matters of international education. It acts as a central clearinghouse, and its reference library includes data on the activities of organizations in the exchange-of-persons field, catalogues of United States and foreign educa-tional institutions, and other pertinent materials. Overseas offices have been established in Nairobi, Kenya; Lima, Peru; and Bangkok, Thailand. A European office is scheduled to open in 1965.

Particularly useful are two *Handbooks on International Study,* published by the Institute of International Education. One is intended primarily for United States nationals and provides information on nearly 100 countries.[8] The other, for foreign nationals, is a guide to study, training, and other opportunities in the United States.[7] They cost $3.50 each, or $6 for the two-volume set. The IIE also has a free pamphlet on *Fellowships Offered by Foreign Governments, Universities, and Private Donors,* as well as a list of other available publications.[9]

In most countries to which graduate students are sent under the provisions of the Fulbright-Hays Act, binational commissions administer the educational exchanges and supervise the grantees. Where no commission has been established, educational programs are the responsibility of the respective United States embassies. Persons wishing to explore opportunities under the Fulbright program in the United States may direct initial inquiries to these commissions or the educational officers attached to United States embassies.

World Health Organization

From its beginning in 1949, the World Health Organization [15] has emphasized the importance of international collaboration in the training of health personnel. The WHO fellowship program [16] has become one of the most effective ways of implementing the goal of improving standards of training, advancing research, and strengthening national health services. Fellowships are granted for either individual studies or for group educational activities. Individual programs may be arranged to suit the needs of the fellow. For group endeavors, fellows are chosen to suit the requirements of a specific activity with a predetermined content and scope. In its essentials, the award of a WHO fellowship means that an appropriate program of advanced study abroad is planned and arranged for an individual and that the fellow is provided with the necessary financial assistance.

A WHO fellowship implies the acceptance of an individual, *on the recommendation of his government,* as a person who, given the opportunity to study abroad, will increasingly contribute toward furthering the objectives of WHO. An application for and the award of a fellowship constitute a joint undertaking by WHO, the fellow, and his government. This means that WHO will make appropriate study plans, handle the necessary arrangements with countries and training centers, and provide the required funds. The fellow promises that, on his return, he will place his services at the disposal of his national health organization. The government concerned states, as specified on the application form, that it will make full use of the knowledge and experience gained by the fellow and that his study leave will not adversely affect his status, seniority, salary, pension, and similar rights.

WHO fellowships are awarded to qualified persons for attendance at group educational activities organized or assisted by WHO, for formal postgraduate training, and for the observation of practices and techniques or research. The usual time is six to twelve months, although exceptions may be made. Applications should reach WHO during the first six months prior to the year in which the fellowship is to begin. Interested individuals would be well advised to read *WHO Fellowship: An Information Booklet*,[16] available from WHO regional offices or from the headquarters in Geneva, Switzerland.

According to the *WHO Chronicle*,[20] in the period from December, 1962, to October, 1963, WHO awarded 2,058 fellowships; recipients came from 147 countries and studied in 84 other lands. There were 81 fellowships in mental health and related subjects during 1963. In all, from the beginning of the program in 1949 to mid-1964, a total of 1,073 fellowships were awarded in the mental health field.[18]

A most significant advance in the WHO mental health program occurred in April, 1964, when the First WHO Scientific Group on Mental Health Research was convened in Geneva. It was reported in the October, 1964, *WHO Chronicle:* [17]

> The Group considered that absolute priority should be given to the promotion of epidemiological research on the distribution of mental disorders in different countries, and on the effectiveness of curative and preventive services. . . . Emphasis was placed on the importance of cultural and environmental factors affecting mental health. . . . But it is especially important to remember the links connecting genetics with biological psychiatry and epidemiology. . . . The mental disorders of childhood should be made the subject of more comprehensive and better directed research. . . . The mental disorders of old age are an increasingly important problem. . . . Research on conditional reflex activity is of vital interest to the study of mental health and disease, as it helps us to understand the nature and dynamics of the physical processes of the brain, to establish links between the internal laws governing higher nervous activity and environmental influences, to integrate the data obtained by other methods in an over-all picture of man's behavior under normal and pathological conditions, and to devise psychiatric treatment based on sound scientific knowledge. . . . Besides these important questions, the Group discussed many others concerning research to be done in biological psychiatry, psychosomatic disorders, psychotherapy, alcoholism and drug abuse, the repercussions of industrialization on mental health, and forensic psychiatry.*

The scientific group's report was considered and approved in June, 1964, by the WHO Advisory Committee on Medical Research, which

> . . . recommended that WHO expand its research activities regarding the classification and epidemiology of mental disorders and the operation of

* For full text see chap. 26.

programs of social psychiatry; and that emphasis be given to WHO support for biological research into the causes and treatment of mental disorders.[19]

Great impetus was given to the development of the mental health research program by the provision of funds for the appointment of two new medical officers to the Mental Health Unit in Geneva. The ground has thus been prepared for a major expansion of WHO's role in international mental health research.

Private American Foundations

The size and scope of private foundations in the United States is exceedingly well described in the 1,000-page 1964 edition of the *Foundation Directory*,[14] prepared by the Foundation Library Center, an educational institution in New York City established in 1956 by the Russell Sage Foundation "to collect, organize and make available to the public reports and information about foundations." Its extremely useful annual reports are published for the center by the Russell Sage Foundation. The *Directory* contains a descriptive listing of 6,007 foundations, with combined assets totaling 14.5 billion dollars and grants for the latest year of record of 779 million dollars.

For each foundation, the *Directory* includes, insofar as they are available, the legal name and present address; data on establishment; names of donors, officers, and trustees; a statement outlining general purposes, present fields of interest, and any specific limitations; the amount of assets; and, for the most recent available year, total new gifts to the foundation and expenditures, including grants.

In an analytical introduction, F. Emerson Andrews, director of the Foundation Library Center, tabulates and summarizes the data included in the *Directory*. He reports on the scope of foundation activities and estimates grants for a specific field. There are three indexes: foundations classified by fields of interest, a list of more than 16,000 trustees and officers, and an alphabetical list of foundations. Reasonably priced at $10, the volume is available from the Russell Sage Foundation, 230 Park Avenue, New York, New York 10017, U.S.A. Also useful are the foundation's publications on philanthropic activities[2] and their legal aspects,[3] both written by Mr. Andrews.

Particularly relevant for the field of mental health is a survey of private foundations conducted by the International Section in the Research Grants and Fellowships Branch of the National Institute of Mental Health.[4] Starting in the fall of 1958, Dr. Jeanne L. Brand undertook to query, by letter and questionnaire:

> . . . 1,182 foundations and other national granting agencies which might be expected to offer support for some phase of mental health research, training, or service. Responses were obtained from 782 organizations, a

66.1 percent over-all return. These responses, together with supporting research in the files of the Foundation Library Center in New York and in annual reports and interviewing, provided a group of 142 private foundations and other organizations which have indicated that they have support available for mental health related activities.

Dr. Brand emphasized:

> Organizations which awarded funds primarily on a local, state, or regional basis were excluded from the survey, as were research institutes which were non-grant-awarding agencies, universities, research libraries, the donations of private individuals, and of business corporations which awarded funds directly rather than through company foundations.

Thus, the results of the survey refer only to support available on a national level from participating philanthropic or other tax-exempt organizations. It should also be noted that the degree of interest in mental health varied considerably among these 142 organizations. While mental health was the core program for some, for many others it was only one area of interest and possibly a minor one at best.

In personal conversation, Dr. Brand has cautioned that her list is not current and that some of the information provided may no longer be accurate. The participating foundations were not queried on whether or not they were prepared to award grants abroad. Many are handicapped by the terms of their charters, which frequently limit support to organizations possessing Federal tax-exempt status in the United States, a legal procedure many voluntary, nonprofit, and nongovernmental international organizations have found rewarding.

In view of the paucity of available data, it is informative to note the pattern of grants given by those 21 organizations whose average annual level of support for mental health exceeded $100,000. Research grants head the list, followed by support for training, service, and demonstration projects. Funds for travel are meager, as are grants for construction and building. Support for conferences is mentioned only occasionally. Of all the 142 foundations studied, 53 indicate that they award grants only to organizations and not to individuals and 13 follow a policy of selecting their own grantees.

Summarizing her observations, Dr. Brand cites several cautions in interpreting her findings. While some foundations maintain the same programmatic interests for a number of years, others operate quite flexibly, feeling a need for more frequent assessment and change to meet altered situations. It should also be noted that if it had been feasible to include private state and local agencies supporting mental health, it is probable that the survey estimate for service grants would have been proportionally higher. Many local organizations give the major share of their funds to assist in the operation of hospitals, clinics, and other community programs.

Applying to Private American Foundations

At the 1961 Annual Meeting of the American Psychological Association, Dr. Francis H. Palmer, then with the Social Science Research Council, presented an informative survey of the role of the private foundations.[11] Among his many cogent comments was the observation that large foundations are competitive. They are well aware of each other's activities and attempt to channel their resources in directions with which they can become more or less uniquely identified. For example, the Carnegie Foundation of New York has been particularly alert to supporting studies designed to upgrade the educational system, the Ford Foundation to research on juvenile delinquency, and the Rockefeller Foundation to areas related to public health in the developing countries. In making application to a foundation, it might well be useful to identify interests by reading available annual reports. Conceivably, much effort could be saved and potential rejections avoided if a proposal were not submitted to a foundation which has never evinced any interest in a given area while one of its competitors has.

Dr. Palmer also noted that several of the larger foundations employ professional staffs qualified to consider a proposal to the extent that research interests expressed are consistent with current programs. Most proposals which are ultimately supported have a history of advice and consent with a staff officer. Indeed, such an officer may suggest that a particular investigator submit a proposal if the investigator has been productive in the area of the foundation's interests. It is often very useful to learn who the relevant staff officer in a given foundation is, how to get in touch with him, and perhaps arrange to explore potential joint interests. Obviously the best time for such an acquaintance is before submitting a proposal. If there is no person on a foundation staff interested in or knowledgeable about a certain area of interest, this may well be a predictor of the chances of support from that particular foundation.

Once a proposal has been received by a foundation, the staff officer best informed about the area will review it, request further clarifying information if needed, determine whether it fits the foundation's goals, and discuss it with experts in the field to the extent deemed desirable. Since far more numerous proposals are usually submitted than can be supported, many are rejected at this stage without benefit of review by higher administrative echelons or boards. The rejection will often be in the name of the board, which is factual to the extent that the staff officer is a board representative. Obviously, if there has been communication with a staff officer before submitting a proposal, chances of reaching the next higher review level are better. If a proposal survives to the point of being presented to the board (usually by a staff officer, although not necessarily the same one), the final decision will be made by the board itself.

An unusual insight into the operations of a unique foundation is provided by the *Tenth Annual Report* of the Foundations' Fund for Research in Psychiatry,[5] reviewing activities for the decade from 1953 to 1963. Historical development, grants made, and changes in policy are discussed. A growing trend of supporting international research was noted; during 1962–1963, seventeen of the twenty-four grants given were awarded to psychiatric researchers outside the United States.

Perusal of the more than 150 research grants given during the decade under review indicates that the FFRP has supported research endeavors spanning the entire spectrum of sciences relevant to behavior and psychiatry. It appears that interdisciplinary projects have been particularly encouraged, as has cross-disciplinary research training. Fundamental studies are emphasized, with a marked trend in recent years toward social psychiatry, cross-cultural endeavors, and child development. A service-oriented clinical project is not likely to receive support unless it holds obvious potential for advancing basic knowledge or research techniques. Narrowly limited studies and conferences are considered to fall outside the scope of the FFRP. Most grants are in the range from $5,000 to $20,000 per annum. The overall average grant was $15,381, including overhead allowances, and was for about three years; the average new grant was for a period of little more than two years.

The basic policy of the FFRP appears to be one of accepting high risk: "Faith will be placed on the ability of the investigator, on the potential for growth in the location, and on the importance of the problem." The fund indicated that it is itself stimulating applications, instead of passively waiting for them; it anticipates expanded support of research abroad, particularly "in unusual, neglected areas of study."

Potential applicants would be well advised to review the Foundations' Fund's *Annual Report*, available from 100 York Street, New Haven 11, Connecticut, U.S.A.

United States Government Support Abroad

Among the many grant-giving agencies of the United States government, the National Institutes of Health constitute the largest single source of funds for the support of research and training in the medical and biological sciences in the United States and abroad. Established to promote the health needs of the American people, the NIH have an essentially domestic mission. Recognizing that science by its very nature is international and that participation in the international scientific community makes available additional resources and talents, the NIH have supported research abroad.[10]

International activities permit the NIH to utilize unique opportunities by joining with foreign scientists and institutions in attacking problems of mutual interest. The NIH provide direct costs of certain research projects abroad when they are of specific interest to their program objectives and when these projects utilize resources, conditions, or talents not available in the United States. In each case the foreign institution shares in the investment. The NIH also participate in supporting the research programs of such international agencies as the World Health Organization, the Pan American Health Organization, and other international scientific organizations when the resources of these groups present special opportunities to advance both the program objectives of the NIH and those of the cooperating organization. NIH foreign grants may provide funds for such items as equipment, supplies, and salaries of technical personnel. Construction costs and salaries of senior investigators are usually paid by the cooperating institution.

In response to growing international responsibilities, the NIH established an Office of International Research in 1961 as part of the Office of the Director. OIR is responsible for coordinating all international activities of the National Institutes of Health. It advises the Director and the Office of the Surgeon-General on matters relating to the international aspects of medical research training and assists the several institutes in the development of their international programs. It is specifically responsible for administration of the NIH special foreign currency program and for coordinating Institute proposals for research under this program in foreign countries. It also administers the international centers program, the international fellowship program, and the international research career development program. While less than 5 per cent of NIH activities have direct and substantial foreign implications, in 1963 these international extensions represented an annual investment of approximately 30 million dollars. Specific requests for support of mental health research abroad are considered primarily through the International Section in the Research Grants and Fellowships Branch of the National Institute of Mental Health.

Foreign currencies generated from the sale of surplus American agricultural products are available for medical research in a limited number of countries. The NIH uses these funds to support collaborative agreements with institutions on problems important both to the country concerned and the research effort of the Public Health Service.

To facilitate communication and improve administration and evaluation of foreign programs, the OIR opened offices in Europe, Latin America, and the Far East. In 1961, the European office was established in Paris, and a science representative stationed in London. In 1962, the Latin American office was organized in Rio de Janeiro, a Far East office activated in Tokyo, and a science representative assigned to New Delhi. These overseas officers are prepared to interpret current trends and review possibilities for closer cooperation between research programs abroad and the international activities of NIH.

Grant Proposals and Problems

It has been reported by Dr. Ernest M. Allen [1] that during the fiscal year 1959 the National Institutes of Health received and acted upon nearly six thousand competitive applications for funds to initiate or continue projects in medical or related biological research in the United States. Approximately two thousand were disapproved by thirty-odd study sections consisting of research scientists connected with universities and other research institutions throughout the United States.

To explore the reasons for disapproval of so large a percentage of applications, Dr. Allen analyzed the minutes kept by thirty-three different study sections, which during their spring meetings of 1959 rejected 605 applications. The results of his classifications are listed in Table 1.

TABLE 1

Shortcomings Found in Research Proposals *

No.	Shortcoming	Percentage
	Class 1: Problem (58 per cent)	
1.	The problem is of insufficient importance or is unlikely to produce any new or useful information.	33.1
2.	The proposed research is based on a hypothesis that rests on insufficient evidence, is doubtful, or is unsound.	8.9
3.	The problem is more complex than the investigator appears to realize.	8.1
4.	The problem has only local significance, is one of production or control, or otherwise fails to fall sufficiently clearly within the general field of health-related research.	4.8
5.	The problem is scientifically premature and warrants, at most, only a pilot study.	3.1
6.	The research as proposed is overly involved, with too many elements under simultaneous investigation.	3.0
7.	The description of the nature of the research and of its significance leaves the proposal nebulous and diffuse and without a clear research aim.	2.6
	Class 2: Approach (73 per cent)	
8.	The proposed tests, methods, or scientific procedures are unsuited to the stated objective.	34.7
9.	The description of the approach is too nebulous, diffuse, and lacking in clarity to permit adequate evaluation.	28.8
10.	The overall design of the study has not been carefully thought out.	14.7
11.	The statistical aspects of the approach have not been given sufficient consideration.	8.1
12.	The approach lacks scientific imagination.	7.4
13.	Controls are either inadequately conceived or inadequately described.	6.4

14. The material the investigator proposes to use is unsuited
    to the objectives of the study or is difficult to obtain.   3.8
15. The number of observations is unsuitable.   2.5
16. The equipment contemplated is outmoded or otherwise
    unsuitable.   1.0

Class 3: Man (55 per cent)

17. The investigator does not have adequate experience or
    training, or both, for *this* research.   32.6
18. The investigator appears to be unfamiliar with recent
    pertinent literature or methods, or both.   13.7
19. The investigator's previously published work in *this* field
    does not inspire confidence.   12.6
20. The investigator proposes to rely too heavily on insuffi-
    ciently experienced associates.   5.0
21. The investigator is spreading himself too thin; he will be
    more productive if he concentrates on fewer projects.   3.8
22. The investigator needs closer liaison with colleagues in
    this field or in collateral fields.   1.7

Class 4: Other (16 per cent)

23. The requirements for equipment or personnel, or both,
    are unrealistic.   10.1
24. It appears that other responsibilities would prevent the
    devotion of sufficient time and attention to this research.   3.0
25. The institutional setting is unfavorable.   2.3
26. Research grants to the investigator, now in force, are
    adequate in scope and amount to cover the proposed
    research.   1.5

* Shortcomings found in study-section review of 605 disapproved
research-grant applications, April–May, 1959. All percentages are
to the base number 605. Published with permission from *Science,*
132:1532–1534, 1960.

Taking the four primary classes, it will be noted that in 58 per cent of
the applications there are questions about the problem: its importance or
timeliness, in the general area covered by the NIH program, is not considered sufficient to warrant support. In 73 per cent the approach is
involved: the method of attack, as proposed, is not deemed to yield
sufficiently useful data. In 55 per cent there is concern about the scientific
competencies to be brought to bear on the research, and in 16 per cent
other, miscellaneous issues are raised.

In setting up these four classes, Dr. Allen recognized that failure to
choose a meritorious or timely problem (class 1) and failure to plan an
adequate approach (class 2) reflect upon the investigator's judgment or
the adequacy of his information regarding recent advances in the chosen
area of research or in collateral areas. To combine class 1 and class 2
criticisms and put them in class 3 would, however, defeat the purpose of

spreading the spectrum of criticism to permit examination of the intensity of each portion.

The shortcomings noted by the study sections are arranged under the four category headings in Table 1. The list contains twenty-six items, each of which is a blend of closely related but variously phrased criticisms. The phraseology adopted in each instance can be regarded as a kind of verbal mode or mean for the group of criticisms represented. In Dr. Allen's view, the "averaging" has in no instance distorted significantly the meaning of any of the criticisms as actually phrased in the study-section records.

Just as the percentages corresponding to the four main classes add up to more than 100 per cent, so also those within any one of the four groups total more than the percentage for that group. In both cases the excess results from the fact that a given research proposal may have more than one adverse characteristic. For the 605 applications, one or another of the twenty-six criticisms occurred an overall total of 1,558 times.

Dr. Allen correctly cautions that the criticisms are not mutually exclusive and not of the same order of comprehensiveness or importance. Criticism 11, for example, is general enough to embrace criticisms 13 and 15. The criticisms far down the list in each of the first three classes are clearly of less importance than the leading items and in some instances would obviously not in themselves warrant disapproval of an application. Such differences are to be expected when the basic material for the analysis is, as here, taken from a summary record of free and unconstrained discussion of a research proposal.

The criticisms that occurred in the discussions summarized in the study-section minutes were, of course, voiced primarily in an effort to arrive at a balanced judgment of the merits of each research proposal, not to aid investigators in perfecting their techniques of preparing research proposals. Nevertheless, the total list of twenty-six adverse characteristics could well be used as a checklist for criticism of grant applications prior to submission, no matter to what public or private granting agency.

Summary

Following a review of individual opportunities for study or training abroad, the activities of American foundations are surveyed. The role of the United States government in supporting international research is cited, and the problems and pitfalls of preparing and evaluating grant applications are discussed.

References

1. Allen, Ernest M.: "Why Are Research Grant Applications Disapproved?" *Science,* 132:1532–1534, 1960.
2. Andrews, F. Emerson: *Philanthropic Foundations,* Russell Sage Foundation, New York, 1956.

3. ———: *Legal Instruments of Foundations,* Russell Sage Foundation, New York, 1958.
4. Brand, Jeanne L.: *Private Support for Mental Health,* U.S. Public Health Service Publication 838, 1963.
5. Foundations' Fund for Research in Psychiatry: *Tenth Annual Report for the Years 1953–1963,* New Haven, Conn., 1964.
6. Institute for International Education: *Annual Report, 1963,* New York, 1964.
7. ———: *Handbook on International Study: For Foreign Nationals,* New York, 1964.
8. ———: *Handbook on International Study: For U.S. Nationals,* New York, 1964.
9. ———: *Publications List,* New York, 1964. (Free.)
10. National Institutes of Health: *International Activities of the National Institutes of Health of the U.S.A.,* Bethesda, Md., 1963. (Mimeographed.)
11. Palmer, Francis H.: "The Role of the Private Foundations," unpublished paper presented at the Annual Meeting of the American Psychological Association, New York, 1961.
12. United Nations Educational, Scientific and Cultural Organization: *Study Abroad,* 15th ed., Paris, 1963.
13. ———: *Handbook of International Exchanges,* Paris, 1964.
14. Walton, Ann D., and Marianna O. Lewis (eds.): *The Foundation Directory,* 2d ed., Russell Sage Foundation, New York, 1964.
15. World Health Organization: *Annual Reports of the Director-General,* Geneva.
16. ———: *WHO Fellowship: An Information Booklet,* 8th ed., Geneva, 1962.
17. ———: "Mental Health and Research," *WHO Chronicle,* 18:380–383, 1964.
18. ———: *Personal communication,* 1964.
19. ———: *WHO Ment. Hlth. News,* no. 15, 1964.
20. ———: "The Work of WHO in 1963," *WHO Chronicle,* 18:150, 1964.

28. Mental Health Films

Thomas L. Pilkington

Introduction

Film is one of the most potent and exact means of communication at our disposal today. It can present abstractions and convey fine shades of difference in emotions and moods. It can encompass time by showing events separated by months or years, and transcend space by comparing activities that could not otherwise be brought together. It is a form of non-verbal communication whose meaning is retained independently of its language.

The World Federation for Mental Health has always been keenly aware of the value of films, and programs of films from many countries have been increasingly featured in its meetings and congresses. In 1952, the first edition of the *International Catalog of Mental Health Films* was produced under the editorship of Henk Nieuwenuize; the second edition, edited by myself in 1960, details about 550 films with its 1962 supplement. In the past two years, a number of new and stimulating films on mental health have been produced, and a WFMH member body, the Mental Health Film Board of New York, is currently engaged, in collaboration with the WFMH Film Section, on a further elaborate and detailed compilation of all the world's mental health films.

Varieties of Films

Of the several types, promotional (or "propaganda") films aimed at the general public form a large group. They are particularly effective in presenting emotional disturbances of childhood, the value of the mental hospital, aspects of alcoholism, acceptance of the mentally disabled by the community, removal of the stigma of mental disease, etc. The difficulties of showing the exact nature of mental health work and the relative isola-

Especially prepared for this volume.

tion of most mental hospitals have led to the production of many films of the recruitment type. The most effective of these are made by the realistic, rather than the romantic, school: nobody makes a surgical film without showing blood. Films for the specific training of mental health personnel are being increasingly produced, and many contain either clinical material or acted-out problems in psychodynamics. The new eight-millimeter "concept" films, lasting a few minutes, are significant additions to this field.

Films about research and particular forms of treatment often use special production techniques, such as hidden cameras. Films may also be aids in the direct treatment of patients by, for example, raising moral issues for discussion. Other types, such as those dealing with the history of psychiatry, the analysis of psychomotor movements, and the recording of reactions under specific stresses, continue to be explored. The international use of psychiatric films represents an area open for considerable expansion. The visual component is unaffected by any language barrier, and a number of useful films have been made with a sound track of only secondary importance. The possibilities for comparison of similar psychiatric syndromes from different countries and diverse culture patterns are essential for viewing mental health problems in a wider perspective. Furthermore, the technical development of multimagnetic sound tracks permits a given film to carry its sound in several languages simultaneously.

The Value of Mental Health Films

When considering mental health films in an educational program, it is useful to discuss their particular value. Mental health is the most important factor in coping with life in present-day civilizations, and most persons are acutely aware of its significance. Because of association with the fear that they may see mental weakness in themselves, however, many members of the general public are resistant to the consideration of psychiatric problems. At the same time, they have a deep curiosity about mental mechanisms and their possible introspective application to themselves. Account must be taken of this ambivalence in any program designed to educate the public in mental health matters.

Film provides a most useful medium for several reasons. It is viewed in a captive group, so that the individual, whilst being influenced both by the content of the film and by the attitude of his fellow audience, can still deal personally with his individual impressions and reactions. This element of group participation has a heightened value over, for example, television presentations or published articles.

By the process of identification, film has a strong emotional appeal, which can be turned to good value in affecting the attitudes and standards of an audience. It should be remembered, however, that the local culture pattern plays a strong part in this influence. A film with a setting which reflects values and an approach to life elsewhere will have a limited impact and may even cause resistance to the message it contains.

The Presentation of Films

Film presentations fall under two headings: the mechanics and the general setting. The physical arrangements for a film show deserve much greater attention than they usually get; the impact on the audience is easily affected by distractions. At the present time, it is virtually only necessary to think in terms of sixteen-millimeter sound projection. There are very many suitable machines available locally, either in relation to a hall or on hire from nearby dealers. Most of these render an excellent performance, but even the best will show a poor picture with inaudible sound in a badly blacked-out room with a built-in echo. Furthermore, the audience must *see* the picture. The screen should be at a good height; in this respect, a smaller (and therefore brighter) picture is very much better than a larger one produced by a projector placed at the back of a long hall without the appropriate lens.

An experienced projectionist, amateur or professional, will see to all these things if he is given time for preparation. He will also make sure that he has a spare lamp and that the show does not start with a series of disconcerting leader flashes and the sound either remain nonexistent or come in with a roar. A key person is the individual in charge of projection, properly briefed and with adequate time for placing the apparatus.

The general setting of a film presentation is in the hands of the organizer; he must decide, for example, how long the show will last and how many films should be included. It is a good working rule to allow at least as long again as the film for a period of discussion, led by an informed person, who should also say a few words of introduction. Mental health films are very meaty material, and to show too many of them promotes intellectual strain and confusion. One or two films, depending upon their length, are enough for one session, although a third can usefully be added to break the concentration, if it is short and reasonably entertaining and continues the general theme.

Choosing Mental Health Films

Mental health films fall into various categories, and some are made for only very specialized and technically knowledgeable audiences. It is thus most important to choose films carefully, with particular reference to the objectives for which they were made and the audience for which they are intended. Although a detailed selection of films can be made from many sources, there are still the particular approach of the local community and the particular theme of a program or series to be considered.

Films vary considerably in their individual impact. Whenever possible, it is a very good plan to preview a film for its suitability. In any case, this is essential for the introducer if he is to bring out the main points and guide the discussion usefully; he is not likely to be able to prepare many thoughts on the subject if he has only a hasty viewing on the day of the actual showing.

In planning a series of films to support an educational program, it should be remembered that the most useful films are booked several months in advance, especially during the winter. It is poor policy to substitute films in an arranged program. If the fullest use is to be made of this medium, adequate time should be allowed for preparation.

The Objectives of Using Film

As with all activities of this nature, a clear idea of the goal and purpose of a film presentation is necessary for success. Films can be used to attain several objectives. They can, for example, convey information which widens the knowledge of the audience; films dealing with problems of mental hospital patients, with rehabilitation services, and with specific forms of treatment fall into this group. Other films are designed to promote sympathy for certain groups, e.g., mentally handicapped children, and to foster changes in public attitudes. Some films show new ideas and how they can be made to work, such as the concept of open-door hospitals, psychiatric treatment in general hospitals, and industrial therapy activities. Still other films are frankly provocative so as to stimulate discussion, showing, for example, the effects of hospitalization on the young child or the integration of the nurse into the full life of the mental hospital patient.

Summary

From the international point of view, film is the most realistic and convenient medium through which different cultures can be presented and studied. The principles here discussed remain the same whether viewing is direct or through the intermediary of television. Film represents a basic approach to the deeper international understanding essential for world mental health.

References

The UNESCO film coupon scheme enables institutions and individuals in UNESCO member states to buy educational films from other countries. Details are available from the UNESCO Coupon Office, 9 Place de Fontenoy, Paris viie, France. Useful references include the following:

1. *Catalogue of National Film Board of Canada,* Post Office Box 6100, Montreal 3, Canada.
2. *Films on Psychology and Psychiatry,* 1960 edition, Scientific Film Association, 55a Welbeck Street, London W.1., England.
3. *Psychological Cinema Register,* Audio-visual Aids Library, Pennsylvania State University, University Park, Pennsylvania, U.S.A.
4. *UN Film Catalogue,* European Office of the Technical Assistance Administration,

Palais des Nations, Geneva, Switzerland. (Films from the UN Library are available from the local United Nations representative.)

5. *World Mental Health Films,* 1960 edition with 1962 supplement; obtainable from the World Federation for Mental Health, 1 Rue Gevray, Geneva, Switzerland, or 124 East 28th Street, New York, N.Y., 10016, U.S.A., or from the Mental Health Film Council, 39 Queen Anne Street, London W.1., England.

29. Mental Health Pocketbooks

Benjamin Schlesinger

Anthropology

Barnett, H. G.: *Being a Paluan,* Holt, Rinehart and Winston, Inc.

Beals, Alan R.: *Gopalpur: A South Indian Village,* Holt, Rinehart and Winston, Inc.

Beattie, John: *Bynyove: An African Kingdom,* Holt, Rinehart and Winston, Inc.

Boas, Franz: *The Mind of Primitive Man,* Collier Books, a division of Crowell-Collier Publishing Co.

Chiang, Yee: *A Chinese Childhood,* W. W. Norton & Company, Inc.

Fried, Morton: *Readings in Anthropology,* vol. II, *Cultural Anthropology,* Thomas Y. Crowell Company.

Friedl, Ernestine: *Vasilika: A Village in Modern Greece,* Holt, Rinehart and Winston, Inc.

Hart, C. W. M., and A. P. Pilling: *The Tiwi of North Australia,* Holt, Rinehart, and Winston, Inc.

Hoebel, E. Adamson: *The Cheyennes: Indians of the Great Plains,* Holt, Rinehart and Winston, Inc.

Kroeber, A. L.: *Anthropology: Biology and Race,* Harbinger, HO17.

Kuper, Hilda: *The Swazi: A South African Kingdom,* Holt, Rinehart and Winston, Inc.

Lewis, Oscar: *Tepoztlau: Village in Mexico,* Holt, Rinehart and Winston, Inc.

Mead, Margaret: *Anthropology: The Human Science,* Insight Books, D. Van Nostrand Company, Inc., 22.

Montagu, Ashley: *Anthropology and Human Nature,* McGraw-Hill Book Company.

Posposil, Leopold: *The Kapauku Papuans of West New Guinea,* Holt, Rinehart and Winston, Inc.

From the more than 25,000 English-language paperbound books in print, Dr. Benjamin Schlesinger compiled approximately seven hundred references for training and research in mental health. This extensive list appeared in Supplement 43 to the September–October, 1964, issue of *Canada's Mental Health,* the complimentary bi-monthly journal edited by Carl Birchard and published in English and French by the Mental Health Division, Department of National Health and Welfare, Ottawa, Canada. About three hundred references particularly suited to this volume are re-printed here in categories originally edited for *Canada's Mental Health.*

Ramos, Samuel: *Profile of Man and Culture in Mexico,* McGraw-Hill Book Company.

Salisbury, R. F.: *Structures of Custodial Care: An Anthropological Study of a State Mental Hospital,* University of California Press.

Taylor, William X.: *Anthropology,* Collier Books, a division of Crowell-Collier Publishing Co., AS1040.

Warner, Lloyd: *A Black Civilization,* Harper Torchbooks, Harper & Row, Publishers, Incorporated, TB3056.

Wiser, William, and Charlotte Wiser: *Behind Mud Walls, 1930–1960 (Indian),* University of California Press.

Clinical Psychology

Dean, John P., and Alex Rosen: *A Manual of Intergroup Relations,* Phoenix Books, The University of Chicago Press.

Dollard, John, et al.: *Frustration and Aggression,* Yale University Press, Y34.

Fromm, Erika, and Leonore D. Hartman: *Intelligence: A Dynamic Approach,* Random House, Inc., PP16.

Grinker, R., and J. Spiegel: *Men under Stress,* McGraw-Hill Book Company.

Gross, Martin L.: *The Brain Watchers* [Psychological Tests], Signet Books, New American Library of World Literature, Inc., T2382.

Hart, C.: *The Psychology of Insanity,* Cambridge University Press.

Jourard, Sidney M.: *The Transparent Self: Self Disclosure and Well-being,* Insight Books, D. Van Nostrand Company, Inc.

Lynch, K. A. (ed.): *Personal Problems,* Deus Books.

Maier, Norman: *Frustration,* Ann Arbor Paperbacks, The University of Michigan Press, 48AA.

May, Rollo: *The Art of Counseling,* Apex Books, Abingdon Press.

Menninger, K.: *Love against Hate,* Harvest Books, Harcourt, Brace & World, Inc., HB28.

————: *Man against Himself,* Harvest Books, Harcourt, Brace & World, Inc., HB21.

Moustakas, C. E.: *Loneliness,* Spectrum Books, Prentice-Hall, Inc., S15.

Mullahy, Patrick: *Oedipus Myth and Complex,* Evergreen Books, Grove Press, Inc., E23.

————: *A Study of Interpersonal Relations,* Evergreen Books, Grove Press, Inc., 76.

Palmer, James O., and Michael T. Goldstein: *The Experience of Anxiety: A Casebook of Abnormal Psychology,* Oxford University Press.

Pavlov, I. P.: *Conditioned Reflexes,* Dover Publications, Inc., S614.

Quay, H. C. (ed.): *Readings in Psychopathology,* Insight Books, D. Van Nostrand Company, Inc., 11.

Selye, Hans: *The Stress of Life,* McGraw-Hill Book Company.

Sprott, W.: *Human Groups,* Penguin Books, Inc., A346.

Watson, Robert I.: *The Clinical Method in Psychology,* Science Editions, Inc.

Werner, H.: *Comparative Psychology of Mental Development,* Science Editions, Inc., 852-S.

Dictionaries

Bradley, David G.: *A Guide to the World's Religions,* Spectrum Books, Prentice-Hall, Inc.

Drever, J.: *A Dictionary of Psychology,* Penguin Books, Inc., R5.

Fairchild, H. P.: *Dictionary of Sociology,* Littlefield, Adams & Co., H120.

Filler, *Dictionary of American Social Reform,* The Citadel Press, C108.

Fodor, Nandor, and Frank Gaynor (eds.): *Freud: Dictionary of Psychoanalysis,* Premier Books, Fawcett Publications, Inc., T187.

Freud, Sigmund: *Dictionary of Psychoanalysis,* Wisdom Library Paperbacks, Philosophical Library, Inc., WL34.

Hariman and Jones: *Dictionary of Psychological Terms,* Littlefield, Adams & Co.

Uvarov, E. B., and D. R. Chapman: *A Dictionary of Science,* Penguin Books, Inc.

Winick, *Dictionary of Anthropology,* Littlefield, Adams & Co., 31.

Family Life

Barrett, Donald N. (ed.): *The Problem of Population: Moral and Theological Considerations,* Notre Dame Pocket Library, University of Notre Dame Press, PL3.

Carstairs, G. M.: *This Island Now,* Penguin Books, Inc., 2133.

Cavan, Ruth: *Marriage and Family in the Modern World* [Readings], Thomas Y. Crowell Company.

Davis, Fred: *Passage through Crisis: Polio Victims and Their Families,* The Bobbs-Merrill Company, Inc.

De Forrest, H.: *Planned Parenthood,* Monarch Books, Inc.

Doyle, C. H.: *Cana Is Forever,* Image Books, Doubleday & Company, Inc., D62.

Egleson, Jim, and Janet Egleson: *Parents without Partners,* Ace Star, K190.

Elkin, Frederick: *The Family in Canada,* Canadian Conference on the Family, Ottawa.

Farber, S. M., and R. H. L. Wilson (eds.): *The Potential of Women,* McGraw-Hill Book Company.

Fletcher, R.: *The Family and Marriage,* Penguin Books, Inc., S210.

Friedan, Betty: *The Feminine Mystique,* Dell Publishing Co., 2498.

Garigue, Philippe: *La vie familiale des canadiens français,* University of Montreal Press.

Goode, William J.: *The Family,* Prentice-Hall, Inc.

Gosse, E.: *Father and Son: A Study of Two Temperaments,* W. W. Norton & Company, Inc.

Gray, Madeline: *The Changing Years (Menopause),* Dolphin Books, Doubleday & Company, Inc., C242.

Kelly, Msgr. George A.: *Catholic Family Handbook,* Chapel Books, Dell Publishing Co., Inc., S30.

———: *Overpopulation: A Catholic View,* Paulist Press.

Lewis, Oscar: *The Children of Sanchez,* Vintage Books, Random House, Inc., VG1.

———: *Five Families,* Science Editions, Inc., 425S.

Malinowski, B.: *The Family among the Australian Aborigines,* Schocken Books, Inc.

Mavry, Marican (ed.): *Birth Rate and Birth Right,* Macfadden Publications, Inc., 60-118.

Mead, Margaret: *Male and Female,* Mentor Books, New American Library of World Literature, Inc., MD150.

Parenthood: Design or Accident, Ernest Benn Paperbacks, Ernest Benn, Ltd.—Benn Bros., Ltd.

Patai, Raphael: *Sex and the Family in the Bible and the Middle East,* Dolphin Books, Doubleday & Company, Inc., C40.

——— (ed.): *Women in Modern Afro-Asia,* Dolphin Books, Doubleday & Company, Inc.

——— (ed.): *Women in the Modern Western World,* Dolphin Books, Doubleday & Company, Inc.

Puxom, Margaret: *The Family and the Law,* Pelican Books, A644.

Queen, S., R. Habenstein and J. Adams: *The Family in Various Cultures*, Perceptor, P1.

Schifferes, Justus J.: *The Older People in Your Life*, Pocket Books, Inc. (Permabooks), M75-7.

Schlesinger, Benjamin: *Under One Roof* [Family Life in Canada], Canadian Broadcasting Corporation.

Somerville, Rose: *Family Insights through the Short Story*, Bureau of Publications, Teachers College, Columbia University.

Stephens, William N.: *The Family in Cross-cultural Perspective*, Holt, Rinehart and Winston, Inc.

Sussman, Marion B.: *Source Book in Marriage and the Family* [Readings], Houghton Mifflin Company.

Townsend, Peter: *The Family Life of Old People*, Pelican Books, A634.

Yoe, Shway: *The Burman: His Life and Notions*, W. W. Norton & Company, Inc.

Young, M., and P. Wilmott: *Family and Kinship in East London*, Pelican Books, A595.

Problems of Childhood

Adler, Alfred: *Difficult Child*, Capricorn Books, G. P. Putnam's Sons, 33.

Burns, C.: *Mental Health and Childhood*, Fides Dome, 16.

Clark, K.: *Prejudice and Your Child*, Beacon Press.

Despert, T. L.: *Children of Divorce*, Dolphin Books, Doubleday & Company, Inc.

Driscoll, Gertrude: *Child Guidance in the Classroom*, Columbia University Press.

Foster, C., and Spurgeon English: *Fathers Are Parents Too*, Belmont Books, L92-548.

Frampton, M. E., and E. D. Gall: *Mental Health and Guidance for Exceptional Children*, Porter Sargent.

Franklin, *Care of Invalid and Crippled Children*, Oxford University Press.

Gesell Institute, Frances Ilg, and Louise Ames: *Child Behavior*, Dell Publishing Co., Inc., LC120.

Goodman, May Ellen: *Race Awareness in Young Children*, Collier Books, a division of Crowell-Collier Publishing Co., BS200.

Goodman, Paul: *Growing Up Absurd*, Vintage Books, Random House, Inc., V32.

Jersild, Arthur T.: *When Teachers Face Themselves*, Columbia University Press.

Ostrovsky, E.: *Children without Men*, Collier Books, a division of Crowell-Collier Publishing Co., A5464.

———: *Father to the Child*, Collier Books, a division of Crowell-Collier Publishing Co.

Psychiatry

Barker, R., and Bert Kaplan (eds.): *Dreams of American College Students*, University of Kansas Press.

Bellak, Leopold: *Contemporary European Psychiatry*, Evergreen Books, Grove Press, Inc., E285.

Brussels, James A.: *The Layman's Guide to Psychiatry*, Barnes & Noble, Inc.

The Burden on the Community: The Epidemiology of Mental Illness [A Symposium], Oxford University Press.

Clark, D. Stafford: *Psychiatry Today*, Pelican Books, A262.

Crow, Lester, and Alice Crow (eds.): *Mental Hygiene for Teachers*, Collier Books, a division of Crowell-Collier Publishing Co.

Day Hospital, Grune & Stratton, Inc.

Dewit, Gerard A.: *Symbolism of Masculinity and Femininity*, Springer Publishing Co., Inc.

Goffman, E.: *Asylums: Mental Hospitals and Patients*, Anchor Books, Doubleday & Company, Inc., A277.
———: *The Presentation of Self in Everyday Life*, Anchor Books, Doubleday & Company, Inc., A174.
Goldstein, Kurt: *Human Nature in the Light of Psychopatholgy*, Schocken Books, Inc.
Goldstein, Michael T., and James O. Palmer: *The Experience of Anxiety: A Casebook*, Oxford University Press.
Gottman, Erving: *Stigma*, Spectrum Books, Prentice-Hall, Inc., S73.
Grinker, Roy: *Psychosomatic Research*, Grove Press, Inc., E313.
Hadfield, J. A.: *Dreams and Nightmares*, Pelican Books, A294.
Hinsie, L.: *Understandable Psychiatry*, Collier Books, a division of Crowell-Collier Publishing Co., AS332.
Hook, Sidney (ed.): *Dimensions of the Mind*, Collier Books, a division of Crowell-Collier Publishing Co., BS38.
Hunt, Morton M.: *Mental Hospital* (foreword by Robert H. Felix), Pyramid Books, R762.
Hyde, Robert M.: *Experiencing the Patient's Day*, G. P. Putnam's Sons.
Jones, Ernest: *Hamlet and Oedipus*, Anchor Books, Doubleday & Company, Inc., A31.
———: *Treatment of the Neuroses*, Schocken Books, Inc.
Kolle, A.: *Introduction to Psychiatry*, The Citadel Press, C120.
Kraepelin, Emil: *100 Years of Psychiatry*, The Citadel Press.
Kubie, L.: *Neurotic Distortion of the Creative Process*, Noonday Books, Farrar, Straus & Cudahy, Inc., N213.
McCord, William: *The Psychopath: An Essay on the Criminal Mind*, Insight Books, D. Van Nostrand Company, Inc.
Neumann, Erich: *The Origins and History of Consciousness*, Harper Torchbooks, Harper & Row, Publishers, Incorporated, vol. I, TB2007; vol. II, TB2008.
Orlando, Ida J.: *The Dynamic Nurse-Patient Relationship*, G. P. Putnam's Sons.
Pavlov, I. P.: *Essays in Psychology and Psychiatry*, The Citadel Press, C110.
A Psychiatric Glossary, American Psychiatric Association.
Redlich, F., and J. Bingham: *The Inside Story: Psychiatry and Everyday Life*, Vintage Books, Random House, Inc., V99.
Roback, A.: *History of Psychology and Psychiatry*, The Citadel Press.
Roheim, Geza: *Magic and Schizophrenia*, Midland Books, Indiana University Press.
Ropp, Robert S. de: *Drugs and the Mind*, Grove Press, Inc., E218.
Sargent, W.: *Battle for the Mind* [Brainwashing], Pan-Piper, XP12.
Seidman, Jerome M.: *Educating for Mental Health: A Book of Readings*, Thomas Y. Crowell Company.
Shneidman, Edwin S., and Norman L. Farberow (eds.): *Clues to Suicide*, McGraw-Hill Book Company, 56981.
Simeons, A. T. W.: *Man's Presumptuous Brain*, Dutton Everyman Paperbacks, E. P. Dutton, Co., Inc.,
Suttie, J.: *Origins of Love and Hate*, Pelican Books, A444.
Thouless, Robert H.: *Experimental Psychical Research*, Pelican Books, A623.
Thruelsen, A., and B. Kodker: *Adventures of the Mind*, Vintage Books, Random House, Inc., V109.
Umbarger, Dalsimer, Morrison, and Breggin: *College Students in a Mental Hospital*, Grune & Stratton, Inc.
United States Joint Commission on Mental Illness and Health: *Action for Mental Health*, Science Editions, Inc., 102-S.
Walter, W.: *The Living Brain*, Pelican Books, A256.
Wooldridge, Dean E.: *The Machinery of the Brain*, McGraw-Hill Book Company, 71841.

Psychoanalytic Thought

Adler, Alfred: *Practice and Theory of Individual Psychology,* Littlefield, Adams & Co.
——: *Problem of Neurosis,* Harper Torchbooks, Harper & Row, Publishers, Incorporated, TB1145.
——: *Understanding Human Nature,* Premier Books, Fawcett Publications, Inc., D52.
——: *What Life Should Mean to You,* Capricorn Books, G. P. Putnam's Sons, 3.
Adler, Kurt A.: *Essays in Individual Psychology,* Danica Deutsch (ed.), Evergreen Books, Grove Press, Inc., E180.
Alexander, F., and H. Ross: *Impact of Freudian Psychiatry,* Phoenix Books, The University of Chicago Press, 462.
Baker, Rachel: *Sigmund Freud for Everybody,* Popular Library Inc., G712.
Bennet, E. A.: *C. J. Jung,* Dutton Everyman Paperbacks, E. P. Dutton & Co., Inc., D98.
Brill, A.: *Freud's Contribution to Psychiatry,* Norton Library.
Brown, T. A. C.: *Freud and the Post Freudians,* Pelican Books, 522.
Chaplin, (ed.): *The Unconscious,* Ballantine Books, Inc., F443K.
Clark, R. A. *Six Talks on Jungian Psychology,* Boxwood Press.
Clouzet, Maryse (Choisy): *Sigmund Freud: A New Appraisal,* The Citadel Press, C122.
Evans, Richard I.: *Conversations with Jung and Reactions from Ernest Jones,* Insight Books, D. Van Nostrand Company, Inc., 23.
Ferenczi, S. *Sex in Psychoanalysis and Development of Psychoanalysis,* Dover Publications, Inc., T324.
Fordham, Freda: *An Introduction to Jung's Psychology,* Pelican Books, A273.
Freud, Philip: *The Myth of the Birth of the Hero and Other Essays of Otto Rank,* Vintage Books, Random House, Inc., K70.
Freud, Sigmund: *Beyond the Pleasure Principle,* Bantam Books, Inc., FC49.
——: *Civilization and Its Discontents,* Anchor Books, Doubleday & Company, Inc. A130.
——: *Collected Papers,* Collier Books, a division of Crowell-Collier Publishing Co., *Character and Culture,* BS193V; *Dora: An Analysis of a Case of Hysteria,* AS581V; *Early Psychoanalytic Writings,* BS188V; *General Psychological Theory,* AS582V; *The History of the Psychoanalytical Movement,* AS580V.
——: *Collected Papers,* Collier Books, a division of Crowell-Collier Publishing Co., *Studies in Parapsychology,* ASS83V; *Sexuality and the Psychology of Love,* BS192V; *Therapy and Technique,* BS189V; *Three Case Histories,* BS191V; *The Sexual Enlightenment of Children,* BS190V.
——: *On Creativity and the Unconscious: Papers on the Psychology of Art, Literature, Love, Religion,* B. Nelson (ed.), Harper Torchbooks, Harper & Row, Publishers, Incorporated, 45.
——: *Delusion and Dream,* Beacon Press, BP19.
——: *On Dreams,* W. W. Norton & Company, Inc., N144.
——: *The Ego and the Id,* W. W. Norton & Company, Inc., N142.
——: *Future of an Illusion,* Anchor Books, Doubleday & Company, Inc., A99.
——: *General Introduction to Psychoanalysis,* Pocket Books, Inc., M5001.
——: *Group Psychology and the Analysis of the Ego,* Bantam Books, Inc., FC58.
——: *The Interpretation of Dreams,* Science Editions, Inc.
——: *Jokes and Their Relation to the Unconscious,* W. W. Norton & Company, Inc., N145.
——: *Leonardo,* Pelican, A519.

———: *Leonardo da Vinci: A Study in Psychosexuality*, Modern Library Paperbacks, Random House, Inc., P11.

———: *Origin and Development of Psychoanalysis*, Gateway Books, 6009.

———: *Origin of Psychoanalysis*, Anchor Books, Doubleday & Company, Inc., A112.

———: *Psychopathology of Everyday Life*, New American Library of World Literature, Inc., MD67.

———: *Three Contributions to the Theory of Sex*, Dutton Everyman Paperbacks, E. P. Dutton & Co., Inc., D105.

———: *Totem and Taboo*, Modern Library Paperbacks, Random House, Inc., P67.

———: *Two Short Accounts of Psychoanalysis*, Pelican Books, A511.

——— and J. Breuer: *Studies in Hysteria*, Beacon Press, PB59.

Fromm, Erich: *Forgotten Language* [Dream and Myth], Evergreen Books, Grove Press, Inc., E47.

———: *Psychoanalysis and Religion*, Yale University Press, Y12.

———: *Sigmund Freud's Mission*, Black Cat Books, BB51.

Glover, E.: *Freud or Jung*, Meridian Books, Inc., M34.

Hall, Calvin S. (ed.): *Primer of Freudian Psychology*, New American Library of World Literature, Inc., MO271.

Jacobi, Jolande: *The Psychology of C. J. Jung*, Yale University Press, Y75.

Jones, Ernest: *Life and Work of Sigmund Freud*, Anchor Books, Doubleday & Company, Inc., A340.

———: *Papers on Psychoanalysis*, Beacon Press, BP119.

Jung, Carl: *Modern Man in Search of a Soul*, Harvest Books, Harcourt, Brace & World, Inc., HB2.

———: *Psyche and Symbol*, Pelican Books, A136.

———: *Psychological Reflections*, Harper Torchbooks, Harper & Row, Publishers, Incorporated, TB2001.

———: *Psychology and Religion*, Yale University Press, Y14.

———: *Symbols of Transformation* (*Schizophrenia*), Harper Torchbooks, Harper & Row, Publishers, Incorporated, vol. I, TB2009; vol. II, TB2010.

———: *Two Essays on Analytical Psychology*, Meridian Books, Inc., M28.

———: *Undiscovered Self*, New American Library of World Literature, Inc., M28.

Justrow, Joseph: *Freud: His Dream and Sex Theories*, Pocket Books, Inc. (Permabooks), M4134.

Nelson, B. (ed.): *Freud and the Twentieth Century*, Meridian Books, Inc., M45.

Progoff, Ira: *Jung's Psychology and Its Social Meaning*, Evergreen Books, Grove Press, Inc., E24.

Puner, Helen Walker: *Freud: His Life and Mind*, Dell Publishing Co., Inc., LC137.

Reich, Wilhelm: *Character Analysis*, Noonday Books, Farrar, Straus & Cudahy, Inc., N202.

———: *The Functions of the Organs*, Noonday Books, Farrar, Straus & Cudahy, Inc., N219.

———: *Selected Writings*, Noonday Books, Farrar, Straus & Cudahy, Inc., N217.

———: *Sexual Revolution*, Noonday Books, Farrar, Straus & Cudahy, Inc., N235.

Reik, Theodor: *The Compulsion to Confess*, Grove Press, Inc., E316.

———: *Haunting Melody*, Evergreen Books, Grove Press, Inc., E215.

———: *Jewish Wit*, Gamut Press, A1.

———: *Listening with the Third Ear*, Evergreen Books, Grove Press, Inc., E34.

———: *Of Love and Lust*, Evergreen Books, Grove Press, Inc., E135.

———: *Masochism and Modern Man*, Evergreen Books, Grove Press, Inc., E79.

———: *Masochism in Sex and Society*, Black Cat Books, BD13.

————: *Psychology of Sex Relations*, Evergreen Books, Grove Press, Inc., E276.

———: *Ritual,* Evergreen Books, Grove Press, Inc., E22.
———: *The Search Within,* Evergreen Books, Grove Press, Inc., E107.
———: *Secret Self,* Evergreen Books, Grove Press, Inc., E243.
———: *Sex in Man and Woman,* Noonday Books, Farrar, Straus & Cudahy, Inc., N200.
Richman, J.: *A General Selection from the Works of Sigmund Freud,* Anchor Books, Doubleday & Company, Inc., A115.
Rieff, P.: *Freud: The Mind of the Moralist,* Anchor Books, Doubleday & Company, Inc., A278.
Stekel, Wilhelm: *Auto Erotism,* Evergreen Books, Grove Press, Inc., E288.
———: *Frigidity in Women,* Evergreen Books, Grove Press, Inc., vol. I, E353; vol. II, E354.
———: *Patterns of Psychosexual Infantilism,* Evergreen Books, Grove Press, Inc., E185.
———: *Sadism and Masochism,* Evergeen Books, Grove Press, Inc., vol I, E362; vol. II, E363.
Way, Lewis: *Adler's Place in Psychology,* Collier Books, a division of Crowell-Collier Publishing Co., BS101.
———: *Alfred Adler: An Introduction to His Psychology,* Pelican Books, A366.
Wells, Harry K.: *Sigmund Freud: A Pavlovian Critique,* New World Paperbacks, NW13.
Whyte, L.: *The Unconscious before Freud,* Anchor Books, Doubleday & Company, Inc., A286.
Wittels, Fritz: *Freud and His Time,* The Universal Library, Grosset & Dunlap, Inc., 34UL.
Zilboorg, Gregory: *Freud and Religion,* The Newman Press.
———: *Sigmund Freud: His Exploration of the Mind of Man,* Evergreen Books, Grove Press, Inc., E239 .

Sociology and Social Work

THE COMMUNITY

Anderson, N.: *Dimensions of Work,* McKay Social Science Series.
Blau, P. M.: *Bureaucracy in Modern Society,* Random House, Inc., S512.
Buckingham, Walter: *Automation: Its Impact on Business and People,* Mentor Books, New American Library of World Literature, Inc., MP525.
Caplow, Theodore: *The Sociology of Work,* McGraw-Hill Book Company, 09778.
Carr, J.: *Crack-up in Suburbia,* Monarch Books, Inc.
Conant, J. B.: *Slums and Suburbs,* McGraw-Hill Book Company.
Dubriner, W.: *Class in Suburbia,* Spectrum Books, Prentice-Hall, Inc., S50.
Fortune Magazine: *The Exploding Metropolis,* Anchor Books, Doubleday & Company, Inc., A146.
Galbraith, John Kenneth: *The Affluent Society,* Mentor Books, New American Library of World Literature, MT534.
Gordon, Milton M.: *Assimilation in American Life,* Oxford University Press.
———: *Social Class in American Sociology,* McGraw-Hill Book Company, 23786.
Lundberg, George A.: *America's Sixty Families,* The Citadel Press, C65.
Moore, Wilbert: *Social Change,* Prentice-Hall, Inc.
Nisbet, C.: *Community and Power,* Oxford University Press.
Packard, Vance: *The Hidden Persuaders,* Pocket Books, Inc., C288.
———: *The Waste Makers,* Pocket Books, Inc., GC612.
Peterson, W.: *American Social Patterns,* Anchor Books, Doubleday & Company, Inc., A126.

Schermer, R. A.: *Society and Power in Modern Society*, Random House, Inc., S518.
Seeley, John, Alexander Sim, and E. W. Loosley: *Crestwood Heights*, University of Toronto Press.
Spectorsky, A. C.: *The Exurbanites*, Berkley Publishing Corporation, BG108.
Vidich, A., and J. Beirsman: *Small Town in Mass Society*, Anchor Books, Doubleday & Company, Inc., A216.
Wylie, Laurence: *Village in the Vaucluse [France]*, Harper Colophon Books, CN24.

CROSS-CULTURAL

Barison, W.: *Continuity and Change in African Culture*, Phoenix Books, The University of Chicago Press, P85.
Barnett, H. G.: *Innovation: The Basis of Cultural Change*, McGraw-Hill Book Company, 03793.
Benedict, Ruth: *Patterns of Culture*, Mentor Books, New American Library of World Literature, Inc., MD89.
Du Bois, Cora: *The People of Alor*, 2 vols., Harper Torchbooks, Harper & Row, Publishers, Incorporated, TB1042–43.
Handlin, O.: *The Newcomers: Puerto Ricans and Negroes*, Anchor Books, Doubleday & Company, Inc., A283.
Hansen, Marcus Lee: *The Immigrant in American History*, Harper & Row, Publishers, Incorporated.
Kluckhohn, C.: *Mirror for Man*, Premier Books, Fawcett Publications, Inc., D58.
Lee, Dorothy: *Freedom and Culture*, Spectrum Books, Prentice-Hall, Inc., 56.
Linton, R.: *The Tree of Culture*, Vintage Books, Random House, Inc., V76.
Malinowski, B.: *The Dynamics of Culture Change*, Yale University Press, Y47.
Mead, Margaret: *Cultural Patterns and Technical Change*, Mentor Books, New American Library of World Literature, Inc., MD134.
———: *Male and Female*, Mentor Books, New American Library of World Literature, Inc., MD150.
———: *New Lives for Old*, Mentor Books, New American Library of World Literature, Inc., MD324.
Radcliffe-Brown: *African Systems of Kinship and Marriage*, Oxford University Press.
Redfield, R., and A. Rojas: *Chan-Kon: A Village That Chose Progress*, Phoenix Books, The University of Chicago Press, P86.
Sapir, E.: *Culture, Language, and Personality*, University of California Press.
Shapiro, Harry (ed.): *Man, Culture and Society*, Galaxy Books, Oxford University Press, GB32.
Spiro, M. E.: *Kibbutz Venture in Utopia*, Schocken Books, Inc.
Van Gennep, A.: *The Rites of Passage*, Phoenix Books, The University of Chicago Press, P64.
Weingarten, M.: *Life in a Kibbutz*, Reconstructionist Press.
Williams, Raymond: *Culture and Society*, Pelican Books, A520.
Zborowski, Mark, and E. Herzog: *Life Is with People: The Culture of the Shtetl*, Schocken Books, Inc., SB20.
Zinkin, T.: *Caste Today*, Oxford University Press.

SPECIAL PROBLEMS

Anderson, N.: *The Hobo*, Phoenix Books, The University of Chicago Press, P71.
Black, H.: *Buy Now Pay Later*, Pocket Books, Inc., GC139.
Brightbill, Charles K.: *The Challenge of Leisure*, Spectrum Books, Prentice-Hall, Inc., 567.
Dollard, John: *Caste and Class in a Southern Town*, Anchor Books, Doubleday & Company, Inc., A95.

Felder, W. Michael: *It's Cheaper to Die,* Monarch Books, Inc., MB514.

Fyrel, T. R.: *Insecure Offenders,* Pelican Books, A608.

Harrington, Michael: *The Other America,* Penguin Special, Penguin Books, Inc., S223.

Lolli, G.: *Social Drinking,* Collier Books, a division of Crowell-Collier Publishing Co., BS2.

Lucia, S. P. (ed.): *Alcohol and Civilization,* McGraw-Hill Book Company.

McGee, Reece: *Social Disorganization in America,* Chandler Publishing Company.

O'Connor, Philip: *Vagrancy,* Penguin Special, Penguin Books, Inc., S219.

Richmond, A. H.: *The Colour Problem,* Penguin Books, Inc., A328.

Thrasher, Frederick L.: *The Gang,* The University of Chicago Press.

30. Mental Health in Other Lands: Selected References

Henry P. David and Hans J. Priester

In concluding this volume, it seems useful to cite selected references on developing trends in mental health programs and psychiatric services in seventy-three countries. All are post-1960 publications and may generally be obtained through major libraries, interlibrary loan, or the respective publishers.

The selection of references was based on material available to the compilers. Major professional and abstracting journals were searched. The resources of the World Federation for Mental Health and the Mental Health Unit of the World Health Organization, both located in Geneva, were of considerable assistance. The scheme of geographic presentation follows the model of the six WHO regions.

There is no claim to be exhaustive or authoritative. With the continuing proliferation of mental health publications in many lands and numerous languages, it is most probable that some key papers were missed. In a few countries, notably the United States, we may have been too sparse, preferring to suggest sources of current information to which specific inquiries can be addressed.

As part of its continuing service program, the World Federation for Mental Health has expanded its Information Centre, which, in cooperation with member associations and individual members, is attempting to compile major references on mental health programs and services in all parts of the world. Readers are cordially invited to send pertinent material to the Federation at 1 Rue Gevray, Geneva, Switzerland.

Africa

GENERAL

Lambo, T. A. (ed.): *Report of First Pan-African Psychiatric Conference,* Government Printer, Ibadan, Nigeria, 1962.
   Especially prepared for this volume.

Leighton, A. H., T. A. Lambo, C. C. Hughes, et al.: "Psychiatric Disorders in West Africa," *Amer. J. Psychiat.*, 120:521–527, 1963.

CAMEROUN

Tschoungi, S. P., and P. Zumbach: "Diagnostic de la délinquance juvénile au Cameroun," *Int. Rev. Crim. Pol.*, no. 20, pp. 35–47, 1962.

CONGO (LÉOPOLDVILLE)

Veil, C.: "Contribution to Mental Health in the Congo (Léopoldville)," *World Ment. Hlth.*, 15:125–130, 1963.

ETHIOPIA

Hylander, F. B.: "Summary Information on Mental Diseases in Ethiopia," Commission for Technical Cooperation in Africa South of the Sahara, no. 35, London, 1960.

GHANA

Field, M. G.: *Search for Security and Ethno-psychiatric Study of Rural Ghana,* Northwestern University Press, Evanston, Ill., 1960.
Forster, E. B.: "The Theory and Practice of Psychiatry in Ghana," *Amer. J. Psychother.*, 16:7–51, 1962.

KENYA

Crawford, B. K. A.: "Developing Psychiatric Services in Kenya," in T. A. Lambo (ed.), *Report of First Pan-African Psychiatric Conference,* Government Printer, Ibadan, Nigeria, 1962.

LIBERIA

"Social Changes and Mental Health Problems in Liberia," *Harefuah,* 65:224–228, 1963.

MOZAMBIQUE

"Mental Hygiene and Mental Health in Mozambique," Commission for Technical Cooperation in Africa South of the Sahara, no. 35, London, 1960.

NIGERIA

Lambo, T. A.: "Mental Health in Nigeria," *World Ment. Hlth.*, 13:135–141, 1961.

RWANDA AND BURUNDI

Vyncke, J.: "L'assistance psychiatrique au Ruanda-Urundi," Commission for Technical Cooperation in Africa South of the Sahara, no. 35, London, 1960.

SENEGAL

Ortigues, M. C.: "Problèmes de psychologie clinique concernant les enfants sénégalais," *Neuro-psychiatrie,* Université de Dakar, Dakar, Senegal, 1963.

SOUTH AFRICA

Archer, B. C.: "Psychiatry in South Africa," *S. Afr. Med. J.*, 37:467–471, 1963.
Hurst, L. A., H. E. Reef, and S. B. Sachs: "Neuropsychiatric Disorders in the Bantu," *S. Afr. Med. J.*, 35:750–754, 1961.

TANZANIA

Smartt, C. G. F.: "Problems and Prospects of Psychiatry in Tanganyika," *E. Afr. Med. J.*, 37:480, 1960.

UGANDA

"Mental Health: Trends and Problems in Uganda," in T. A. Lambo (ed.), *Report of First Pan-African Psychiatric Conference*, Government Printer, Ibadan, Nigeria, 1962, pp. 183–185.

Americas

GENERAL

Bermann, S.: "La asistencia psiquiátrica en Latinoamérica," *Acta Psiquiat. Psicol. Argent.*, 9:56–71, 1963.
"Mental Health in Latin America," *WHO Chronicle*, 18:328–334, 1964.
Velasco Alzaga, J. M.: "La salud mental en las Américas," *Bol. Oficina Sanit. Panamer.*, 54:492–512, 1963.

ARGENTINA

Etchegoyen, R. H.: "Estado actuel de la psicotherapie en la Argentina," *Acta Psiquiat. Psicol. Argent.*, 9:93–113, 1963.

BRAZIL

Maia, E.: "Realidade de assistência psiquiatrica do Brasil," *Rev. Psicol. Norm. Patol.*, 9:270–279, 1963.

CANADA

Lazure, Denis: "Intégration de l'hygiène mentale au programme d'action des unités sanitaires," *Union Med. Canada*, 93:344–346, 1964.
More for the Mind: A Study of Psychiatric Services in Canada, Canadian Mental Health Association, Toronto, 1963.

CHILE

For information, write Asociación Chilena pro Salud Mental, Casilla 9319, Santiago, Chile.

CUBA

Bustamante, José A. (ed.): *Annals*, Institute for Research in Higher Nervous Activity, University of Havana, Havana, 1963.

HAITI

Bordeleau, Jean-M., and Nathan S. Kline: "Experience in Developing Psychiatric Services in Haiti," *World Ment. Hlth.*, 14:170–182, 1962.

MEXICO

Velasco Suárez, M., et al.: "Present Status of Psychiatry in Mexico," *Amer. J. Psychiat.*, 120:160–163, 1963.

PERU

Caravedo, B., and J. S. Garcia: "Estado actuel de la asistencia psiquiátrica en el Peru," Ministry of Public Health and Social Assistance, Lima, 1964.

Seguin, C. A.: "The Theory and Practice of Psychiatry in Peru," *Amer. J. Psychother.*, 18:188–211, 1964.

TRINIDAD AND TOBAGO

Government of Trinidad and Tobago: *Report of the Committee to Produce a Comprehensive Plan of the Mental Services of Trinidad and Tobago*, Government Printing Office, Port of Spain, 1960.

UNITED STATES

Action for Mental Health: Final Report of the Joint Commission on Mental Illness and Health, Basic Books, Inc., Publishers, New York, 1961.

Douglass, Joseph H.: "Current Trends in the United States," in H. P. David (ed.), *Population and Mental Health*, H. Huber Verlag, Bern, 1964; Springer Publ. Co., New York, 1964.

Felix, R. H.: "Community Mental Health," *Amer. J. Orthopsychiat.*, 33:788–795, 1963.

Ridenour, Nina: *Mental Health in the United States: A Fifty Year History*, Harvard University Press, Cambridge, Mass., 1961.

It is suggested that specific inquiries about mental health programs in the United States be addressed to the National Clearinghouse for Mental Health Information, National Institute of Mental Health, United States Public Health Service, Bethesda 14, Md., U.S.A.; or to the National Association for Mental Health, 10 Columbus Circle, New York, N.Y., U.S.A.; or to both.

VENEZUELA

Mateo Alonso, A.: "The Organization of Mental Health Services in Venezuela and Other Underdeveloped Countries," *Exerpta Med.*, International Congress Series, no. 45., 1961.

Southeast Asia

CEYLON

Fernando, G. P. S., and C. M. S. Jayewardene: "Mental Illness in Ceylon," *Probat. Child Care*, Colombo, June, 1963.

INDIA

Gaitonde, M. R.: "Psychiatric Problems in Emerging Countries—India," *Comprehen. Psychiat.*, 5:75–79, 1964.

Kohlmeyer, W. A., and X. Fernandes: "Psychiatry in India: Family Approach in the Treatment of Mental Disorders," *Amer. J. Psychiat.*, 119:1033–1037, 1963.

INDONESIA

Kline, Nathan S.: "Psychiatry in Indonesia," *Amer. J. Psychiat.*, 119:809–815, 1963.

MALAYSIA

Schmidt, K. E.: "Aufbau eines psychiatrischen Gesundheitsdienstes in einem entwicklungslande Südost-Asiens (Sarawak)," *Nervenarzt*, 34:397–401, 1963.

THAILAND

Ratanakorn, Prasop: *Neurological and Psychiatric and Mental Health Service in Thailand,* Neurological Research Institute, Bangkok, 1962.

Europe

GENERAL

Barton, Walter H. (ed.): *Impressions of European Psychiatry,* American Psychiatric Association, Washington, D.C., 1961.
Bellak, Leopold (ed.): *Contemporary European Psychiatry,* Grove Press, Inc., New York, 1961.

ALBANIA

Aleksandrovskii, A. B.: "The Development of Psychiatry in Albania," *Zh. Nevropat. Psikhiat.,* 60:109–114, 1960.

ALGERIA

Staff of Blida Mental Hospital: "Causes principales de morbidité psychiatrique chez las musulmans algériens," *Hyg. ment.,* 50:261–286, 1961; *Transcult. Psychiat. Res. Newsltr.,* October, 1962.

AUSTRIA

Hoff, H., and O. M. Arnold: "Austria," in Leopold Bellak (ed.), *Contemporary European Psychiatry,* Grove Press, Inc., New York, 1961, pp. 43–142.
Schindler, R.: "Follow-up of Psychoses by the Public Health Service in Vienna," *Wien. Z. Nervenheilk.,* 21:70–78, 1963.

BELGIUM

Barton, Walter H. (ed.): "Notes on Belgium," *Impressions of European Psychiatry,* American Psychiatric Association, Washington, D.C., 1961.

BULGARIA

Penchev, P.: "The Scope of Neurological and Mental Invalidity in Bulgaria," *Neurol., Psychiat., Neurochir.,* 3:82–88, 1964.

CZECHOSLOVAKIA

Prokupek, J.: "Development of Psychiatric Care in C.S.S.R. in 1962 and Next Tasks in Mental Health," *Cesk. Zdravot.,* 11:465–470, 1963.

DENMARK

Langfeldt, Gabriel: "Scandinavia (Denmark)," in Leopold Bellak (ed.), *Contemporary European Psychiatry,* Grove Press, Inc., New York, 1961, pp. 219–279.
Udsen, P.: "Fifty Years of Danish Psychiatry, 1934–1984: A Review of the State of the Profession and a Prognosis for the Near Future," *Ugeskr. Laeger,* 126:81–91, 1964.

FINLAND

Achte, K. A.: "Requirement of Psychiatric Beds for Care of the Mentally Ill in Helsinki, Finland," *Suomen Lääkärilehti Finlands Läkärtidning,* no. 28, pp. 1761–1766, 1963.

FRANCE

Ey, H.: "Psychiatric Therapy in France," *Current Psychiat. Ther.*, 2:266–269, 1962.
Flavigny, H., and H. Basquin: "The Current Situation of French Child Psychiatry," *Acta Paedopsychiat.*, 31:290–294, Basel, 1964.
Pichot, Pierre: "France," in Leopold Bellak (ed.), *Contemporary European Psychiatry*, Grove Press, Inc., New York, 1961, pp. 3–39.

GERMANY (DEMOCRATIC REPUBLIC)

Müller-Hegemann, D.: "Psychiatry in a Changing World; Methodologic Approaches in Psychotherapy: Current Concepts in East Germany," *Amer. J. Psychother.*, 17:554–568, 1963.

GERMANY (FEDERAL REPUBLIC)

Ehrhardt, H.: "Mental Health Program and Public Health Planning in Germany Today," *Ger. Med. Monthly*, 8:211–216, 1963.
Hoff, Hans, and O. H. Arnold: "Germany," in Leopold Bellak (ed.), *Contemporary European Psychiatry*, Grove Press, Inc., New York, 1961, pp. 43–142.

GREECE

Alivisatos, G., and G. Lyketsos: "A Preliminary Report into the Attitudes of the Families of Hospitalized Mental Patients," *World Ment. Hlth.*, 14:1–20, 1962.
Vassiliou, George: "The Behavioral Sciences in Greece," *Amer. J. Orthopsychiat.*, 34:979–980, 1964.

ICELAND

Petursson, E.: "Psychiatry in Iceland," *Int. J. Soc. Psychiat.*, 9:154–156, 1963.

IRELAND

Browne, Ivor W.: "Psychiatry in Ireland," *Amer. J. Psychiat.*, 119:816–819, 1963.

ITALY

Cerletti, Ugo: "Italy," in Leopold Bellak (ed.), *Contemporary European Psychiatry*, Grove Press, Inc., New York, 1961, pp. 187–216.
Rose, Arnold M.: "The Prevalence of Mental Disorders in Italy," *Int. J. Soc. Psychiat.*, 10:87–100, 1964.

MOROCCO

For information, write Ligue Marocaine pour la Santé Mentale, Ministère de la Santé Publique, Rabat, Morocco.

NETHERLANDS

Mental Health in the Netherlands, Ministry of Social Affairs and Public Health and National Federation for Mental Health, The Hague, 1964.

NORWAY

Astrup, C.: "Patterns of Discharge and Readmission into Psychiatric Hospitals in Norway, 1926–1955," *Ment. Hyg.*, 45:185–193, 1961.
Langfeldt, Gabriel: "Scandinavia (Norway)," in Leopold Bellak (ed.), *Contemporary European Psychiatry*, Grove Press, Inc., New York, 1961, pp. 219–279.

POLAND

Jus, A.: "Theory and Practice of Psychiatry in Poland," *Amer. J. Psychother.*, 16:676–692, 1962.

PORTUGAL

Alvim, F., et al.: "Mental Health and Public Health," *J. Med.*, 54:397–399, Lisbon, 1964.

Fontes, Victor: "La psychiatrie infantile au Portugal," *Acta Paedopsychiat.*, 31:340–346, Basel, 1964.

RUMANIA

Prokupek, J.: "À propos de tâches incombrant aux services de santé mentale dans une société socialiste (Romania)," *Santé Publ.*, 5:329–334, 1962.

SPAIN

López-Ibor, J.: "Letter from Spain," *Comprehen. Psychiat.*, 5:128–129, 1964.

Santo-Domingo, C. J.: "La higiene mental y la asistencia psiquiátrica ambulatoria en Espagna," *Arch. Neurobiol.*, 26:22–50, Madrid, 1963.

SWEDEN

Langfeldt, Gabriel: "Scandinavia (Sweden)," in Leopold Bellak (ed.), *Contemporary European Psychiatry*, Grove Press, Inc., New York, 1961, pp. 219–279.

Lundquist, G.: "Fifty Years of Swedish Care of the Mentally Ill," *Psychiat. Quart.*, 36:475–483, 1962.

SWITZERLAND

Benedetti, G., and C. Muller: "Switzerland," in Leopold Bellak (ed.), *Contemporary European Psychiatry*, Grove Press, Inc., New York, 1961, pp. 327–359.

Répond, André: *Hygiène et santé mentale en Suisse*, World Federation for Mental Health, Geneva, 1964.

TURKEY

Geneviere, J. M.: "Nationalization of Health Services in Turkey," *UNICEF News*, January, 1964.

UNION OF SOVIET SOCIALIST REPUBLICS

Aronson, J., and Mark G. Field: "Mental Health Programming in the Soviet Union," *Amer. J. Orthopsychiat.*, 34:913–924, 1964.

David, H. P., and T. S. David: "Soviet Mental Health Facilities and Psychology," in R. A. Bauer (ed.), *Some Views on Soviet Psychology*. American Psychological Association, Washington, D.C., 1962.

Field, Mark G., and J. Aronson: "The Institutional Framework of Soviet Psychiatry," *J. Nerv. Ment. Dis.*, 138:305–322, 1964.

Gilyarovsky, V. A.: "The Soviet Union," in Leopold Bellak (ed.), *Contemporary European Psychiatry*, Grove Press, Inc., New York, 1961, pp. 283–323.

Kline, Nathan S.: "The Organization of Psychiatric Care and Psychiatric Research in the U.S.S.R.," *Ann. N.Y. Acad. Sci.*, 84:147–224, 1960.

UNITED KINGDOM

Clark, J.: "Mental Health and Community Care," *J. Roy. Inst.*, 25:271–274, 1962.

Freeman, H., and J. Farndale (eds.): *Trends in the Mental Health Services,* Pergamon Press, Oxford, 1963; The Macmillan Company, New York, 1963.

Jones, K.: *Mental Health and Social Policy,* Routledge & Kegan Paul, Ltd., London, 1960.

Leigh, Denis: *The Historical Development of British Psychiatry,* Pergamon Press, Oxford, 1961.

Lewis, Aubrey: "Great Britain," in Leopold Bellak (ed.), *Contemporary European Psychiatry,* Grove Press, Inc., New York, 1961, pp. 145–183.

YUGOSLAVIA

Kline, Nathan S.: "Psychiatry in Yugoslavia," *Psychiat. Quart.,* 37:245–252, 1963.

Ugcesiv, B.: "Organization and Development of Mental Health Services," *Narodno Zdravlje,* 20:12–17, 1964.

Eastern Mediterranean

ADEN

Steele, Robin: "Psychiatric Observations in Aden," *Transcult. Psychiat. Res. Newsltr.,* no. 15, pp. 69–70, 1963.

IRAN

Bash, K. W.: *Mental Health Section of the Imperial Iranian Ministry of Health: A Short Report,* Ministry of Health, Department of Public Health, Teheran. (Mimeographed.)

ISRAEL

Lyons-Bergman, R.: "Israel's Mental Health Program—Provides a Network of Varied Services," *Nurs. Outlook,* 12(6):40–42, 1964.

Miller, Louis: "Community Psychiatry in Israel," *Israel Ann. Psychiat. Relat. Discipl.,* 2:41–46, 1964.

KUWAIT

Kline, Nathan S.: "Psychiatry in Kuwait," *Brit. J. Psychiat.,* 109:766–774, 1963.

LEBANON

Habib, A.: *L'Hôpital Psychiatrique de la Croix,* L'Imprimerie Sonahine, Beirut, 1962.

PAKISTAN

Ashgar, G. A.: "Development of Psychiatric Services in Pakistan," *J. Pak. Med. Ass.,* 13:45–48, 1963.

SUDAN

Baasher, T. A.: "Some Aspects of the History of the Treatment of Mental Disorders in the Sudan," *Sudan Med. J.,* 1:44–48, 1962.

TUNISIA

Ammar, S.: "Les désordres psychiques dans la société tunisienne," *Tunisie Med.,* no. 1., pp. 37–53, 1964; *Inform. Psychiat.,* 40:605–612, 1964.

UNITED ARAB REPUBLIC

Girgis, Sabry: *Psychiatry and Mental Health in the United Arab Republic,* Ministry of Health, Cairo, 1964.

Western Pacific

ASIA

Lin, T. Y.: "Historical Survey of Psychiatric Epidemiology in Asia," *Ment. Hyg.*, 47:351–359, 1963.

AUSTRALIA

Dax, Eric C.: *Asylum to Community: The Development of the Mental Hygiene Service in Victoria, Australia*, F. W. Cheshire, Melbourne, 1961.

Youngman, N. Y.: "Psychiatry, Medicine, and the Community," *Med. J. Aust.*, 1:603–608, 1963.

CHINA

Cerny, J.: "Psychiatry in China," *Ceskoslov. Psychiat.*, 59:273–282, 1963.

Lazure, Denis: "The Family and Youth in New China: Psychiatric Observations," *Canad. Med. Ass. J.*, 86:179, 1962.

———: "Politics and Mental Health in the New China," *Amer. J. Orthopsychiat.*, 34:925–933, 1964.

JAPAN

Caudill, William, and L. Takeo Doi: "Psychiatry and Culture in Japan," chap. 12 of this volume.

MONGOLIA

Cerny, J.: "Psychiatry in Mongolia," *Ceskoslov. Psychiat.*, 57:413, 1961.

NEW ZEALAND

Medlicott, R. W.: "Psychiatry and the Practice of Medicine in New Zealand," *Med. J. Aust.*, 2:86–89, 1964; *N.J. Med. J.*, 63:65–68, 1964.

PHILIPPINES

Maguigad, L. C.: "Psychiatry in the Philippines," *Amer. J. Psychiat.*, 121:21–25, 1964.

TAIWAN

Lin, Tsung-yi: "Evolution of Mental Health Program in Taiwan," *Amer. J. Psychiat.*, 117:961–971, 1961.

Author Index *

Aichhorn, A., 282, 292, 301
Aikin, W. A., 227
Ainsworth, M. D., 267
Ajuriaguerra, J. de, 313
Albee, George W., 419
Allen, Ernest M., 328–330
Alt, H., 267
Amado, G., 259, 267
Anderson, R. H., 178, 181
Andrews, F. Emerson, 323, 330

Baan, P. A. H., 79, 313
Babcock, Charlotte, 310
Barton, W. Russell, 96
Beers, Clifford Whittingham, 78, 79
Bindman, Arthur J., 7, 194, 209, 225
Bixby, F. L., 282, 292
Bovet, D., 313
Bower, E. M., 209, 227
Bowlby, J., 20, 22, 75, 216
Brand, J. L., 323, 324, 331
Bransby, E. R., 182, 191
Brim, O. G., Jr., 309, 310
Broadwin, I., 181, 191
Brooke, E. M., 96
Buckle, Donald F., 7, 223, 227, 245, 304, 313
Burgess, E. W., 283, 292
Burn, M., 224, 227
Burnet, Sir MacFarlane, 13, 22
Burns, C., 183, 191

Campbell, J., 183, 191
Caplan, G., 209
Carstairs, G. M., 307, 310, 313
Caudill, William, 6, 129, 145, 155, 313
Chisholm, Brock, 79
Cloutier, François, 6, 78
Collomb, Henri, 4, 9, 303, 310
Conolly, John, 95

David, Henry P., 3, 303, 319, 347
Davidson, M., 267
Davidson, S., 189, 191
Davy, B. W., 189, 191
Deutsch, H., 186, 191
Dix, Dorothea, 4
Dixon, J. J., 185, 191
Doi, L. Takeo, 6, 129, 145, 155
Dore, R. P., 141, 145
Dörken, Herbert, 6, 109, 120, 158
Durkheim, E., 280, 291

Eisenberg, Leon, 6, 63, 75, 82, 191, 309, 313
El Mahi, Tijani, 150
Elias, Albert, 8, 280, 291, 308
Esquirol, J. E. D., 53

Fein, R., 22
Felix, R. H., 75, 313
Forstenzer, H. M., 209
Frank, J., 75
Freud, Anna, 227
Freud, Sigmund, 4, 225, 297

Getzels, J. W., 175, 181
Glueck, E. T., 75
Glueck, S., 75
Goldfarb, W., 25
Goodlad, J. I., 178, 181

Hallock, A. C. K., 209
Hansen, Asger, 8, 293, 308
Hargreaves, Ronald, 79
Harrington, M., 183, 191
Hassan, J., 183, 191
Hersov, L. A., 181, 185, 191
Hill, Gardiner, 95

* Country names and additional reference sources are listed in the Subject Index.

357

Hitchcock, A., 182, 191
Hobbs, Nicholas, 4, 9, 304
Howells, J. G., 267
Hume, Portia B., 209
Hunt, R. C., 209

Jackson, P. W., 175, 181
Jahoda, Marie, 18, 109, 120
Johnson, A. M., 183, 184, 191, 226
Jones, Kathleen, 7, 87, 96, 156

Kahn, Jack H., 7, 181, 190, 192, 225, 226
Kaketa, Katsumi, 140, 146
Karnes, M. B., 177, 181
Kellmer Pringle, M. L., 75
Kerbikov, O. V., 313
Kirk, S. A., 209, 268
Kitami, Yoshio, 140, 146
Klebanoff, Lewis B., 7, 194, 209, 225
Klineberg, Otto, 3, 9
Kora, Takehisa, 146
Krapf, E. E., 5, 23, 79, 81
Krugman, M., 209

Laing, R. D., 187, 192
Lambo, T. Adeoye, 6, 147, 153, 155, 313
Larsson, S., 268
Laycock, Samuel R., 7, 171, 181, 224
Lebedev, B. A., 6, 121, 163, 313
Lebovici, Serge, 6, 7, 97, 163, 165, 228, 245, 304
Leighton, A., 153
Léon, C. A., 313
Levitt, E. E., 244
Lewin, Kurt, 220, 224
Lewis, Marianne O., 331
Lewis, W. W., 7, 231, 304
Lichter, S., 177, 181
Lin, T., 313
Lowrey, L. C., 220

McCorkle, L. W., 282, 291, 292
McKay, H. D., 283, 292
Mackintosh, J. M., 34, 53
McWhinnie, J. B., 183, 192
Maslow, A. H., 173, 181
Matsumoto, Y. S., 141, 146
Miller, Louis, 7, 154

Miller, Neal, 313
Mitchell, S. Weir, 137, 146
Morita, Shōma, 137–139, 146
Moser, Joy, 5, 23, 81, 313
Mulock-Houwer, D. Q. R., 268

Nagler, Shmuel, 7, 210, 225
Newell, Nancy, 209
Nieuwenuize, Henk, 332
Nursten, Jean P., 7, 181, 190, 192, 225, 226

Ojemann, Ralph H., 174, 181

Palmer, Francis H., 325, 331
Palsvig, Kurt, 296
Partridge, J. M., 181, 192
Pasamanick, B., 66
Paumelle, Philippe, 6, 97, 163, 165
Penningroth, Paul, 306, 310
Pfister, Maria, 313
Pilkington, Thomas L., 8, 332
Pinel, Philippe, 4, 38
Priester, Hans J., 8, 347

Querido, Arie, 5, 32, 87, 96

Redl, F., 268, 282, 292, 301
Redlich, F.C., 75
Rees, J. R., 5, 13, 79, 81
Rees, T. P., 37
Reischauer, Edwin O., 141, 146
Riess, B. F., 3
Riessman, Frank, 177, 181
Rush, Benjamin, 4

Sangsingkeo, Phon, 6, 55, 81
Sato, Koji, 146
Scheer, Simon van der, 37
Schlesinger, Benjamin, 8, 337
Shaftesbury, Lord, 95
Shaw, C. R., 283, 292
Sidebotham, R., 96
Sivadon, P., 37, 96, 313
Slater, E. T. O., 313
Snow, John, 19
Speijer, N., 306, 310

Sperling, M., 189, 192
Stürup, Georg K., 300, 301
Suttenfield, V., 181, 192

Thrasher, F. L., 283, 292
Tizard, J., 7, 245, 304, 313
Tooth, G. C., 96
Torrance, E. Paul, 180
Tuke, William, 4
Tunley, Roul, 307, 310

Vail, David, 309, 310

Vaughan, W. T., 209
Vogel, Ezra R., 143, 144, 146
Vogel, Suzanne H., 143, 146

Wall, W. D., 228
Walton, Ann D., 331
Warren, W., 183, 192
Wills, W. D., 282, 292
Winslow, C. E. A., 53
Wolf, Alexander, 283

Yerbury, E. C., 209

Subject Index

Aden, 354
Administration, local, 52
   national, 23, 51–52
   regional, 24
   in U. S., community services, 109–119
Admission procedures, 27–28
Adolescent offenders (see Delinquency;
   Highfields; Viby program for se-
   verely maladjusted girls)
Adult psychiatric services, 103–104
Africa, 147–153, 347
Aftercare, 105
Aging, 317
Albania, 351
Alcoholism, 97
Algeria, 351
Americas, references, 349–350
Anthropology, 337–338
Argentina, 349
Asia, 355
Attitudes, study of, 43, 316
Australia, halfway houses, 27
   references, 355
Austria, 25, 351

Beds per 100,000 population, 27
Behavior therapy, 318
Belgium, 351
Binet Center for Child Guidance, 99–101
Biological psychiatry, 316
Brazil, halfway houses, 27
   references, 349
Bulgaria, 351

Cameroun, 348
Canada, administration, 24
   day hospitals, 27
   halfway houses, 27
   mental health association, 79
   psychiatry, 25
   references, 349

Carnegie Foundation, 325
Case registers, 316
Ceylon, 350
Child care worker, 266
Childhood problems, 340
Children's services, aims, 257
   case study, 194–207
   community programs, 194–195
   European inpatient facilities, com-
      mentary, 304–306
   consultation, 263–264
   extent of problem, 249–250
   facilities, 248–249
   family relations, 254
   group psychotherapy, 262
   individual psychotherapy, 257, 259–
      262
   placement criteria, 252–253
   preliminary observations, 255–256
   psychiatric treatment in hospital,
      263
   references, 267–268
   residential services, 246–249
   staff roles, 264–265
   therapeutic climate, 257–259
   types of centers, 250–252
   Paris, 99–103
   psychiatric treatment, 255–257
   U.S.S.R., 127
   WHO recommendations, 317
Chile, 349
China (Taiwan), 355
Clinical psychology, 338
Colombia, 25
Community organizer, 166
Community services, commentary,
      154–167
   continuity of care, 163
   definition, 93
   dimension, 90
   financing, 91–92, 115–116
   function, 92, 162
   history, 88–89, 154–155

Community services, hospital, 113
  location, 114–115
  needs, 160–161
  neighborhood organization, 165
  philosophy, 109
  planning, 162
  professional participation, 116–117
  references, 119–120, 344–355
  salaries, 117–118
  standards, 92, 94
  team practice, 164
Conditioned reflex activity, 317
Congo, 348
Consultation, 46, 194–207, 241–242
Continuity of treatment, 100, 163
Coordination of services, 105
Costa Rica, 25
County references, 347–355
Cross-cultural differences, 224
Cuba, 349
Cultural change, 15–16, 57
Czechoslovakia, 351

Day hospitals, 14, 27, 148
Delinquency, causes, 308
  peer group, 284
  references, 291–292
  socio-cultural patterns, 67, 281
  treatment, 281, 308–309
  values, 281, 283
  world-wide, 307
Delinquent boys (see Highfields)
Delinquent girls (see Viby program for
  severely maladjusted girls)
Denmark, genetic studies, 316
  references, 351
  Viby, 293–301
Deprivation syndrome, 66–68
Developing countries, 55–62
Dictionaries, 338–339

Éducateur, 266
Education, commentary, 223–227
  mental health, 106–107
El Salvador, 25
Emergency services, 104
Emotionally disturbed children, Europe
  and U.S., 304–306
  (See also Project Re-ED)
England (see United Kingdom)
Epidemiology, 50, 314–315

Ethiopia, 348
Europe, inpatient psychiatric services for
  children, 245–268
  references, 351
European League for Mental Hygiene,
  79
Exchange of persons, 319

Family life, 339–340
Family planning, 317
Films (mental health), Mental Health
  Film Board, 332
  objectives, 335
  presentation, 334
  references, 335–336
  value, 333
  varieties, 332–333
Finland, administration, 25
  mental health association, 79
  psychiatry, 25
  references, 351
Ford Foundation, 325
Foundation Directory, 323
Foundation Library Center, 323
Foundations, American, 323–324
  private, 323–326
  applications, 325
  survey of support, 323–324
Foundations' Fund for Research in Psychiatry, 326
France, administration, 24
  day hospital, 27
  halfway houses, 27
  references, 352
  Thirteenth Arrondissement, 97–108
Fulbright-Hays Act, 320

Genetics, 316
Germany (Democratic Republic), 352
Germany (Federal Republic), 25, 352
Ghana, 147, 348
Girls, maladjusted (see Viby program
  for severely maladjusted girls)
Grants, 319–330
  application and evaluation, 328–329
  references, 331
  support abroad, 326–327
Greece, 352
Guatemala, 25

Hague, The, 269–279

Haiti, 349
Halfway houses, 27
Health education, 123
Health insurance, 132
Herstedvester, 300
Highfields, assumptions, 283
　commentary, 308–309
　community adjustment, 290
　evaluation, 291
　guided group interaction, 288–290
　history, 282–283
　methods, 282–285
　program, 287–290
　residents, 285–286
　staff, 286–287
History, cyclical movement in Britain, 94–95
　mental health movement, 78–80
Honduras, 27
Hospitals, beds per 100,000 population, 27
　psychiatric facilities, 40–41, 157–158
　(See also Mental hospitals)
Hostels, 93

Iceland, 352
Incidence studies, 111
India, 350
Indonesia, 350
Industrialization, 58
Information dissemination, 316, 318
Inpatient psychiatric services for children in Europe, 245–268
Institute for International Education, 320
International Committee for Mental Hygiene, 79
International Committee against Mental Illness, 79
International exchange, 320
International perspective, 13–21, 78–83
Iran, 25, 354
Ireland, administration, 24
　day hospitals, 27
　references, 352
Israel, administration, 24
　children's court, 19
　community services, 154–167
　group social work, 165–166
　halfway houses, 27
　kibbutz children, 210–221
　manpower ratios, 163
　prevention, 19

Israel, psychiatry, 25–26
　references, 354
　social changes, 155–156
　work villages, 27, 159
Italy, 352

Japan, administration, 24
　collaterality, 140–143
　delinquency, 307
　health insurance, 132
　historical pattern, 131
　manpower, 131
　Morita-therapy, 137–139
　nursing, 136–137
　organic treatment, 136–137
　patient-physician relationship, 132–134
　psychiatric services, 129–141
　psychoanalytic treatment, 139–140
　references, 145–146, 335
　resources, 30
　tsukisoi, 136–137
　values, 141–144
　Zen Buddhism, 138
Joint Commisison report, 63, 96, 310
Juvenile delinquent (see Delinquency; Highfields; Viby program for severely maladjusted girls)

Kenya, 348
Kibbutz, definition, 210
　genetic-dynamic factors, 213–217
　psychiatric disturbances in children, 212–213
　references, 221–222
　school age and adolescence, 217–220
Kuwait, 354

Learning problems, 218, 297
Lebanon, 25
Legislation, United Kingdom, 89, 95
Liberia, 348

Malaysia, 350
Manpower, 4, 25–26
　Israel, 163
　Japan, 131
　maldistribution, 45
　ratios, 44

Mental health, definition, 18, 32, 172
  education, 100–107, 123
  promoting in school, 171–180
  resources, 23–31
Mental health consultation, children's services case study, 194–208
  references, 208–209
Mental health movement, aims, 80
  history, 78–80
  values, 81–83
Mental hospitals, aftercare, 39
  British policy, 89
  costs per day, 28
  custodial care, 37
  duration of stay, 28
  open door, 38
  overcrowding, 35
  roles, 36–37
  therapeutic community, 37
Mental illness, costs, 17
  incidence, 15
  recovery rate, 14
Mental retardation (see Retardation)
Mexico, 349
Migration, 56
Minnesota Community Mental Health Program, 119
Mongolia, 355
Morita-therapy, 137–139
Morocco, 352
Mozambique, 348
Multiple-problem family, 112
Multiple therapy, 151

National Association for Mental Health, 79
National Committee for Mental Hygiene, 79
Need surveys, 43
Netherlands, programs for retarded, 269–279
  references, 352
Neuropsychiatric dispensaries, 124–125
Neuropsychiatric hospitals, 127
New Zealand, administration, 24
  psychiatry, 25
  references, 355
Nigeria, community program, 147
  cultural components, 313
  day hospital, 148
  multiple therapy, 151
  traditional healers, 149–150

Nigeria, village care, 149–150
Night hospitals, 27
Norway, genetic research, 316
  references, 352
Nursing, Japan, 136–137
  U.S.S.R., 126

Oranim Child Guidance Clinic, 211
Organization of mental health activity, 44–47
Outpatient facilities, 29, 40

Pakistan, psychiatry, 25
  references, 354
  resources, 30
Paperbound books, bibliography, 337–346
Parent-child relations, 225
Paris, 97–108
Patient-therapist relations, 133–134, 156–157
Payment, 131–132
Pedagogical-psychological treatment, 294–301
Peru, psychiatry, 25
  references, 350
  social work, 26
Philippines, 355
Pocketbooks, bibliography, 337–346
Poland, 353
Population trends, 60–61
Portugal, day hospitals, 27
  psychiatry, 25
  references, 353
  working village, 27
Prejudice, 20–21
Prevalence studies, 111
Prevention, 63–74
  community services, 112, 160–161
  goals, 16–20, 64–65, 121–123
  references, 75–76
Professional services, salaries, 117–118
Professional standards, 118–119
Programmed learning, 177
Project Re-ED, follow-up, 242–244
  history, 231–233
  liaison with home and school, 241
  mental health consultation, 241
  observations, 236–240
  program, 233–236
  schools, 233
  teacher-counselor, 240

Psychiatric facilities, general hospitals, 40–41, 157–158
  hospitals (*see* Mental hospitals)
  regional organization, 158–159
  WHO survey, 27
Psychiatrists, private practice, 25
  public service, 25
Psychiatry, references, 340–341
Psychoanalysis, in mental health, 69–71
  references, 342–344
Public health care, definition, 32
  planning, 32–52
  references, 53–54

Research, 30–31, 50
Retardation, 68, 306
  Netherlands, 269–279
    adult services, 277
    BLO schools, 272
    children of school age, 275–276
    commentary, 306–307
    interagency services, 273
    postschool age, 276
    preschool community care, 275
    residential care, 274
    social pedagogic center, 270
    workshops, 278–279
Rockefeller Foundation, 325
Rumania, 353
Russell Sage Foundation, 323
Rwanda-Burundi, 348

School mental health, achievement sense, 175
  climate, 173, 226
  commentary, 223–227
  definition, 174, 224
  educational practice, 223
  examinations, 177
  grade structure, 178
  learning and behavior, 174–175
  promotion policies, 176
  regulations, 178
  teachers' mental health, 172–173
  team services, 162
School phobia (*see* School refusal)
School refusal, attitudes, of community, 183–184
  of professionals, 184
  definition, 181
  incidence, 183

School refusal, psychopathology, 185–188
  references, 190
  review of literature, 181–183
  treatment, 188–189
Scotland (*see* United Kingdom)
Screening, 41
Sectorization, 97–108
Senegal, 4, 348
Sheltered workshops, 27
Social change, 55–62, 110, 155–156
Social disorganization, 57
Social psychiatry, 40, 316
Sociology, 344–346
South Africa, mental health association, 79
  psychiatry, 25
  references, 348
  resources, 30
Soviet Union (*see* Union of Soviet Socialist Republics)
Spain, 353
Study abroad, 319–323
Sudan, 17, 47, 354
Suicide, 314
Sweden, administration, 24
  delinquency, 307
  references, 353
Switzerland, genetic studies, 316
  psychiatry, 25
  references, 353
  working village, 27

Taiwan, cultural components, 313
  day hospital, 27
  psychiatry, 25
  references, 355
Tanzania, 349
Teamwork, 46, 263–264
Thailand, psychiatry, 25
  references, 351
  resources, 30
  urbanization, 56–57
Therapy (*see* Treatment)
Training, advanced countries, 49
  community development, 59
  cultural background, 48
  international personnel, 59–60
  medical, 26–27
  priorities, 43–44
  psychiatric, 17, 72–73
  recommendations, 48–50, 309
  research, 315
Transference, 48

Treatment, advances in, 13–15
    community, in Africa, 147–153
        in Britain, 87–96
        in Israel, 154–167
        in Japan, 130–141
        sectorization in Paris, 97–108
        in U.S.S.R., 123–127
    Highfields program, 280–291
    inpatient, of children in Europe, 245–267
    project Re-ED, 231–244
    of school phobia, 185–189
    Viby program, 293–302
Trinidad and Tobago, 350
Tunisia, 354

UNESCO, 79, 320–321
Union of Soviet Socialist Republics, administration, 23
    children's services, 127
    conditioned reflex activity, 317
    day hospital, 27
    halfway houses, 27
    mental hygiene program, 121–128
    neuropsychiatric dispensaries, 123–125
    neuropsychiatric hospitals, 127
    nursing, 126
    preventive programs, 121–123
    psychiatry, 25
    references, 353
    resources, 30
    working village, 27
United Arab Republic, 25, 254
United Kingdom, administration, 23
    community care, 87–96
    day hospitals, 27
    Mental Health Act, 89
    references, 353–354
    reforms, 94–96
United States of America, administration, 24, 109–119
    children's services case study, 194–208
    community mental health, 109–119
    conditioned reflex research, 317
    day hospitals, 27
    delinquency, 307

United States of America, halfway houses, 27
    Office of International Research, NIH, 327
    prevention, 63–69
    psychiatric training, 69–73
    psychiatry, 25
    psychology, 26
    references, 350
    resources, 30
    sheltered workshops, 27
    U.S. government support abroad, 326–327
Urbanization, 56

Venezuela, 350
Viby program for severely maladjusted girls, commentary, 308–309
    pedagogical-psychological treatment, 294–301
    referrals, 293–295
    therapeutic climate, 301
Village care in Nigeria, 149–150

Wales (see United Kingdom)
Witch doctors, 149
Working villages, 27, 159
World Federation for Mental Health, 9, 15, 55
    films, 332
    history, 79
    relation to WHO, 81
    resources, 347
World Health Organization (WHO), fellowships, 321–322
    history, Mental Health Unit, 79
    reports, 23–31, 32–54, 245
    research recommendations, 313–316
    resources, 347
    scientific group, 313–318, 322
World Psychiatric Association, 79–80

Yoruba, 153
Yugoslavia, 354